copies of period tables, desks, chairs and cabinets. Naturally, these pieces are produced by our own master craftsmen who are used to the exceptional standards required by the international market. This in-house team includes cabinet makers, carvers, french polishers, desk top leather liners, upholsterers, marble masons and metal workers. Their talents and the use of only the best genuine materials make us confident in claiming a standard of furniture unsurpassed in this century.

We would strongly recommend and welcome a visit to our showrooms so that you can experience at first hand our commitment to quality.

LAPADA
Registered Member

BRITISH ANTIQUE INTERIORS

THE GUILD OF MASTER CRAFTSMEN

BRITISH ANTIQUE INTERIORS,
School Close, Queen Elizabeth Avenue, Burgess Hill, West Sussex RH15 9RX, England.
Telephone BURGESS HILL (04 44) 245577.   Fax (04 44) 232014.

A MEMBER OF THE BRITISH ANTIQUE EXPORTERS GROUP OF COMPANIES

Cover illustrations
La Maison de Mimi Pinson a Montmartre **by Maurice Utrillo** *(Christie's)*
And Every Lad May Be Aladdin (Crackers in Bed) **by Norman Rockwell** *(Christie's)*
Deux Anglaises **by Jules Pascin** *(Christie's)*
The sleeping babe **by Rudolf Epp** *(Christie's)*
A fair beauty **by Herbert Gustave Schmalz** *(Christie's)*
A cockerel and hens, a rabbit in a hutch nearby **by Edgar Hunt** *(Christie's)*
The centre of attraction **by Cornelius Bouter** *(Christie's)*

All prices quoted in this book are obtained from a variety of auctions in various countries during the twelve months prior to publication and are converted to dollars at the rate of exchange prevalent at the time of sale.

The publishers wish to express their sincere thanks to the following for their involvement and assistance in the production of this volume:

NICKY FAIRBURN (Art Editor)
EELIN McIVOR (Sub Editor)
CHARLES BORTHWICK (Sub Editor)
LESLEY MARTIN
TRACEY BLACK
GILLIAN EASTON
ANNETTE CURTIS
LOUISE SIMPSON
JONN DUNLOP
KERRY McCONNEL
ANTONIA MURPHY
DOREEN RILEY
FRANK BURRELL
ROBERT NISBET
EILEEN BURRELL
RICHARD SCOTT

A CIP catalogue record for this book is available from the British Library.

ISBN 0-86248-113-9

Copyright © Lyle Publications MCMLXXXIX
Glenmayne, Galashiels, Scotland.

Printed and bound by Butler & Tanner, Frome, Somerset.

THE LYLE OFFICIAL

ARTS
REVIEW 1990

PHILLIPS SCOTLAND

Phillips Scotland hold over 140 auctions a year, in our Edinburgh and Glasgow branches. These include **Antique Furniture, Oil Paintings, Watercolours, Ceramics, Glass, Silver, Jewellery, Books, Oriental Works of Art; Dolls, Textiles & Costume; 20th Century Decorative Arts; Arms & Armour and Golfing Memorabilia.**
Our specialists are always happy to give free advice and auction valuations.
For further details please contact **Rebecca Fairweather** in Edinburgh, **Jennifer Whyte** in Glasgow or **Michael Finlay** in Carlisle.

PHILLIPS SCOTLAND
65 George Street, Edinburgh EH2 2JL. Tel. 031-225 2266
207 Bath Street, Glasgow G2 4HD. Tel. 041-221 8377
48 Cecil Street, Carlisle, Cumbria CA1 1NT. Tel. 0228 42422

Thirty five salerooms througout the United Kingdom
Members of the Society of Fine Art Auctioneers.

ILP

Introduction

Published annually and containing details of thousands of oil paintings, watercolours and prints, The Lyle Official Arts Review is the most comprehensively illustrated reference work on the subject available at this time.

Each entry is listed alphabetically under the Artist's name for easy reference and includes a description of the picture, its size, medium, auctioneer and the price fetched at auction during the twelve months prior to publication.

As regards authenticity of the works listed, this is often a delicate matter and throughout this book the conventional system has been observed:

The full Christian name(s) and surname of the artist denote that, in the opinion of the auctioneer listed, the work is by that artist.

The initials of the Christian name(s) and the surname denote that, in the opinion of the auctioneer listed, the work is of the period of the artist and may be wholly or partly his work.

The surname only of the artist denotes that, in the opinion of the auctioneer listed, the work is of the school or by one of the followers of the artist or painted in his style.

The word 'after' associated with the surname of the artist denotes that, in the opinion of the auctioneer listed, the picture is a copy of the work of the artist. The word 'signed' associated with the name of the artist denotes that, in the opinion of the auctioneer listed, the work bears a signature which is the signature of the artist.

The words 'bears signature' or 'traces of signature' denote that, in the opinion of the auctioneer listed, the work bears a signature or traces of a signature which may be that of the artist.

The word 'dated' denotes that the work is dated and, in the opinion of the auctioneer listed, was executed at that date.

The words 'bears date' or 'inscribed' (with date) denotes that, in the opinion of the auctioneer listed, the work is so dated and may have been executed at about that date.

All pictures are oil on canvas unless otherwise specified. In the dimensions (sight size) given, the height precedes the breadth.

Although the greatest possible care has been taken to ensure that any statement as to authorship, attribution, origin, date, age, provenance and condition is reliable, all such statements can only be statement of opinion and are not to be taken as statements or representations of fact.

The Lyle Official Arts Review offers a unique opportunity for identification and valuation of paintings by an extremely broad cross section of artists of all periods and schools.

Unless otherwise stated descriptions are placed immediately underneath the relevant illustrations.

We firmly believe that dealers, collectors and investors alike will treasure this and subsequent annual editions of the Lyle Official Arts Review (published in September each year) as changing trends in the fluctuating world of art values are revealed.

Tony Curtis

8

ARTS
REVIEW 1990

Genius, in the case of Van Gogh, was next to madness, and his name these days is certainly enough to cause a kind of madness in the fine art market. Ever since 'Irises' sold for £30.2 million and 'Sunflowers' sold for £24.2 million, the merest rumour that one of his paintings might be coming on the market is enough to cause great ripples of excitement. In fact, the market in general has a slightly crazy feel about it at present. The Impressionists are certainly still topping the bill, and enthusiasm for them shows no signs of abating. And it's not just the first-rate works by first-rank painters that are fetching huge sums. Good paintings by artists generally considered to be of the second rank are also right up there. Maybe it's because the Impressionist style is now familiar and the subject matter usually easily appreciable.

Paul Gauguin – Mata Mua (In Olden Times), 1892. (Sotheby's)
$24,200,000 £14,578,313

9

Alberto Magnelli – L'Uomo Ubriaco – signed and dated – oil on canvas – 39¼ x 29½in. (Christie's) $94,622 £50,600

Charles Sheeler – Grey Barns – signed and dated – tempera on board – 14 x 20½in. (Christie's) $165,000 £88,709

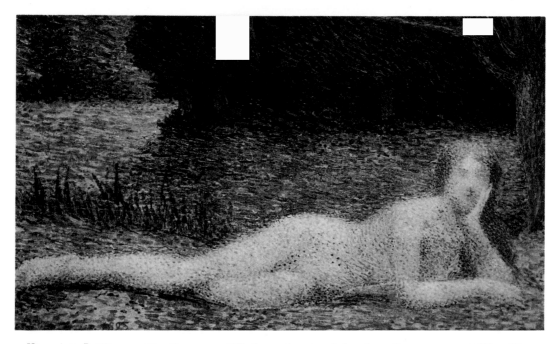

Hippolyte Petitjean – Nu allonge sur l'Herbe – signed and dated – oil on canvas – 10½ x 18in.
(Christie's)   *$41,624 £24,200*

Whatever the reason, in New York in May, Sotheby's and Christie's between them sold $¼ billion worth of Impressionist works in two days, with Christie's taking $103 million in the space of one and a half hours.

One result of this is that many owners of Modern and Impressionist paintings are now tempted to put them on the market in the hope of cashing in on the current craze. A rather sad reflection on the state of the art market. There was in the past a kind of unwritten law that dictated that no work which appeared and reappeared on the market could hope to retain its credibility for long. Alas, this seems to be no longer the case in a market where great art is traded like so many stocks and shares. The 'buzz' now, it would appear, comes no longer from the possession of a beautiful masterpiece, but from the excitement of buying and selling it.

Pierre-Auguste Renoir – La Promenade – signed and dated – 81.3 x 65cm. (Sotheby's)
$17,578,000 £10,340,000

In basic terms, the rationale now seems to be not the pleasure one might have in owning a superb work of art but "If I buy it now, how much profit will I make by selling it next month". Perhaps after all we shall before long be seeing Monet and Renoir quoted alongside 3M and Rio Tinto Zinc in the City pages of the national dailies!

A further rather disquieting spin-off of spiralling prices is that, as usual where there's the prospect of a fast buck, middlemen are entering the arena. Major auction houses and dealers are reporting an upsurge in agent trading, ie. the offering of pictures for sale by people who do not own them. The idea is that the self-appointed agent, often completely unknown to the real owner, hunts for a buyer for a certain work, on the assumption that, if he can come up with a good enough offer, he may then be able to persuade the owner to sell, and he can then claim his commission. According to some galleries, things have reached the state that they now hardly dare to send out pictures or transparencies of desirable works in case they are used for such purposes.

Jackson Pollock — Number 8. (Sotheby's) $11,550,000 £6,700,000

T. Noel Smith — A Somerset Cottage — signed — watercolour — 26 x 35cm. (Henry Spencer)   *$2,422 £1,400*

Pierre-Auguste Renoir – Jeune Fille au Chapeau. (Sotheby's)   *$13,750,000 £8,136,095*

Alfred de Breanski − Ben Vorlich − signed and inscribed on the reverse − oil − 74 x 126cm. (Henry Spencer) $35,700 £21,000

Edward Robert Hughes − A Viking − signed − watercolour −52 x 32cm. (Henry Spencer) $4,056 £2,400

Wilfred Gabriel de Glehn — The Avon near Great Durnford — signed — oil on canvas —
20¼ x 30¼in. (Bonhams) $27,200 £16,000

Coming back to Van Gogh, 'Sun-flowers' has now surfaced in the Yasuda Fire and Marine Insurance Co in Tokyo, where it can be viewed by the public for the equivalent of £1. The Japanese are continuing to buy in strength in all the major auction centres. It appears, too, that they have now extended their shopping lists from the traditional Impressionists such as Renoir and Monet, to include more minor masters such as Utrillo and Vlaminck and are now looking for 18th century French and 19th century English paintings as well. De Breanski and even Turner are now sought after in the Land of the Rising Sun as are gentle English cottage garden watercolours and contemporary art. It seems that the Jackson Pollock 'No 8 of 1950' sold at Sotheby's for £6.7 million may have finished up there. Their tastes are nothing

if not catholic, and it seems as difficult to analyse their buying rationale as it does to find out who the actual Japanese purchaser may be. In contrast to the razamatazz which surrounds many Western buyers, the Japanese are discreet and even secretive in the extreme. Certainly, the taxation laws governing such acquisitions make it of paramount importance that the purchaser should remain unknown and the use of dealers is commonplace. In many cases too, unlike 'Sunflowers', the paintings are stored rather than hung, again for fear of the taxman. Nevertheless it does seem that the Japanese buy for prestige, and this, while still not exactly a purist approach, may seem marginally preferable to the out-and-out mercenary attitude which exists in other parts.

Walt Kuhn – The Performer – signed and dated – oil on canvas –102 x 76.5cm. (Christie's) $50,600 £27,204

Haydn Reynolds Mackey – Jazz Drummer – signed and inscribed – oil on panel – 36 x 28in. (Christie's) $66,946 £37,400

Jose Luis Caballero – St Sebastian (?) and St Catherine (?) – signed – pencil, water-colour and body colour – 14¼ x 10¼in. (Christie's) $5,874 £3,300

Theo van Rysselberghe – Baigneuse – oil on canvas – 50 x 37in. (Christie's) $37,840 £22,000

Vincent van Gogh — Mas a Saintes-Maries — Reed pen and sepia ink and pencil — 30.5 x 47.4cm.
(Sotheby's)   *$3,927,000 £2,310,000*

Georges Rouault-Automne — aquatint in colour — 19¾ x 25¾in. (Phillips) $40,710 £23,000

Peter Breughel – La Retour de la Kermesse. (Phillips)   *$916,000 £539,000*

Wolfgang Adam Topffer – A Village Fair – 81 x 104cm. (Bearne's)   *$528,000 £300,000*

The Japanese, too, have been instrumental in keeping up the price of Old Masters, which, but for their interest, might have fallen back even more than they are reported to have done. Of course there will always be a ready market for the high fliers, and Phillips recently sold a Peter Breughel the Younger for £539,000 to a European client. One theory for the decline in the market for Old Masters is that they are 'too difficult' for modern taste. Certainly their full appreciation demands a knowledge of history and often also of scripture and it may be that less serious collectors simply can't be bothered to make the effort, preferring something rather more accessible. However, it has been noted that the Italians, and Dutch, for example, maintain a lively interest in British sales of their Old Masters,

and frequently come over to buy them back.

The 'going home' theme, indeed, seems to be one which is being played ever more strongly. The auctioneers, Henry Spencer, based in the eastern side of the country, report many Germans, Scandinavians and Dutch bidding for their own artists and they also sold a Skinner Prout with strong Australian associations to an Australian buyer. Bearne's too say that their most successful sale was of Swiss pictures. They did their homework and mounted a substantial publicity campaign in Switzerland, which reaped excellent results in terms of interest and prices paid, with the two Topffers on offer fetching £300,000 and £410,000 respectively. Jacobs and Hunt also sold a Verschuur for £49,000.

Wouter Verschuur — Horses and Riders at Drinking place — oil on canvas — 43½ x 28½in. (Jacob & Hunt) $85,260 £49,000

Fernando Botero – Princess Margarita after Velasquez – signed and dated – 215 x 192cm. (Christie's) $444,000 £267,470

Diego Rivera – La Mujer del Chal Rojo – signed, dedicated and dated – oil on canvas – 31½ x 29½in. (Christie's) $181,500 £109,337

Needless to say, this is all good for business, if 'business' is to be the sole criterion, and there's even a certain sentimentality in the thought of all these works of art finding their way back to their place of origin. On the other hand, however, it is perhaps worth mentioning that the value of antiques and fine arts exported from the UK according to the last set of D.T.I. yearly figures available amounted to £1216 million, while imports totalled only £1109 million. That means a net loss of art from the UK, and while the deficit is half that of the previous year it means we still have a fair way to go before enough domestic buying clout (or the government interest which might engender it) is established to turn the tide the other way. It seems, however, that we are not alone in this situation, and it may cause a wry smile on some faces to learn that that arch-predator of British arts and antiques, the United States, is now beginning to suffer from a similar problem. At Sotheby's New York in May, Pontormo's masterpiece of Cosimo I de 'Medici was safely sold to the Getty Museum for the sum of $35.2 million (£22.3 million). Nothing so dramatic in that, one might say, but the fear that a US bid might **not** be successful was enough to provoke the headline in the New York Times a week or so before the sale 'Vanishing art: Cultural Heritage on Auction Block'. The writer went on to quote a list of works of art which had been lost to foreign buyers over the past couple of years. Europe appears at last to be striking back though it seems unlikely that the UK will be in a position to benefit much, for the present at least.

Jacopo da Carucci, called Pontormo – Portrait of Duke Cosimo I de'Medici – oil on panel transferred to canvas – 92 x 72cm. (Christie's) $35,200,000 £22,300,000

Remedios Varo – Vuelo Magico o La Zamfonia – signed and dated – oil on masonite with mother-of-pearl – 86 x 105cm. (Christie's) $385,000 £231,928

Away fron the world centres, trends are similar, with the modern Impressionists much to the fore, and the Scottish colourists again an important section. At Christie's, in Glasgow, a Peploe made £506,000, and the interest is not merely local, as Christie's in New York are devoting a sale entirely to these artists. The turn of the century Scottish painters in general are reckoned to be worth watching and it may well be that prices for their works will continue to rise still further.

Samuel John Peploe — Girl in white, a portrait of Peggy MacRae 1909 — signed — oil on canvas — 33¼ x 24¼ in. (Christie's) $946,220 £506,000

Edward Atkinson Hornel — The Butterfly — signed and dated — 50 x 60cm. (Phillips)   *$21,054 £12,100*

Samuel John Peploe – The Harbour, Royan – signed – oil on board – 27 x 35cm. (Phillips)
$86,130 £49,500

John Duncan Fergusson – Paris Plage – signed, inscribed and dated – oil on board –
27.5 x 35.5cm. (Phillips) *$153,120 £88,000*

Dorothea Sharp − On the Jetty − signed − 63 x 75cm. (Phillips) $38,280 £22,000

Raymonde Lynde − Mother's Pride − signed − 20 x 30in. (Bonhams) $14,240 £8,000

Robert Gemmell Hutchison — On the Creel — signed — on panel — 22 x 30cm. (Phillips)
$34,452 £19,800

Jeno Jendrassik — Close Companions — signed and dated — 46 x 33¼in. (Christie's)
$9,240 £5,280

Other areas which are proving popular at present are animal paintings. Bonham's again held their 'Crufts' sale this year, a specialised selection of paintings timed to coincide with the Show, and this was by no means the only sale devoted to Man's Best Friend. Marine and topographical pictures are also finding a ready market. Portraits, however, seem at present to be arousing less general interest, and miniatures in particular could be underpriced at this time.

Not far behind the Impressionists at the top of the ladder, however, are contemporary artists. Picasso is tipped by some to rival Van Gogh's dizzy heights, while a Jasper Johns recently sold for millions at Sotheby's. In this field American and British sales tend to be entirely different in content, with the Americans concentrating more on their own artists, while the British tend to feature the Europeans. The interest in modern artists seems set to continue. At a recent London exhibition by artists of the generation which has just left the Royal College, works by completely unknown painters were selling for as much as £4,000. A vote of confidence indeed in the future of British art!

Pablo Picasso – Yo Picasso. (Sotheby's)   *$47,850,000 £28,313,610*

Another potential growth area is Latin American art, which up to now has found its market mainly in the States, where paintings by artists such as Botero, Rivera and Varo sell for hundreds of thousands of dollars. There has, however, been a recent exhibition at the Hayward Gallery in London which is to move on to Stockholm and Madrid, and this may well serve to increase European awareness of this rich source of artistic inspiration.

That much talked of Glasnost has had its effect on the art market as well, and there are now a number of works by modern Russian painters appearing for sale. The German auction house of Hauswedell & Nolte held such a sale recently and buying was brisk.

Jasper Johns — Colored Alphabet, 1959 — paper collage with oil and encaustic on masonite — 30.48 x 26.4cm. (Christie's)

$3,520,000 £2,046,511

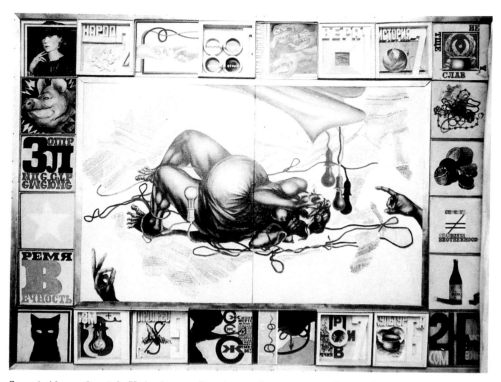

Sergei Alexandrovich Volochov — Russia — oil, tempera and mixed media on canvas and wood — 26 parts — signed and dated — 192 x 260cm. (Hauswedell and Nolte)

$25,982 £15,106

Apart from crazy prices, however, perhaps the major event of the last year was the death of one who might be described by some in similar terms, Salvador Dali. While he had throughout his life tended towards the flamboyant and eccentric, Dali's final years were almost as surreal as the most bizarre of his works. Following the death of his wife Gala, with whom he could be said to be obsessed, he became a complete recluse at the top of a tower in his museum/mausoleum at Figueras, ministered to by a handful of acolytes. There followed the 1984 fire, the discovery of his acute malnutrition, and the scandal that he had been allegedly signing print editions which were not his own work. All this may have a bearing, one way or the other, on how his later works are assessed. There can, however, be no doubt at all of the power of his earlier paintings, perhaps in particular those dating from the troubled period of the 1930's, and it is almost certain that these will continue to rise in value.

Salvador Dali — La Sorciere et la Belle Miroir — signed and dated — watercolour and gouache on paper — 50.8 x 41cm. (Christie's)
$52,976 £30,800

Salvador Dali — Les Deux Harlequins — signed, inscribed and dated — oil on canvas 85½ x 141in. (Christie's)

Maurice Utrillo – Rue enneigee – signed – oil on canvas – 33 x 46cm. (Christie's)
$178,695 £104,500

Salvador Dali – Le sentiment de la vitesse –
signed and dated – oil on canvas – 13x9½in.
(Christie's) $394,680 £214,500

Another artist currently much under the microscope for authenticity is, of course, Utrillo. This is thanks largely to the tireless efforts of the French sleuth M. Jean Fabris, who in April had the gendarmerie whisk all seven Utrillos off from beneath the nose of the unfortunate Paris auctioneer who was about to sell them, to be 'tried' as fakes. It is hardly surprising that M. Fabris is unloved by the major auction houses, and indeed he is said to hold the record for the number of ejections in one week from Christie's and Sotheby's!

One of the problems is that Utrillo was thought to have spent most of his painting life under the influence of alcohol or drugs, and many of his works, particularly after 1916, are prosaic and banal in the extreme. (Quite often they were drawn from picture postcards.) The question therefore whether one of his works is a fake or whether it was painted by him, so to speak, on a bad day, really, (if the art market were governed by realism) should become a bit academic. That said, however, a Japanese buyer did pay £297,000 for a scene of Montmartre even after M. Fabris had denounced it as a fake.

An Italian 17th century carved and gilded tabernacle frame with scrolling foliate frieze. (Christie's) $5,513 £3,080

A Venetian early 16th century carved and gilded tabernacle frame, 18¾ x 15½in. (Bonhams) $30,600 £18,000

Paul Cezanne – Pichet et Fruits sur une Table
(Sotheby's)   *$11,550,000 £6,834,320*

Tsuguharu Foujita – Mere et deux Enfants.
(Phillips)   *$577,500 £330,000*

Turning, finally, from the dizzy prices being paid for some paintings at auction, we find that there is also a lively market for something to put them in, and frames too are engendering a good deal of interest. Of course, if one is paying several million for a picture, an extra three or four thousand for a good frame, assuming it needs one, could be regarded as so much chickenfeed. However, there are a number of sales devoted exclusively to frames and these sort of prices are quite commonplace. Bonham's, for instance, sold a tabernacle example recently for £18,000.

At the end of the day, or of the past year at least, fine art at most levels remains a very buoyant market. Whether one has a million pounds to spend or a hundred, there are worthwhile investments to be made, and it will certainly be interesting for those of us who are not rich enough to be involved at the very top levels of the art market, to sit back over the next few months and watch the further shenanigans which seem bound to occur there.

EELIN McIVOR

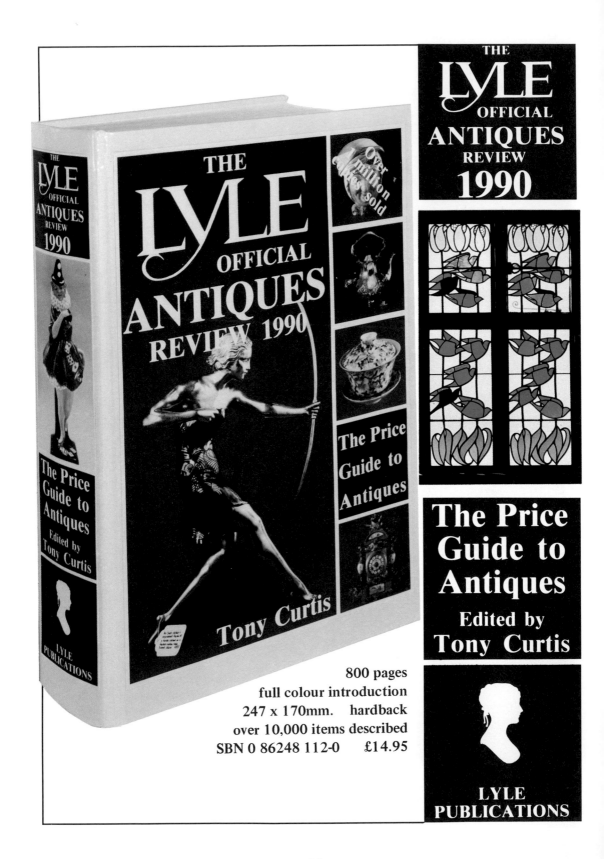

THE LYLE OFFICIAL ANTIQUES REVIEW 1990

The Price Guide to Antiques

Edited by Tony Curtis

LYLE PUBLICATIONS

800 pages
full colour introduction
247 x 170mm.   hardback
over 10,000 items described
SBN 0 86248 112-0   £14.95

ARTS
REVIEW 1990

JOHN WHITE ABBOTT – Buckland Abbey, Devon – inscribed and dated – 13.5 x 20cm.
(Christie's) **$5,236 £3,080**

PATRICK WILLIAM ADAM – Irises around a garden pond – signed – oil on canvas – 51 x 83 cm.
(Phillips) **$4,976 £2,860**

PAUL ABRAM – A young Breton girl sitting in the shade of a tree – signed and dated – black chalk and watercolour – 19¼ x 13in.
(Christie's) **$532 £308**

CHARLES JAMES ADAMS – "Palethorpe . . ." – signed and dated – watercolour – 14 x 20in.
(Fellows & Sons) **$3,380** **£2,000**

CHARLES PARTRIDGE ADAMS – Autumn Haystacks – signed and dated – watercolour on paper – 24.7 x 33.3cm.
(Robt. W. Skinner Inc.) **$275** **£162**

WAYMAN ADAMS — Woman with a Parasol —
signed — oil on board — 20 x 15¼in.
(Robt. W. Skinner Inc.)   **$3,000 £1,704**

EDMUND ADLER — "The snowman", depicts
children making a snowman — signed — oil on
canvas — 22 x 27in.
(Du Mouchelles)   **$7,500 £3,968**

C. F. AHL — A view of Lubeck with the Agidien-
kirken from the river Trave — signed and dated —
18 x 23¾in.
(Christie's)   **$1,122   £660**

BJORN AHLGRENSON — Study of a seated girl —
pencil — 8¾ x 13½in.
(Christie's)   **$305   £165**

SIGISMOND VON AJDUKIEWICZ — The vegetable
seller — signed and dated — oil on board — 9½x7½in.
(Christie's)   **$743   £440**

JOSEPH VAN AKEN — A lady buying vegetables
from a barrow beside an inn — oil on copper —
15½ x 20½in.
(Phillips)   **$7,160   £4,000**

CECIL ALDIN – A Prize-winning Hunter in Hand
– signed – pastel – 34¼ x 49½in.
(Phillips)   **$11,830**   **£7,000**

CECIL ALDIN – A bay Hunter and two Hounds
– signed – pastel – 34¼ x 47½in.
(Phillips)   **$14,365**   **£8,500**

JOHN ALDRIDGE – Quinces and Artichokes –
signed and dated – oil on board – 18 x 25½in.
(Christie's)   **$3,044**   **£1,760**

CECIL ALDIN – Grey Mare and Foal – signed –
pastel – 28 x 37¾in.
(Phillips)   **$6,422**   **£3,800**

JOHN ALDRIDGE – The River Bank – signed –
oil on board – 10½ x 14in.
(Christie's)   **$1,468   £825**

FREDERICK B. ALLEN – Ogunquit – signed and dated – watercolour on paper – 12 x 18in.
(Bruce D. Collins) **$110** **£58**

CLIFFORD GREAR ALEXANDER – "The grey silence" – signed and dated – oil on canvas – 32 x 32in.
(Robt. W. Skinner Inc.) **$4,500 £2,556**

HELEN ALLINGHAM – Lessons – signed – watercolour – 14 x 19¼in.
(Phillips) **$60,840** **£36,000**

PAUL ALFRED – Autumn – one of three – signed – watercolour and bodycolour – 10¼ x 13¼in.
(Christie's) **Three** **$1,174** **£660**

HARRY EPWORTH ALLEN – Evening in the Hills – signed – oil on card – 13 x 19¼in.
(Christie's) **$761** **£440**

ALESSANDRO ALLORI, Follower of – The infant Saint John the Baptist greeting the Holy Family, on the return from Egypt – on copper – 8¾ x 6¾in.
(Christie's) **$1,332 £770**

ABBEY ALSTON – "Olivia", study of a girl –
oil on canvas.
(Morphets) **$3,168 £1,800**

ALEXANDRE ALTMANN – Village au Bords de
Riviere – signed – oil on canvas – 73.5 x 92cm.
(Christie's) **$6,930 £3,960**

AMERICAN SCHOOL – Hudson River landscape –
Oil on board – 9 x 12in.
(Bruce D. Collins) **$231** **£122**

ALEXANDRE ALTMANN – Maisons et Riviere
– signed – oil on canvas – 93 x 73.5cm.
(Christie's) **$6,160 £3,520**

AMERICAN SCHOOL – One of a pair of nudes –
watercolour on paper – 10 x 11½in.
(Bruce D. Collins) **Two** **$83 £43**

AMERICAN SCHOOL – Garden in full bloom –
signed – Watercolour on paper – 12 x 8in.
(Bruce D. Collins) **$28** **£14**

AMERICAN SCHOOL – Artist sketching along
coastline – oil on canvas – 18 x 22in.
(Bruce D. Collins) **$165** **£87**

AMERICAN SCHOOL, 19th/20th Century –
In the Park – inscribed – oil on panel –
9.2 x 15.6cm.
(Robt. W. Skinner Inc.) **$700** **£414**

AMERICAN SCHOOL, 20th Century – The
Hockey Game – illegibly signed – oil on particle
board – 56.2 x 120.7cm.
(Robt. W. Skinner Inc.) **$800** **£473**

AMERICAN SCHOOL – George Washington – oil
on canvas – 29 x 24in.
(Christie's) **$3,300 £1,813**

AMERICAN SCHOOL, 20th Century –
American Tragedy – signed – tempera on gessoed
metal mounted on Masonite – 63.8 x 89.2cm.
(Robt. W. Skinner Inc.) **$700**   **£414**

AMERICAN SCHOOL, 20th Century – Spring
Pastures – signed – oil on canvas – 24 x 30in.
(Robt. W. Skinner Inc.) **$850**   **£502**

AMERICAN SCHOOL, 20th century – Spanish
Mission – signed indistinctly – oil on canvas –
18 x 24in.
(Christie's)   **$1,045**   **£574**

AMERICAN SCHOOL, 20th Century – He Refused
to be Entangled in the Concerns of Fairyland –
signed – ink on paper – 42.2 x 32.7cm.
(Robt. W. Skinner Inc.) **$1,700**   **£1,005**

AMERICAN SCHOOL, 20th century – View of
the Summer Cottage – indistinctly signed and
dated – oil on panel – 16¾ x 34in.
(Robt. W. Skinner Inc.)   **$850**   **£482**

JACOPO AMIGONI, Manner of – Esther at the
court of Assurro – oil on canvas – 96.5 x 126.5cm.
(Phillips)   **$2,112**   **£1,200**

AMORA

MARIO D. AMORA – Marina Di Pozzvoli, Naples –
signed – 19½ x 29½in.
(Christie's) **$1,131 £605**

AMSTERDAM SCHOOL, Circa 1660 – Portrait
of a lady, half length, wearing a lace ruff and fur-
lined costume; bears coat of arms – oil on panel –
31¾ x 26in.
(Phillips) **$1,760 £1,000**

ANNA ANCHER – An interior with a woman
looking in a mirror – signed and dated – on canvas
laid down on board – 29 x 28.5cm.
(Christie's) **$26,455** **£14,300**

MICHAEL ANCHER – A garden party; the young
girl's arrival – signed and dated – 26½ x 33¾in.
(Christie's) **$22,385** **£12,100**

MICHAEL ANCHER – The fishermen's return –
signed – 39½ x 55in.
(Christie's) **$44,770** **£24,200**

ANDERS ANDERSEN-LUNDBY – A wooded lake
landscape with figures seated on a bench – signed –
on board – 34 x 42cm.
(Christie's) **$3,052** **£1,650**

WILHELM ANDERSEN – Chrysanthemums in a vase on a window-sill – signed – 47.5 x 42cm.
(Christie's) **$5,698** **£3,080**

MAGDA ANDRADE – Village de Chantilly – signed and titled – oil on panel – 8½ x 12¾in.
(Christie's) **$550** **£312**

ALBERT ANDRE – Bouquet de Zinias – signed – oil on canvas – 46.5 x 41.5cm.
(Christie's) **$15,400 £8,800**

HENRY ANDERTON – Portrait of a lady, seated three-quarter length in a black dress trimmed with pearls, her left arm resting on a plinth, by a sculpted urn – signed – 49½ x 39½in.
(Christie's) **$4,540** **£2,640**

FREDERICO ANDREOTTI – A love story – signed – oil on canvas – 28½ x 22½in.
(Christie's) **$13,013 £7,700**

ANKARCRONA

HENRIK ANKARCRONA – A desert landscape –
signed and dated – 48 x 73cm.
(Christie's) **$9,768** **£5,280**

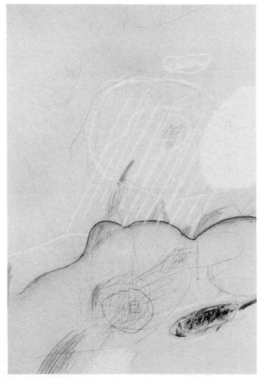

HORST ANTES – Untitled – signed and dated –
oil, coloured crayon, pencil and black chalk on
paper – 29 x 20½in.
(Christie's) **$13,244 £7,700**

HORST ANTES – Paar (Blinder) – signed – acrylic
on canvas – 39½ x 47¼in.
(Christie's) **$34,056** **£19,800**

THOMAS POLLOCK ANSHUTZ – The Farmer and
His Son at Harvesting – signed and dated – oil on
canvas – 24¼ x 17¼in.
(Christie's) **$1,540,000** **£827,956**

LOUIS APOL – A canal in winter – signed and dated – on panel – 52.3 x 83.2cm.
(Christie's) $9,724 £5,720

KAREL APPEL – Les Oiseaux – signed and dated – coloured chalk, coloured crayon, gouache and watercolour on paper – 22½ x 30½in.
(Christie's) $11,313 £6,050

KAREL APPEL – Untitled – signed and dated – on board – 28 x 39½in.
(Christie's) $13,244 £7,700

ANDREA APPIANI, Circle of – Cupid and Psyche – oil on canvas – 53.5 x 41cm.
(Phillips) $875 £500

ANDREA APPIANI, Attributed to – Portrait of an officer of the Guard Hussars of the Kingdom of Naples, bust length, wearing the Royal Order of the two Sicilies – oil on canvas – 26¼ x 23½in.
(Phillips) $6,336 £3,600

APPLEYARD

RAFFAELE ARMENISE – A close family –
signed – 33½ x 25½in.
(Christie's)   **$11,594**   **£6,820**

FRED APPLEYARD – A scented moment –
signed – watercolour – 11 x 6½in.
(Anderson & Garland)   **$3,163 £1,850**

EDWARD JEFFREY IRVING ARDIZZONE –
Cribbage at the cider bar – watercolour –
15 x 19in.
(Christie's)   **$8,179 £4,840**

GEORGE ARMFIELD – Terriers at a rabbit hole
– signed – oil on millboard – 9¾ x 9¾in.
(Anderson & Garland)   **$2,970**   **£1,650**

GEORGE ARMFIELD – A terrier hunting rabbits
– signed and dated – oil on canvas – 8¾ x 11½in.
(Anderson & Garland)   **$632 £370**

ROMEK ARPAD – Still Life with fruit –
signed – oil on canvas – 32 x 24in.
(Bruce D. Collins) **$1,100** **£582**

EDUARDO ARROYO – Le Carnet de Winston –
each signed and dated – coloured, black and grey
crayon on paper – each 33.3 x 48.9cm.
(Christie's) **Four** **$2,879** **£1,540**

DAVID ADOLF CONSTANT ARTZ – Fisherwoman picking cockles on the sea shore before
drying nets – signed – oil on canvas – 25 x 32in.
(W. H. Lane & Son) **$2,236 £1,300**

WILLIAM F. ASHBURNER – Gathering flowers –
signed – 14 x 10¼in.
(Anderson & Garland) **$2,768 £1,600**

H. ASHBY – An officer, probably of the London
and Westminster Light Horse Volunteers, mounted
on a dark bay charger, ready for battle – signed
and dated – 23½ x 17¾in.
(Christie's) **$5,709 £3,300**

ASHMORE

JOHN ATKINSON – A haystack – signed –
10¼ x 14¾in.
(Anderson & Garland) **$2,057 £1,100**

CHARLES ASHMORE – "The first love letter" –
Young girl in a blue dress, reading a letter in the
woods – initialled – watercolour – 5½ x 4½in.
(W. H. Lane & Son) **$549 £300**

JOHN ATKINSON – Brough Hill Horse Fair –
signed and inscribed – 9¾ x 12¼in.
(Anderson & Garland) **$5,049 £2,700**

ANGELO ASTI – A young woman reading –
signed – 16 x 12¾in.
(Christie's) **$1,870 £1,100**

JOHN ATKINSON – A woodland clearing – signed
– oil on millboard – 11½ x 15½in.
(Anderson & Garland) **$756 £420**

JOHN ATKINSON – The Fish Quay, North Shields
– signed and dated – watercolour – 8¾ x 13¼in.
(Anderson & Garland) **$2,052 £1,200**

JOHN ATKINSON – A three-horse harrow –
signed – watercolour – 10¾ x 15in.
(Anderson & Garland) **$3,078 £1,800**

JOHN ATKINSON – At Haytime – signed –
19¾ x 29½in.
(Anderson & Garland) **$10,440** **£5,800**

JOHN ATKINSON – Stagshaw Bank Fair –
signed – 8¼ x 23¼in.
(Anderson & Garland) **$9,360** **£5,200**

JOHN ATKINSON – Meet at Callerton – signed –
9¼ x 14½in.
(Anderson & Garland) **$1,620** **£900**

JOHN ATKINSON – The opening Meet of the
Haydon Hunt at Newbrough Lodge – signed,
inscribed and dated – 9 x 12in.
(Anderson & Garland) **$2,431 £1,300**

ATTINGER

GASTON AUBERT — Le Marche aux Fleurs —
signed — oil on canvas — 50.5 x 65cm.
(Christie's) $2,117 £1,210

LUCIE ATTINGER — Mon atelier — signed —
15 x 18in.
(Christie's) $8,085   £4,620

FRANK AUERBACH — Portrait of J.Y.M. —
signed and dated — charcoal on joined paper —
86 x 76.5cm.
(Christie's) $41,140 £22,000

FRANK AUERBACH — Seated Model in the Studio
III — Oil on paper — 102.2 x 68.2cm.
(Christie's) $75,680   £44,000

FRANK AUERBACH — Summer building site —
signed — oil on board — 30 x 42in.
(Christie's) $135,388 £74,800

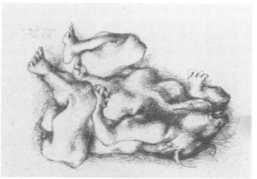

MICHAEL AYRTON – Minotaur – signed and dated – pen and brown ink – 13 x 18in.
(Christie's) **$836 £495**

ALEXANDER AUSTEN – After the shoot; and Weighting the catch – both signed – 15½ x 23½in.
(Christie's) Two **$1,522 £880**

WILLIAM FREDERICK AUSTIN – Pulls Ferry, Norwich – signed and dated – watercolour – 12 x 21in.
(G. A. Key) **$392 £210**

HENDRIK VAN AVERCAMP, Manner of – A winter landscape with villagers skating – on copper – 14 x 21¾in.
(Christie's) **$7,612 £4,400**

OTTO BACHE – A nude lady at her toilet – signed and dated – 60¼ x 30¾in.
(Christie's) **$6,512 £3,520**

OTTO BACHE − A game of croquet − signed with initials − oil on canvas − 11¾ x 15¾in.
(Christie's)   **$1,301 £770**

FRANCIS BACON − Head I − oil on canvas − 24 x 20in.
(Christie's)   **$435,160**   **£253,000**

WILHELM JOHANN BADER − Figure in a mountainous landscape − signed and dated − oil on panel − 62 x 48.5cm.
(Christie's)   **$6,054**   **£3,520**

NATHANIEL HUGHES J. BAIRD — Exmoor
ponies — monogrammed — watercolour —
11 x 21in.
(W. H. Lane & Son)   **$2,580 £1,500**

THOMAS BAKER — Harvest at Radford, Warwick-
shire — signed and dated — 13 x 19in.
(Christie's)   **$4,380**   **£2,420**

WILLIAM BAPTISTE BAIRD — Nice — signed
— on canvas laid down on board — 12½ x 9¼in.
(Christie's)   **$3,720 £2,090**

WILLIAM BAKER — Figures gathering spars from
a wreck — signed — 14¾ x 21¾in.
(Anderson & Garland) **$540**   **£300**

BLANCHE BAKER — Gathering wild flowers —
signed — pencil and watercolour heightened with
white — 16.3 x 25.5cm.
(Christie's)   **$2,081**   **£1,210**

JAMES WALSHAM BALDOCK — Sherwood
Forest — with deer in the bracken — signed and
dated — watercolour — 34 x 49.5cm.
(Henry Spencer)   **$980**   **£580**

BALEN

JAN VAN BALEN, Follower of – The Annunciation – on copper – 37.7 x 30cm.
(Christie's) **$1,332 £770**

McCLELLAND BARCLAY – Depicts boy skating on pond playing fetch with dog – signed – oil on canvas – 30 x 26in.
(Du Mouchelles) **$1,750 £1,035**

ARCHIBALD BARNES – Still Life with Flowers – oil on canvas – 25 x 30in.
(Christie's) **$2,349 £1,320**

McCLELLAND BARCLAY – Girl seated with two Scottish terriers – signed – oil on canvas – 33 x 26in.
(Du Mouchelles) **$4,000 £2,366**

ARCHIBALD BARNES – By The River – signed – oil on canvas – 23½ x 29½in.
(Christie's) **$7,832 £4,400**

JAMES D. BARNETT – On the Canal at Malines – signed and dated – oil on board – 11¾ x 15½in.
(Lawrence Fine Arts) **$608** **£352**

AFRO (BASALDELLA) – Untitled – signed and dated – watercolour on paper – 20½ x 26¼in.
(Christie's) **$11,730 £6,820**

WILLIAM NEWTON BARTHOLOMEW – Split-Rail Fence – signed – watercolour on paper – 9 x 14in.
(Bruce D. Collins) **$94** **£49**

GEORGES BARWOLF – Paris, Place Clichy sous la Neige – signed and dated – oil on canvas – 25½ x 36¼in.
(Christie's) **$4,620 £2,640**

STEPHEN JOHN BATCHELDER – The barge, Sea Breeze, entering Yarmouth Harbour – signed – watercolour – 9 x 6in.
(G. A. Key) **$4,114 £2,200**

BATCHELDER

STEPHEN JOHN BATCHELDER – Boats at
Horning Reach – signed – watercolour –
13 x 22in.
(G. A. Key) $6,358 £3,400

DAVID BATES – A meadow with a fallen tree and
cattle beyond – signed and dated – on board –
9 x 12½in.
(Christie's) $1,493   £825

ARTHUR BATT – Carthorse in a farmyard – signed
and dated – 20 x 24in.
(Woolley & Wallis) $830   £480

ALESSANDRO BATTAGLIA – A lady at her dres-
sing table – signed and dated – 15½ x 19in.
(Christie's) $4,114   £2,420

V. BATURIN – A spring orchard – signed and
dated – oil on canvas – 18½ x 12½in.
(Christie's) $650   £385

ANDRE BAUCHANT – Fleurs de Bois – signed
and dated – oil on canvas – 18¼ x 15in.
(Christie's) **$17,204 £9,350**

THOMAS TENNANT BAXTER – Still Life with
Ewer, Vegetables and Game – oil on canvas –
30¼ x 25¼in.
(Christie's) **$1,468 £825**

ELIJAH BAXTER, JR – Solitude – signed –
oil on canvas – 30.2 x 15.3cm.
(Robt. W. Skinner Inc.) **$1,400** **£828**

CECIL BEATON – Portrait of a young boy
holding a pug – singed and inscribed – watercolour
– 19 x 13in.
(Hy. Duke & Son) **$809 £460**

BEAUDIN

ANDRE BEAUDIN – Nature morte aux Fleurs dans un Vase – signed and dated – oil on canvas – 54.6 x 37.2cm.
(Christie's)   **$7,315 £4,180**

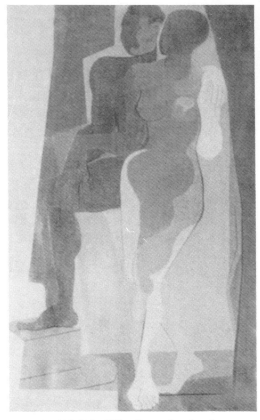

CARL BECKER – At the well – signed and dated – oil on canvas – 137 x 100cm.
(Christie's)   **$12,144 £6,600**

ANDRE BEAUDIN – L'Escalier – signed and dated – oil on canvas – 129.9 x 81.3cm.
(Christie's)   **$11,165 £6,380**

WILLIAM BEAULEY – St Paul's – signed – oil on canvas laid down on panel – 16 x 12in.
(Christie's)   **$770 £423**

WLADIMIR VON BECHTEJEFF – Landschaft bei Murnau – signed – oil on canvas – 20¼ x 27½in.
(Christie's)   **$22,627 £12,100**

MAX BECKMANN – Frau Swarzenski – signed – pencil on paper – 17.5 x 15.5cm.
(Christie's)   **$5,348 £2,860**

JAN VAN BEERS – Portrait study of a dancing ballerina – signed – oil on panel – 30 x 24cm.
(Henry Spencer)   **$1,124**   **£650**

MAX BECKMANN – Nachstilleben mit Sonnen-blumen – signed and dated – oil on canvas – 33½ x 17½in.
(Christie's)   **$155,144**   **£90,200**

ADRIAEN CORNELISZ BEELDEMAKER – Spaniels in a grotto – signed and dated – on panel – 15½ x 19½in.
(Christie's)   **$3,806 £2,200**

WILHELM BEHM – In the mountains – signed and dated – 29¼ x 36¼in.
(Christie's)   **$4,070**   **£2,200**

BELLE

CHARLES-ERNEST DE BELLE — Portrait of Miss
R. M. Heffer, bust length, wearing a black dress —
signed with monogram — charcoal, watercolour
and wash — 16¼ x 12¼in.
(Lawrence Fine Arts) **$380** **£220**

BERNARDO BELLOTTO, Manner of — The
Arsenal, Venice — 25 x 40in.
(Christie's) **$5,709 £3,300**

PIERRE CARRIER-BELLEUSE — L'Arlequin aux
Danseuses — signed and dated — pastel —
78 x 47in.
(Christie's) **$94,600 £55,000**

ANTONIO BELLUCCI, Follower of — The
Magdalen (?) — 31 x 25½in.
(Christie's) **$1,618 £935**

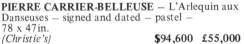

ELINOR BELLINGHAM-SMITH — Boats at
Cookham — oil on canvas — 16 x 20in.
(Christie's) **$3,982 £2,200**

ALMEIDA DE BELMIRO — Un vieil artiste —
signed and dated — oil on panel — 18 x 21½in.
(Christie's) **$15,787 £8,580**

FRANK MOSS BENNETT – The card players –
signed and dated – 20 x 16in.
(Christie's) **$13,937** **£7,700**

FRANK W. BENSON – Cloudy Dawn – signed –
etching on paper – 25.2 x 30.2cm.
(Robt. W. Skinner Inc.) **$400** **£236**

FRANK MOSS BENNETT – After the meet –
signed and dated – oil on canvas – 24½ x 30½in.
(Christie's) **$64,768 £35,200**

THOMAS HART BENTON – The Grand Tetons –
signed – oil on tin – 26.4 x 30.2cm.
(Christie's) **$49,500** **£26,612**

FRANK W. BENSON – Rendezvous – signed –
etching on paper – 9.2 x 12.4cm.
(Robt. W. Skinner Inc.) **$275** **£162**

THOMAS HART BENTON – Fruit on a Pink Cloth
– signed and dated – oil on panel – 35.4 x 43.4cm.
(Christie's) **$16,500** **£8,870**

BERGEN

DIRCK VAN BERGEN – An extensive landscape with travellers at a well, an estuary beyond – signed with monogram – on panel – 72.7 x 107.7cm.
(Christie's) **$9,515 £5,500**

ALFRED BERGSTROM – An extensive landscape at sunset – 16 x 13in.
(Christie's) **$4,070** **£2,200**

EUGENE BERMAN – Maison d'Olivia: La Nuit des Rois – titled and dated – watercolour on paper – 14¼ x 10½in.
(Christie's) **$2,420** **£1,428**

EUGENE BERMAN – Neo-Romantic Landscape – signed and dated – on paper – 11 x 15in.
(Christie's) **$3,300** **£1,947**

EUGENE BERMAN – Gypsy Family – signed and dated – on yellow paper – 12¾ x 10in.
(Christie's) **$1,430** **£843**

LEONID BERMAN – Deux Pecheurs de Nazare, Portugal – signed and dated – oil on canvas – 18 x 25½in.
(Christie's) **$6,600** **£3,894**

THERESA F. BERNSTEIN – Street market scene – signed – oil on canvas laid down on board – 23 x 19½in.
(Christie's) **$1,320** **£725**

LEONID BERMAN – Sandhills – signed and dated – oil on canvas – 17 x 38¾in.
(Christie's) **$5,500** **£3,245**

NATHANIEL L. BERRY – The Marshes in Haying Time – signed – oil on canvas – 20 x 30¼in.
(Robt. W. Skinner Inc.) **$1,100** **£650**

GUNNAR BERNDTSON – On reconnaisance – signed and dated – on panel – 10½ x 8½in.
(Christie's) **$40,700** **£22,000**

JOHANN BERTHELSEN – Vase of flowers – signed – oil on canvasboard – 18 x 14in.
(Christie's) **$1,430** **£785**

BESTLAND

CHARLES BESTLAND – Portrait of Thomas Willoughby, small half length, in a dark brown coat and black stock, in a landscape – signed – on board 11½ x 9½in.
(Christie's)   **$1,229**   **£715**

CHARLES BESTLAND – Portrait of Charlotte Elizabeth Willoughby, seated half length in a blue and white dress and long white gloves, holding papers and a pen, in a landscape – signed – on panel – 14 x 11¾in.
(Christie's)   **$1,608**   **£935**

ROBERT BEVAN – The Beech Tree – oil on canvas – 15¾ x 17¾in.
(Christie's)   **$10,950 £6,050**

CORNEILLE (CORNELIUS GUILLAUME VAN BEVERLOO) – Approche des nuages – signed and dated – 19½ x 23¾in.
(Christie's)   **$24,596 £14,300**

SID BICKFORD – Squaretail trout – signed – oil on canvas – 19 x 19in.
(Bruce D. Collins)   **$550**   **£291**

SID BICKFORD – A string of brookies – signed – oil on canvas – 19 x 19in.
(Bruce D. Collins)   **$770**   **£407**

CARL VON BINZER – A Greek – signed – watercolour – 450 x 320mm.
(Christie's)   **$2,887**   **£1,650**

ALFRED JOHN BILLINGHURST – Young girl holding a soldier doll – gouache, watercolour and charcoal – 22 x 15in.
(Christie's)   **$557**   **£330**

SAMUEL JOHN LAMORNA BIRCH – The Weir – signed – oil on canvas – 23¾ x 28¾in.
(Christie's)   **$39,160**   **£22,000**

SAMUEL JOHN LAMORNA BIRCH – "First flowers of spring", primroses and bluebells on the banks of a wooded stream – signed – oil on canvas – 20 x 24in.
(W. H. Lane & Son)   **$6,880 £4,000**

BIRCH

SAMUEL JOHN LAMORNA BIRCH – Stream,
Lamorna – signed and dated – watercolour,
bodycolour and pencil – 10 x 13½in.
(Christie's)   **$1,370**   **£770**

SAMUEL JOHN LAMORNA BIRCH – The
Farmyard – signed – oil on canvas – 13 x 16in.
(Christie's)   **$3,916**   **£2,200**

SAMUEL JOHN LAMORNA BIRCH – A stream
in winter – signed and dated – oil on canvas –
19 x 23in.
(Christie's)   **$8,811**   **£4,950**

HUGO BIRGER – A Moroccan warrior – signed
– 34½ x 23½in.
(Christie's)   **$24,420**   **£13,200**

PIERRE BITTAR – Harbour Pointe at Harbour
Springs from bluff overlooking the bay – signed
– 22 x 26in.
(Du Mouchelles)   **$6,500**   **£3,845**

SOREN C. BJULF — Fishermen landing their catch at Nyhavn — signed and dated — 48 x 74in.
(Christie's)   **$14,245**   **£7,700**

CHARLES BITTINGER — The Lamp — signed and dated — oil on canvas laid down on board — 80.7 x 64.4cm.
(Christie's)   **$4,400**   **£2,365**

SOREN CR. BJULF — In the park — signed — 21¾ x 25½in.
(Christie's)   **$5,236**   **£3,080**

EUGENE VON BLAAS — An Italian beauty — signed
and dated — pencil and watercolour — 310 x 270mm.
(Christie's)   **$2,695**   **£1,540**

OLIVE PARKER BLACK — New England stream,
early autumn — signed — oil on canvas — 16 x 24in.
(Robt. W. Skinner Inc.)   **$2,100 £1,193**

WILLIAM KAY BLACKLOCK — An old woman
pouring tea at a hearthside — signed — watercolour
— 11¼ x 8¼in.
(Anderson & Garland)   **$5,130 £3,000**

WILLIAM KAY BLACKLOCK — Polperro Harbour
— signed and inscribed — watercolour — 9 x 11½in.
(Anderson & Garland)   **$1,265 £740**

ANTOINE BLANCHARD — Paris street scene —
signed — oil on canvas — 24 x 30in.
(Du Mouchelles)   **$4,500 £2,380**

ANTOINE BLANCHARD — Paris street scene —
signed — oil on canvas — 20 x 24in.
(Du Mouchelles)   **$2,250 £1,190**

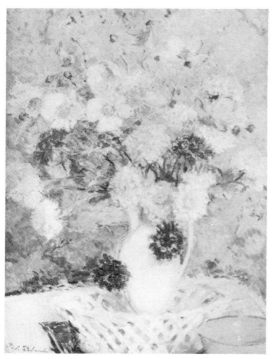

JACQUES EMILE BLANCHE — Nature morte au Bouquet de Fleurs — signed — oil on board — 24¼ x 19½in.
(Christie's) **$19,250 £11,000**

ARBIT BLATAS — Still life — signed — oil on canvas.
(Christie's) **$1,320 £725**

BRUNO BLATTER — Merrymaking in the tavern — signed — oil on canvas — 30.5 x 39in.
(Christie's) **$1,487 £880**

JUAN LUIS BLANES — A Uruguayan Gaucho — signed — on metal — 8 x 6in.
(Christie's) **$1,174 £660**

JABEZ BLIGH — The grass withereth and the flower fadeth — signed — watercolour and bodycolour — 10 x 8¼in.
(Christie's) **$1,135 £660**

BLOCK

L. BLOCK — Still life of books, a quill pen, letters and a pair of spectacles — signed — pen and black ink, watercolour and bodycolour heightened with white — 12 x 20in.
(Christie's) $2,664 $1,540

PIETER VAN BLOEMEN, called STANDARD — Horsemen resting their mounts at a river's edge amongst Classical ruins — oil on canvas — 21 x 30½in.
(Phillips)   Two $10,912 £6,200

BERNARDUS JOHANNES BLOMMERS — The fisherman's children — signed — oil on canvas — 34 x 27in.
(Christie's)
                          $48,576 £26,400

OSCAR F. BLUEMNER — Boat House, Branch Brook Park — monogrammed and inscribed — charcoal on paper — 4½ x 5½in.
(Robt. W. Skinner Inc.) $275 £156

THEOPHILE EMILE ACHILLE DE BOCK — A woodland path — signed — oil on canvas laid down on panel — 23½ x 14½in.
(Christie's)
                           $1,301 £770

JOHANNES BOESEN – Mons klint, Denmark –
signed and dated – 35½ x 57in.
(Christie's)   **$15,262**   **£8,250**

HENRY JOHN BODDINGTON, Attributed to
– A gypsy encampment – 13¼ x 9½in.
(Christie's)   **$1,958**   **£1,100**

JOHANNES BOESEN – A woodland stream –
signed with monogram – oil on canvas –
25 x 37in.
(Christie's)   **$4,833**   **£2,860**

PIERRE LE BOEFF – A Continental market town
– signed – 19¾ x 15¾in.
(Christie's)   **$743 £440**

FRANK MYERS BOGGS – The Louvre and the
Arc du Caroussel – signed – oil on canvas –
24 x 29in.
(Christie's)   **$11,000**   **£5,913**

HENRIK CARL BOGH – In the farmyard –
signed and dated – 16 x 24in.
(Christie's)   **$3,806 £2,200**

C. V. BOIZARD – The circus parade – signed –
oil on canvas – 20 x 30in.
(Du Mouchelles)   **$1,600 £946**

FERDINAND BOL, Follower of – Portrait of a
soldier, bust length – oil on canvas –
29½ x 24in.
(Lawrence Fine Arts)   **$1,903**   **£1,100**

GIOVANNI BOLDINI – Portrait of Diaz Albertini
– signed and dated – 40 x 37½in.
(Christie's)   **$157,850**   **£90,200**

DAVID BOMBERG – Portrait head of Lilian –
oil on canvas – 24 x 16in.
(Christie's)   **$22,896 £12,650**

DAVID BOMBERG – The Alcantara Bridge, Toledo – signed and dated – oil on board – 21 x 26¾in.
(Christie's) $147,334 £81,400

WILLIAM JOSEPH J. C. BOND – A view from The Red Noses to Liverpool, with the Church of St Peter's in the distance – signed – on board – 12 x 18in.
(Christie's) $456 £264

WILLIAM JOSEPH JULIUS CAESAR BOND – A sailing vessel by a jetty – signed – on board – 5½ x 4¾in.
(Christie's) $900 £506

AUGUSTE BONHEUR – Cattle in a coastal landscape – signed – oil on canvas – 24½ x 36½in.
(Christie's) $14,168 £7,700

ROSA BONHEUR – Mother and son – signed – oil on canvas – 13 x 19in.
(Anderson & Garland) $5,363 £3,100

PIERRE BONNARD – Remorqueur sur la Seine a Vernon – signed – on paper – 49.8 x 32.4cm.
(Christie's) $189,200 £110,000

BONNARD

AXEL BORG – A wooded marsh – signed –
on panel – 26.9 x 35.3cm.
(Christie's) **$1,933** **£1,045**

PIERRE BONNARD – Le Negre Constantin –
signed and inscribed – oil on canvas –
20¼ x 15¾in.
(Christie's) **$26,950 £15,400**

CARL OSCAR BORG – The Debate – signed and
inscribed – watercolour – 36.8 x 55.5cm.
(Christie's) **$1,664** **£935**

WILLIAM JACOBUS BOOGAARD – In the Stable – signed – on panel – 10½ x 15in.
(Christie's) **$6,545 £3,850**

GIDEON BORJE – Landscape, Sweden – signed – oil on canvas – 28¾ x 36¼in.
(Christie's) **$4,261** **£2,255**

MABEL WINIFRED BOSTOCK – Cape Province farm – signed and inscribed – on canvas laid down on board – 11½ x 15½in.
(Christie's) **$391** **£220**

R. A. BORSTEL – 'Speedonia', a Clipper off Sydney Heads – signed, inscribed and dated – on canvas – 50.7x76.4cm.
(Christie's) **$1,272** **£715**

FREDERICK ANDREW BOSLEY – Peace at Home – signed and dated – oil on canvas – 183 x 152.5cm.
(Christie's) **$12,100** **£6,505**

FREDERICK JAMES BOSTON – Woman picking flowers – signed – oil on canvas – 30 x 20in.
(Christie's) **$1,650** **£906**

BOSTON

JOSEPH H. BOSTON — Landscape scene — signed
— oil on canvas — 30.5 x 41cm.
(Robt. W. Skinner Inc.)   **$1,500**   **£852**

EUGENE BOUDIN — Port. Les Oriflammes —
signed — oil on board laid on cradled panel —
7¾ x 13in.
(Christie's)   **$94,600**   **£55,000**

FRANCOIS BOUCHER, After — The Cage — oil on
canvas — 73 x 60cm.
(Phillips)   **$2,288**   **£1,300**

EUGENE BOUDIN — Honfleur; Le Port — signed
— oil on panel — 10 x 15in.
(Christie's)   **$86,394**   **£46,200**

PIETER BOUTS and ADRIAEN FRANS BOUDE-
WIJNS — Figures on a path, before a ferry crossing a river and fishermen hauling in nets — oil on
canvas — 16¼ x 23½in.
(Phillips)   **$7,392 £4,200**

EUGENE BOUDIN — La Mer a Douarnenez —
signed, dated and inscribed — oil on panel —
11 x 14in.
(Christie's)   **$48,576 £26,400**

SAMUEL BOUGH – A gypsy girl – signed and dated – 24 x 20in.
(Christie's) **$1,076 £605**

SEBASTIAN BOURDON, After – The infant Christ contemplating the instruments of The Passion displayed by angels – 25¾ x 30in.
(Christie's) **$1,713 £990**

CORNELIS BOUTER – The centre of attraction – signed – 20 x 24in.
(Christie's) **$7,106 £4,180**

WILLIAM ADOLPHE BOUGUEREAU – At the start of the day – signed and dated – oil on canvas – 37½ x 24in.
(Christie's) **$70,840 £38,500**

ANTOINE BOUVARD – A Venetian Canal – signed – 19½ x 25½in.
(Christie's) **$4,114 £2,200**

BOUVARD

ANTOINE BOUVARD — A Venetian backwater —
signed — 19¼ x 25½in.
(Christie's)   **$2,674 £1,430**

AUGUSTUS BOUVIER — Portrait of a young lady
in a white and blue dress, carrying a parasol and
dancing on a rug — 19 x 9in.
(G. A. Key)   **$1,402 £750**

JOSEPH BOUVIER — The Nymph in a Wooded
Glade — signed and dated — watercolour and
bodycolour — 21¾ x 15½in.
(Phillips)   **$1,352   £800**

PASCAL ADOLPHE JEAN DAGNAN BOUVERET
— A young Bacchante — signed and dated —
18¼ x 9¾in.
(Christie's)   **$2,805   £1,650**

ALEXANDER BOWER — Observation Tower,
Cape Elizabeth — signed — watercolour on paper —
18 x 22in.
(Bruce D. Collins)   **$330   £174**

WILLIAM THOMAS NICHOLS BOYCE – Shipping off Sunderland – signed and dated – 13¾ x 20in.
(Anderson & Garland)   **$1,211 £700**

ARTHUR BOYD – Morning on the Shoalhaven River – signed – oil on canvas – 121 x 151cm.
(Australian Art Auctions)   **$27,259 £14,815**

WILLIAM THOMAS NICHOLS BOYCE – Coastal craft on a blustery day – signed and dated – 9¼ x 13in.
(Anderson & Garland)   **$841 £450**

WILLIAM THOMAS NICOLS BOYCE – Herring boats off a headland – signed and dated – 13¾ x 18½in.
(Anderson & Garland)   **$1,107 £640**

CRESWICK BOYDELL – Outside the cottage – signed – on panel – 18 x 10¾in.
(Christie's)   **$1,076   £605**

BOYDELL

CRESWICK BOYDELL – A Gloucestershire thatched cottage in summer – signed – 13¾ x 18¼in.
(Anderson & Garland) **$1,314 £760**

ARTHUR ROYCE BRADBURY – Reclining Nude – signed and dated – oil on canvas – 18¾ x 24in.
(Christie's) **$1,903** **£1,100**

BASIL BRADLEY – Setters in a Landscape – signed – watercolour – 7 x 10in.
(Phillips) **$2,704** **£1,600**

THOMAS SHOTTER BOYS – Waterloo – signed – pencil and watercolour – 26.5 x 17.5cm.
(Christie's) **$14,025 £8,250**

HELEN BRADLEY – Blackpool Station – signed – watercolour and bodycolour – 14 x 21¼in.
(Christie's) **$21,538 £12,100**

ADRIEN FERDINAND DE BRAEKELEER –
The poultry seller – signed and dated – oil on
panel – 14½ x 12in.
(Christie's) **$8,500 £4,620**

FRANK BRAMLEY – Chrysanthemums in a blue
vase – oil on canvas – 23¼ x 30¼in.
(Christie's) **$29,370 £16,500**

FRANK BRAMLEY – Old English roses –
monogrammed and dated – 6 x 10in.
(W. H. Lane & Son) **$4,128 £2,400**

FRANK BRAMLEY – Courtship – oil on canvas
– 30 x 36in.
(Christie's) **$35,244 £19,800**

SIR FRANK BRANGWYN – Canal with workmen
– oil on canvas – 15 x 24in.
(Christie's) **$5,286 £2,970**

CHARLES BROOKE BRANWHITE – Christchurch-
on Avon, Hants – signed and dated – watercolour
– 14 x 24½in.
(Lawrence Fine Arts) **$1,712 £990**

BRAQUE

GEORGES BRAQUE – Grand Nu – signed and dated – on canvas – 91 x 72.5cm.
(Christie's) **$813,560 £473,000**

WILLIAM A. BREAKSPEARE – The reproach – signed – on panel – 7½ x 4¾in.
(Christie's) **$1,762 £990**

VICTOR BRAUNER – Promeneur – signed and dated – oil on canvas – 73 x 60cm.
(Christie's) **$127,534 £68,200**

ALFRED DE BREANSKI – Near Dunkeld, N.B. – signed – 24 x 36in.
(Christie's) **$13,244 £7,700**

ALFRED DE BREANSKI – Ben Lomond –
signed – 16 x 24in.
(Christie's)   **$17,230 £9,680**

ALFRED FONTVILLE DE BREANSKI – A
water mill and a village street – signed – 15 x 22in.
(Anderson & Garland)   Two **$2,422 £1,400**

ALFRED FONTVILLE DE BREANSKI – Grange
near Keswick, Cumbria – signed – oil on canvas –
19½ x 29in.
(Prudential)   **$1,028   £550**

QUIRYN VAN BREKELENKAM – A lady seated
in an interior with a book open on her lap and a
gentleman standing – oil on panel – 15 x 13in.
(Phillips)   **$3,401   £1,900**

HANS ANDERSEN BRENDEKILDE – By the pond
– signed and dated – 15¾ x 19¾in.
(Christie's)   **$34,595   £18,700**

CARL BRENNIR – Cattle by a river in Westmorland – signed – oil on canvas – 19½ x 29½in.
(Anderson & Garland)   **$1,903 £1,100**

BRESSANIN

VITTORIO EMANUELE BRESSANIN — Rejected — signed — oil on canvas — 76.3 x 110.8cm.
(Christie's) $30,360 £16,500

ALFRED THOMPSON BRICHER — Mill Pond at Freeport, Long Island, New York — signed — watercolour, gouache, and pencil on grey paper — 37.2 x 53.9cm.
(Christie's) $24,200 £13,010

ANDRE BRETON — Decalcomanie — inscribed on the reverse — black gouache *decalcomanie* on paper — 11¼ x 8¾in.
(Christie's) $6,050 £3,570

FREDERICK ARTHUR BRIDGMAN — Arabian landscape with figures and camel — signed and dated — oil on canvas
(Hobbs & Chambers) $2,970 £1,650

FREDERICK ARTHUR BRIDGMAN — Arab women sitting in a street — signed with initials and dated — 18¼ x 15in.
(Christie's) **$7,480** **£4,400**

BERNAERT DE BRIDT — Huntsmen with their hounds resting beneath a tree — signed — oil on canvas — 16 x 21¼in.
(Phillips) **$5,370 £3,000**

ARTHUR J. T. BRISCOE — A beam wind — figures setting the sails on a sailing vessel — signed — watercolour — 14 x 21in.
(W. H. Lane & Son) **$3,660 £2,000**

WILLIAM BRODERICK — A Peregrine Falcon — signed with monogram and dated — 30 x 42in.
(Christie's) **$11,356 £6,380**

ADRIAEN BROUWER, Follower of — Boors in a tavern — on panel — 14 x 10in.
(Christie's) **$2,664 £1,540**

CARLYLE BROWN — Poppies — signed and dated — gouache on paper — 17¾ x 22in.
(Christie's) **$1,430** **£843**

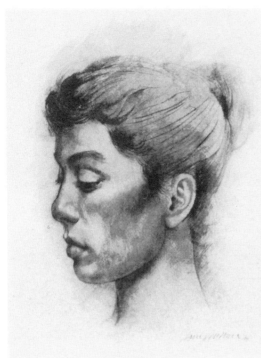

CARLYLE BROWN – Reclining Youth – signed and dated – gouache and watercolour on paper – 13¾ x 17¾in.
(Christie's) **$1,760** **£1,038**

CARLYLE BROWN – Portrait of a Young Girl – signed and dated – watercolour on paper – 13¾ x 10½in.
(Christie's) **$385** **£227**

HUGH BOYCOTT-BROWN – Crab Boats at Cromer – signed – oil on canvas – 24 x 36in.
(Christie's) **$3,916** **£2,200**

CARLYLE BROWN – Portrait – signed and dated – gouache on paper – 22 x 17¾in.
(Christie's) **$385** **£227**

HUGH BOYCOTT BROWN – Fishing Boats, Finisterre, Brittany – signed – oil on canvas – 24¼ x 36¼in.
(Christie's) **$1,958 £1,100**

J. G. BROWN – Grandmother's favourite – signed – oil on canvas – 30 x 24in.
(Du Mouchelles) **$9,000 £4,761**

MARSHALL BROWN – The fisher lass – signed – oil on canvas - 50 x 40cm.
(Phillips) **$21,054 £12,100**

JOHN GEORGE BROWN – A Liberated Woman – signed and dated – oil on canvas – 42 x 32in.
(Christie's) **$55,000** **£29,569**

ROY BROWN – Winter Fields – signed – oil on canvas – 50.5 x 76.2cm.
(Robt. W. Skinner Inc.) **$350** **£207**

W. E. BARRINGTON-BROWNE – Ballyann with Mount Bandan in the distance – signed – oil on canvas – 18 x 24in.
(Christie's) **$1,566 £880**

BROWNELL

PELEG FRANKLIN BROWNELL – Trilliums –
signed with initials – pastel – 12 x 9¼in.
(Christie's) **$626** **£352**

LODEWYK BRUCKMAN – Neptune's Treasure –
signed and dated – oil on canvas – 22 x 14in.
(Robt. W. Skinner Inc.) **$1,000** **£691**

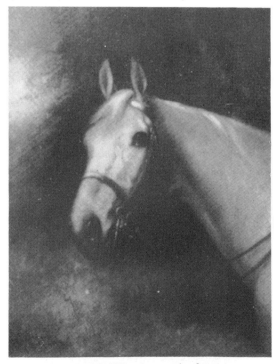

GEORGE BROWNLOW – A portrait of a grey
horse – signed – oil on canvas – 19 x 15½in.
(Anderson & Garland) **$430 £230**

CHARLES LE BRUN, After – The sacrifice of
Jephthah's daughter – circular – 26in. diam.
(Christie's) **$3,045 £1,760**

VIGEE LE BRUN, After — Portrait of the artist — oil on canvas — 10¼ x 8¾in.
(Christie's) $838 £496

GEORGE BUCHNER — A young girl in peasant costume — signed and dated — oil on panel — 8¼ x 6¼in.
(Christie's) $9,108 £4,950

FRANCOIS BRUNERY — Battle of the champagne corks — signed — oil on canvas — 28¼ x 36½in.
(Phillips) $52,624 £28,600

BUCK

ADAM BUCK − Portrait of a lady, said to be the Countess of Cavan, small full length, on a terrace with a portfolio resting on a chair beside her − signed, inscribed and dated − pencil, black and brown chalk and watercolour − 38.5 x 28.5cm.
(Christie's) **$5,984 £3,520**

BERNARD BUFFET − La Route − signed and numbered − colour lithograph − 64.5 x 49.5cm.
(Robt. W. Skinner Inc.) **$3,700 £2,189**
JOHN MICHAEL BUCKLEY − W.P.A. New England Village, Winter − signed − oil on canvas − 25 x 30in.
(Robt. W. Skinner Inc.) **$550 £325**

BERNARD BUFFET – Manoletina – signed and
dated – oil on canvas – 92½ x 117¾in.
(Christie's) **$122,980** **£71,500**

EDGAR BUNDY – A squadron of Moss Troopers
in a landscape with cattle and sheep – signed – oil
on canvas – 28½ x 36in.
(Geering & Colyer) **$1,806** **£1,050**

FELIX-HILAIRE BUHOT – L'Hiver a Paris ou la
Neige a Paris – signed and dated – etching, aquatint
and drypoint on paper – 23.7 x 35cm.
(Robt. W. Skinner Inc.) **$550** **£325**

HEINRICH BUNTZEN – A wooded river landscape
with a huntsman – signed with initials –9½ x 8¾in.
(Christie's) **$1,427 £825**

EDGAR BUNDY – The Cartel – signed –
19½ x 26¼in.
(Anderson & Garland) **$4,325 £2,500**

ARTHUR JAMES WETHERALL BURGESS –
Sun glitter on the sea – signed – watercolour –
10½ x 14¾in.
(Christie's) **$939** **£528**

BURGH

VERONICA BURLEIGH – Gypsies – pen, brown ink, brown wash and pencil – 13½ x 20in.
(Christie's) **$334** **£198**

ALBERT VAN DER BURGH – A Boer playing a mandolin – signed – oil on panel – 17.5 x 15.5cm.
(Phillips) **$2,552 £1,450**

SIR EDWARD COLEY BURNE-JONES – Portrait of a young Woman, bust length, looking downwards to the right – signed – red chalk, watermark MS – 14¾ x 12in.
(Christie's) **$8,415** **£4,950**

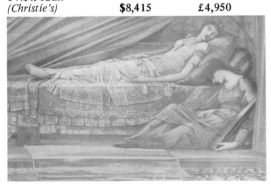

SYDNEY R. BURLEIGH – Portrait of Angela O'Leary – signed with initials – watercolour on paper – 5 x 3in.
(Bruce D. Collins) **$1,045** **£552**

SIR EDWARD COLEY BURNE-JONES – The sleeping princess – signed with initials and dated – gouache with gold paint – 59 x 38¼in.
(Christie's) **$809,600 £440,000**

SIR EDWARD COLEY BURNE-JONES – The lament – oil on canvas – 11 x 15¼in.
(Christie's) **$48,576 £26,400**

ROBERT BURNS – Contemplation – signed – oil on canvas – 46.5cm. diam.
(Phillips) **$5,359 £3,080**

JOHN BURR – The poor helping the poor – signed and dated – oil on canvas – 30 x 45cm.
(Phillips) **$20,097 £11,550**

ROBERT BURNS – The Seamstress – oil on canvas – 111 x 59.5cm.
(Phillips) **$5,359 £3,080**

EDWARD BURRA Music Hall – watercolour – 22½ x 30in.
(Christie's) **$63,712 £35,200**

BUTLER

THEODORE EARL BUTLER – Lili reading –
signed and dated – oil on canvas – 29 x 24in.
(Du Mouchelles) **$25,000 £14,790**

FRANCIS CAMPBELL BOILEAU CADELL –
A rocky shore, Iona – signed – oil on board –
36 x 44cm.
(Phillips) **$19,140 £11,000**

HECTOR CAFFIERI – A boating party on the
Thames at Cookham – signed – pencil and
watercolour – 13¾ x 19½in.
(Christie's) **$10,285** **£6,050**

FRANCIS CAMPBELL BOILEAU CADELL –
Rhum – signed – oil on board – 36 x 44cm.
(Phillips) **$26,796 £15,400**

HECTOR CAFFIERI – A Young Girl in a Meadow
– signed – watercolour – 10 x 8in.
(Phillips) **$5,408** **£3,200**

JAMES HENRY CAFFERTY – Boys Fishing –
oil on canvas – 16 x 20in.
(Christie's) **$4,400** **£2,365**

WALTER WALLOR CAFFYN – A wooded river
landscape with a figure on a bridge – signed and
dated – paper laid down on card – 10 x 14in.
(Christie's) **$796** **£440**

ALEXANDER CALDER – Grand Soleil – signed,
dated and inscribed – gouache on paper –
75 x 110cm.
(Christie's) **$16,456 £8,800**

ANTOINE CALBET – The Spanish dancer – signed
– pencil and watercolour – 12¼ x 8½in.
(Christie's) **$250** **£143**

ALEXANDER CALDER – Composition – signed
and dated – gouache on paper – 43¼ x 29½in.
(Christie's) **$12,298** **£7,150**

ALEXANDER CALDER – Untitled – signed and
dated – mobile of painted sheet metal and rod –
overall approximately 165.5 x 123cm.
(Christie's) **$127,534 £68,200**

ALEXANDER CALDER – Spiral – signed and
dated – gouache on paper – 29½x43¼in.
(Christie's) **$12,298** **£7,150**

CALDECOTT

SIR DAVID YOUNG CAMERON – Evening in Badenoch – signed – oil on canvas – 32.5 x 56cm.
(Phillips) **$9,570 £5,500**

RANDOLPH CALDECOTT – The Farmer's Lunch – signed with initials – pen and ink and water-colour – 8 x 6¾in. – and companion
(Phillips) Two **$2,873** **£1,700**

DUNCAN CAMERON – East Ness Head, Crail, Scotland – signed – oil on canvas – 12 x 20¼in.
(W. H. Lane & Son) **$951 £520**

DUNCAN CAMERON – Harvest time – signed – oil on canvas – 75 x 131cm.
(Phillips) **$4,976 £2,860**

WILLIAM CALLOW – San Giorgio della Greci from the Ponte della Pieta, Venice – signed and dated – pencil and watercolour with touches of bodycolour – 40.5 x 32cm.
(Christie's) **$44,880 £26,400**

SIR DAVID YOUNG CAMERON – Ardlui – signed – oil on canvas – 61 x 92cm.
(Phillips) **$5,359 £3,080**

BLANCHE CAMUS – Le Quai de St Tropez –
signed – oil on panel – 37.2 x 45.7cm.
(Christie's) **$4,158 £2,200**

CHARLES CAMOIN – La Terrasse fleurie, Agay –
signed – oil on canvas – 65 x 81 cm.
(Christie's) **$52,976** **£30,800**

MASSIMO CAMPIGLI – Promenade – signed
and dated – oil on canvas – 17¾ x 22¼in.
(Christie's) **$46,200 £26,400**

BLANCHE CAMUS – Le Port de St Tropez – oil
on panel – 15 x 18½in.
(Christie's) **$4,573 £2,420**

FREDERICO DEL CAMPO – Capri – signed
and dated – oil on canvas – 15½ x 26¼in.
(Christie's) **$30,360 £16,500**

BLANCHE CAMUS – Paysage de Saint Tropez –
signed – oil on canvas – 50 x 61cm.
(Christie's) **$6,737 £3,850**

CAPUTO

ULYSSE CAPUTO – A girl reading in an interior
– signed – oil on panel – 15½ x 19in.
(Christie's) $9,108 £4,950

CLAUDE CARDON – Interior of a barn with calves,
terriers and ducks – signed – watercolour –
27 x 38cm.
(Henry Spencer) $3,114 £1,800

ULYSSE CAPUTO – Apres le Bal – signed –
oil on canvas – 73 x 60cm.
(Christie's) $3,080 £1,760

CLAUDE CARDON – Spring Pastures – signed
and dated – oil on canvas – 14 x 17¼in.
(Lawrence Fine Arts) $2,473 £1,430

GONZALVO CARELLI − Amalfi − signed and inscribed − pencil and watercolour − 13¾ x 9¾in.
(Christie's) **$3,291 £1,760**

SOREN EMIL CARLSEN − Ruby Reflection − signed and dated − oil on canvas laid down on masonite - 37.2 x 40.6cm.
(Christie's) **$22,000** **£11,827**

JOHN WILLIAM CARMICHAEL − Largo d'Iseo: Northern Italy − signed and dated − 18 x 23in.
(Anderson & Garland) **$6,840** **£3,800**

GONZALVO CARELLI − Naples − signed and inscribed − pencil and watercolour − 13½ x 9½in.
(Christie's) **$2,468 £1,320**

JOHN WILSON CARMICHAEL − Sunset: Palazzo d'Este − signed and dated − 18 x 23in.
(Anderson & Garland) **$6,840** **£3,800**

CARMICHAEL

JOHN WILSON CARMICHAEL – Fishwives by a coble – signed and dated – oil on canvas – 16¼ x 23¼in.
(Anderson & Garland) **$5,400** **£3,000**

JEAN CAROLUS – Flowers for the lady – signed and dated – 32¼ x 41¼in.
(Christie's) **$18,287 £10,450**

JOHN WILSON CARMICHAEL – The Gaol from Ha Hill, Morpeth – signed and dated – 11½ x 17½in.
(Anderson & Garland) **$2,340** **£1,300**

JEAN CAROLUS – A visit to Watteau's Studio – signed and dated – oil on canvas – 32 x 41in.
(Christie's) **$13,013** **£7,700**

LEONORA CARRINGTON – Ur of the Chaldees – oil on canvas – 35½ x 21½in.
(Christie's) **$23,100** **£13,631**

LEONORA CARRINGTON – Tuesday – signed, titled and dated – egg tempera on panel – 21¾ x 33¼in.
(Christie's) **$132,000** **£77,893**

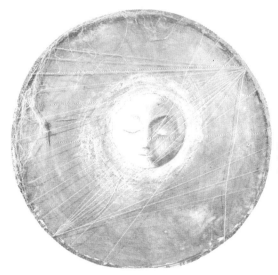

SYDNEY CARTER – A good book – signed and dated – on canvas – 30 x 20in.
(Christie's) **$979** **£550**

LEONORA CARRINGTON – Luna Grande; Luna Blanca – signed and dated – painted plaster relief on wood with threads – 27¾ diam.
(Christie's) **$4,950** **£2,920**

LEONORA CARRINGTON – El Grito – signed and dated – oil on board – 15½ x 34½in.
(Christie's) **$35,200** **£20,771**

A. J. CASSON – Country houses by the river side – signed – oil on panel – 18.7 x 23.2cm.
(Robt. W. Skinner Inc.) **$4,600** **£2,613**

CASTEELS

PIETER CASTEELS III, Circle of — A hawk swooping on ducks in a pond — oil on canvas — 54.5 x 64.5cm.
(Phillips)　　　　**$880**　　　　**£500**

AUGUSTO CECCHI — On guard — signed and dated — 12¼ x 8¾in.
(Christie's)　　　**$1,683**　　　**£990**

F. CATANO — Mosque of the Bar-El Wapar, Cairo — signed — pencil and watercolour heightened with white — 17½ x 10¼in.
(Christie's)　　　　**$370 £198**

THEODORE CERIEZ — The connoisseurs — signed — on panel — 9½ x 7in.
(Christie's)　　　**$1,402**　　　**£825**

PAUL CHABAS – Sous les branches – signed – on panel 9¼ x 12¼in.
(Christie's) $5,610 £3,300

GIACOMO CERUTI, Follower of – An old woman holding a wine glass and a bottle of Chianti – 60.8 x 48.2cm.
(Christie's) $1,427 £825

MARC CHAGALL – Paysage de Peyra-Cava; Le Nuage – signed and dated – oil on canvas – 73 x 60cm.
(Christie's) $714,780 £418,000

PAUL CHABAS – Femme Assise dans un Paysage – signed – oil on board – 17½ x 15in.
(Christie's) $6,160 £3,520

MARC CHAGALL – Fleurs et Amants – signed – coloured chalks on *papier japon nacre* – 19¾ x 15in.
(Christie's) $227,000 £132,000

CHAGALL

MARC CHAGALL – Amoureux au dessous d'un Arbre – signed and dated – watercolour – 26.5 x 20cm.
(Christie's) $17,325 £9,900

MARC CHAGALL – Le Peintre a la Palette – signed and dated – black ink on paper – 20 x 14.5cm.
(Christie's) **$5,390 £3,080**

MARC CHAGALL – Deux Clowns a Cheval (Cirque Vollard) – signed – on paper – 62.8 x 48.3cm.
(Christie's) **$454,080** **£264,000**

MARC CHAGALL – La Ferme, le Village – signed – oil on canvas – 24 x 29in.
(Christie's) **$790,020** **£462,000**

ALFRED EDWARD CHALON – Portrait of Sir Joseph and Lady Mawbry's children – signed – pencil and watercolour – 16.3 x 19.6cm.
(Christie's) **$643** **£374**

CHARLES CHAPLIN – In the boudoir – signed – 20¾ x 11¼in.
(Christie's)   **$14,960   £8,800**

G. B. CHARIGLIONA – The Musketeer's Love Song – signed – pencil and watercolour – 35.3 x 52.7cm.
(Christie's)   **$1,617 £935**

FRANTZ CHARLET – La Mer du Nord – signed and dated – oil on panel – 28.8 x 40cm.
(Christie's)   **$4,781 £2,530**

GEORGE CHARLTON – Sunbathers in a Cornish cove – signed – watercolour – 6 x 10¼in.
(W. H. Lane & Son)   **$384 £210**

WILLIAM HENRY CHARLTON – From Instow N. Devon (Appledore) – signed and dated – oil on canvas – 10¼ x 13¼in.
(Anderson & Garland)   **$1,094 £640**

CHARTON

ERNEST CHARTON – Valparaiso, Chile – signed
inscribed and dated – on canvas – 24½ x 34¼in.
(Christie's)   **$33,286   £18,700**

HENRI LUCIEN CHEFFER – Ready for Ambush
– signed – pencil, watercolour and bodycolour
on buff paper – 24.5 x 31.7cm.
(Christie's)   **$2,854 £1,650**

**FREDERICUS JACOBUS VAN ROSSUM DU
CHATTEL** – A music lesson – signed – oil on
canvas – 25¼ x 21¼in.
(Anderson & Garland) **$1,890   £1,050**

HENRI LUCIEN CHEFFER – Observation a Paris:
Poste d'Observation D.C.A. – signed – pencil,
watercolour and bodycolour on buff paper –
10½ x 8in.
(Christie's)   **$856   £495**

HENRY LUCIEN CHEFFER – Soldiers in their
encampment – pencil and watercolour heightened
with white – 10 x 12¾in. – and a pencil drawing.
(Christie's)   **Two**   **$557   £330**

HENRY LUCIEN CHEFFER – The quiet after the
storm – with pencil and watercolour heightened
with bodycolour on buff paper – 31.4 x 23.8cm.
(Christie's)   **$334   £198**

LILIAN CHEVIOT – Best of friends – signed –
20 x 24in.
(Christie's) **$2,937 £1,650**

H. T. CHEMIELINSKY – Figures in a town street
– signed – 13½ x 19½in.
(Christie's) **$532 £308**

GAETANO CHIERICI – Feeding baby – signed and
dated – 18¾ x 25in.
(Christie's) **$34,650** **£19,800**

CARLO CHERUBINI – Racehorses – signed and
dated – oil on canvas – 16 x 20in.
(Du Mouchelles) **$1,100 £650**

GAETANO CHIERICI – Playing with baby –
signed – 13 x 16½in.
(Christie's) **$100,000** **£57,200**

GEORGIO DE CHIRICO – Roses – signed – oil on board – 12 x 15in.
(Du Mouchelles) **$8,500 £5,030**

GEORGE CHINNERY – Tanka Boats on the Shore – inscribed – pen and brown ink, light brown and light blue wash – 23.5 x 18cm.
(Christie's) **$13,090 £7,700**

J. CHRIST – A shepherd and shepherdess with their flock by a pond, in a wooded landscape – signed and dated – 20½ x 26in.
(Christie's) **$5,610** **£3,300**

GEORGE CHINNERY – Study of an old Chinese, carrying a wide hat and a club – dated – pencil – 10 x 7cm.
(Christie's) **$598 £352**

ANTHONORA CHRISTENSEN – Peaches and grapes in a bowl, with camellia and corn on a table – signed with initials and dated – 15 x 19¾in.
(Christie's) **$1,870** **£1,100**

CHRISTO – Valley Curtain (Project for Aspen, Colorado) – signed and dated – fabric collage, coloured crayon and pencil on board – 70.5 x 55cm.
(Christie's) **$28,798 £15,400**

ANTONIO CIFRONDI, Circle of – A shepherd – oil on canvas – 76.5 x 56.5cm.
(Phillips) **$962 £550**

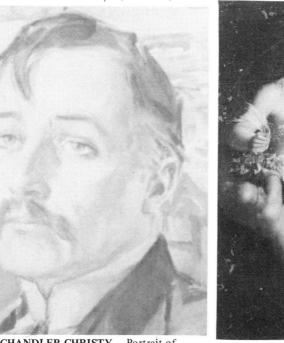

HOWARD CHANDLER CHRISTY – Portrait of John Drew – signed – watercolour on watercolour board – 26.7 x 21.3cm.
(Robt. W. Skinner Inc.) **$175 £99**

CARLO CIGNANI – Venus with two cupids – oil on canvas – 131 x 102cm.
(Phillips) **$28,160 £16,000**

C. MYRON CLARK – U.S. Frigate 'Constitution' – signed and dated – oil on canvas – 19 x 31in. *(Bruce D. Collins)* **$2,420** **£1,280**

ANTONIO CIRINO – October sunlight, Northern New England – signed – oil on board – 18 x 20in. *(Bruce D. Collins)* **$2,420** **£1,280**

JOHN COSMO CLARK – Concarneau Harbour – signed – oil on canvas – 20 x 16in. *(Christie's)* **$1,236** **£715**

WILLIAM ALBERT CLARK – Melbourne Princess and Queen of Ayr, with wagonette and driver – signed and dated – oil on canvas – 19½ x 29½in. *(Prudential)* **$4,325 £2,500**

GEORGE CLAIRIN – The lovers – signed – oil on canvas – 32 x 23½in. *(Christie's)* **$13,763 £7,480**

WILLIAM ALBERT CLARK – "Lunds Janke's Beatty", study of a prize bull standing in an extensive rural landscape – signed and dated – 49.5 x 60cm.
(Henry Spencer) **$3,646 £1,950**

SIR GEORGE CLAUSEN – The roof menders – signed – watercolour and pencil – 9½ x 6½in.
(Christie's) **$1,762 £990**

PIERRE DE CLAUSADE – Le Marais dans la Neige – signed – 21 x 25 in.
(Christie's) **$1,301 £770**

SIR GEORGE CLAUSEN – Landscape and trees – signed – watercolour – 8½ x 11¼in.
(Christie's) **$594 £352**

SIR GEORGE CLAUSEN – Planting a tree – oil on board – 14 x 11¾in.
(Christie's) **$29,370 £16,500**

ELIZABETH CAMPBELL FISHER CLAY – Martin
Eglise, Normandy – 32 x 26in.
(Christie's) **$7,807 £4,620**

ELIZABETH CAMPBELL FISHER CLAY – The
seaside, Eastbourne – signed – on panel –
13¾ x 10in.
(Christie's) **$4,089 £2,420**

ELIZABETH CAMPBELL FISHER CLAY – Red
haired girl in a dark green dress – 24 x 18in.
(Christie's) **$371 £220**

ELIZABETH CAMPBELL FISHER CLAY –
Beguinage Bridge, Bruges – signed – 11½ x 15½in.
(Christie's) **$743 £440**

J. HUGHES CLAYTON – Setting off with the lobster pots – signed – watercolour – 10 x 24in. *(W. H. Lane & Son)* **$3,568 £1,950**

W. P. CLEAVES – Mountain Valley, summer – signed – oil on canvas – 45.7 x 66.4cm. *(Robt. W. Skinner Inc.)* **$900 £511**

JOOS VAN CLEVE, Follower of – The Madonna and child – oil on panel – 16¾ x 12¼in. *(Phillips)* **$6,265 £3,500**

GEORGE CLINT – The Fair Toxopholites – – Exhibited R.A. – watercolour – 12 x 9¼in. *(Anderson & Garland)* **$1,710 £1,000**

SANCHEZ COELLO, Follower of – Portrait of a lady standing three-quarter length beside red drapes wearing a gown with a high lace collar – oil on canvas – 97.5 x 80cm. *(Phillips)* **$2,800 £1,600**

WILLIAM STEPHEN COLEMAN – Girls at play
on the Mediterranean terrace – signed – 17 x 26¾in.
(Christie's) **$8,811 £4,950**

WILLIAM STEPHEN COLEMAN – A classical Nymph
– signed – pencil and watercolour – 35.3 x 25.5 cm.
(Christie's) **$1,496** **£880**

WILLIAM STEPHEN COLEMAN – The flower
girl – signed – 36 x 29in.
(Christie's) **$4,830** **£2,420**

F. G. COLERIDGE – At Shiplake – indistinctly
signed and dated – watercolour heightened with
white – 4¼ x 7¾in.
(Christie's)   **$951   £550**

CHARLES COLLINS – Cattle on a grassy riverbank
– one of a pair – signed and dated – 12½ x 30in.
(Christie's)   **Two**   **$3,132 £1,760**

G. COMBIER – The artist's studio – signed and
dated – oil on canvas – 70½ x 53in.
(Christie's)   **$20,240 £11,000**

JAN TEN COMPE – The Customs House, Amsterdam – signed – oil on panel – 40 x 53cm.
(Phillips)   **$14,080 £8,000**

EDWARD THEODORE COMPTON – The Gross
Glockner from Heiligenblut – signed and dated –
oil on canvas – 16¾ x 24¾in.
(Christie's)   **$15,787 £8,580**

PHILIP CONNARD – Young Sunbathers – signed
with initials and dated – oil on canvas –
19½ x 23½in.
(Anderson & Garland) **$70,200**   **£39,000**

CONTINENTAL SCHOOL

CONTINENTAL SCHOOL, 19th century — The young fisherwoman — signed — oil on canvas — 40.3 x 23.5 cm.
(Robt. W. Skinner Inc.)   **$2,500 £1,420**

E. W. COOKE — A barge at a quayside — signed — 10 x 8in.
(G. A. Key)   **$1,870 £1,000**

GERALD COOPER — Mixed Summer Blossoms — signed — oil on canvas — 30 x 25in.
(Christie's)   **$27,412 £15,400**

MARGARET MURRAY COOKESLEY — The Hookah — signed and dated — on panel — 12 x 18in.
(Christie's)   **$10,406   £6,050**

GERALD COOPER – Irises, Rhododendrons
and Peonies – signed – oil on canvas – 24 x 20in.
(Christie's) **$15,664 £8,800**

THOMAS SYDNEY COOPER – Sheep in an
extensive moorland landscape – signed and dated –
45.4 x 34.6cm.
(Christie's) **$5,482 £3,080**

WILLIAM SIDNEY COOPER – Cattle at a river –
one of a pair – signed and dated – 8 x 11in.
(Anderson & Garland) **Two** **$2,618 £1,400**

THOMAS SYDNEY COOPER – In the meadows
signed and dated 1878 – 20 x 14in.
(Christies) **$6371 £3520**

CHARLES WEST COPE – 'O hush thee my baby!'
– signed with monogram and dated –
(Christie's) **$4,895 £2,750**

COPESTICK

LE CORBUSIER (CHARLES EDOUARD JEANNERET) – Femme et Coquillage – signed and dated – collage, brush and black ink on paper – 15¾ x 13¾in.
(Christie's)   **$18,513 £9,900**

E. COPESTICK – Young girl in a smock amidst corn sheafs – signed – oil on canvas – 22 x 16in.
(W. H. Lane & Son)   **$1,281 £700**

LUIGI CORBELLINI – Girl with a bird – signed – oil on canvas – 22 x 18in.
(Du Mouchelles)   **$650 £343**

LE CORBUSIER (CHARLES EDOUARD JEAN-NERET) – Femme aux Cheveux bleus – signed and dated – pastel, pencil, pen and ink on paper – 12¼ x 8¼in.
(Christie's)   **$8,228 £4,400**

LOVIS CORINTH – Sitzendes Kind – signed –
oil on canvas – 56.5 x 47.4cm.
(Christie's) **$9,625 £5,500**

LE CORBUSIER (CHARLES EDOUARD JEAN-
NERET) – Taureaux – signed, inscribed and
dated – enamel – 19¾ x 9¾in.
(Christie's) **$15,136** **£8,800**

BENJAMIN CORIA – Reclining female nude –
signed, inscribed and dated – on canvas –
25½ x 45¾in.
(Christie's) **$4,111 £2,310**

LOVIS CORINTH – Charlotte mit Wilhelmine –
signed and dated – oil on paper – 26¾ x 19¾in.
(Christie's) **$17,325 £9,900**

CORINTH

LOVIS CORINTH – Thomas mit Hande – signed and dated – oil on board – 48 x 68cm.
(Christie's) **$10,587 £6,050**

DEAN CORNWELL – Holding their own – signed and dated – 34½ x 24in.
(Christie's) **$3,850 £2,115**

ANTONIO CORREGIO, After – 'Marriage of St Catherine' – half length portrait of four figures seated – oil on copper panel – 50 x 40.5cm.
(Henry Spencer) **$1,480 £800**

HERMANN DAVID SALOMON CORRODI – L'Angelus – signed and inscribed – oil on canvas – 65 x 35in.
(Christie's) **$20,240 £11,000**

JEAN BAPTISTE CAMILLE COROT – Prairies avec des Vaches, un Saule a droit et un Village lointain – signed – oil on canvas – 45 x 55 cm.
(Christie's) **$264,880** **£154,000**

EDOUARD CORTES – Paris street scene – signed – oil on canvas – 18 x 22in.
(Du Mouchelles) **$11,000 £6,508**

EDOUARD CORTES – A street scene in winter,
Paris – signed – oil on canvas – 13 x 18¼in.
(Christie's) **$36,432 £19,800**

EDOUARD CORTES – A Paris street scene –
signed – 23½ x 16½in.
(Christie's) **$12,342 £6,600**

GUGLIELMO CORTESE – The martyrdom of St
Andrew – oil on canvas – 42 x 26½in.
(Phillips) **$3,168 £1,800**

COSIMO

MAURICE COURANT – Le Treport – signed and dated – oil on canvas – 18 x 21in.
(Christie's) **$1,925 £1,100**

PIERO DI COSIMO, Manner of – Portrait of a young man, bust length, a landscape beyond – on panel – 22¾ x 19in.
(Christie's) **$1,903 £1,100**

JOHN SELL COTMAN – A figure under the bough of a tree on the shore of a lake – pencil and grey wash – 12 x 8¼in.
(Christie's) **$12,155 £7,150**

GUSTAVE COURBET – Le Chasseur – signed and dated '66 – oil on canvas – 32 x 24¾in.
(Christie's) **$189,200 £110,000**

GUSTAVE CLAUDE ETIENNE COURTOIS – Daphnis and Chloe – signed and inscribed – 115.3 x 114.4cm.
(Christie's) **$5,610 £3,300**

JAN VAN COUVER – Peasants and ducks before a windmill with a village beyond – signed – 34¼ x 44in.
(Christie's)   **$3,740**   **£2,200**

THOMAS COUTURE – A standing soldier – black chalk on manilla matte paper – 16½ x 9½in.
(Christies)   **$1,732**   **£990**

SIR NOEL COWARD – Jamaican figures on a coastal road – signed – oil on canvas – 20 x 24in.
(Christie's)   **$12,139**   **£6,820**

J. VAN COUVER – Marken, Holland – signed – oil on canvas – 20 x 30in.
(Du Mouchelles)   **$1,800 £952**

SIR NOEL COWARD – London's burning – oil on panel – 11½ x 15½in.
(Lawrence Fine Arts)   **$5,328**   **£3,080**

COWARD

SIR NOEL COWARD – Entertainers at the fair –
signed – gouache and felt tip – 16 x 11½in.
(Christie's)   **$7,440   £4,180**

SIR NOEL COWARD – The fruit market – signed
– oil on canvas-board – 11¾ x 8in.
(Christie's)   **$9,790   £5,500**

SIR NOEL COWARD – Coastal town – signed
– oil on board – 19¾ x 15¾in.
(Christie's)   **$8,811   £4,950**

SIR NOEL COWARD – Bathers on the shore –
signed – oil on canvas-board – 8¼ x 10in.
(Christie's)   **$3,328   £1,870**

SIR NOEL COWARD – Theatrical Design, Lady
on a Terrace – signed – watercolour, bodycolour
and pencil – 10½ x 8½in.
(Christie's)   **$1,762   £990**

SIR NOEL COWARD – The Bridge Jamaica –
signed – oil on canvas-board – 19½ x 15½in.
(Christie's)   **$3,720   £2,090**

SIR NOEL COWARD – Two ladies walking by a
lake – signed – oil on canvas – 16 x 12in.
(Christie's)   **$2,251   £1,265**

SIR NOEL COWARD – Wash Day, Jamaica – signed – oil on board – 16 x 20in.
(Christie's)   **$9,790 £5,500**

DAVID COX – The Vale of Llangollen, Wales, figures before a cottage – signed – watercolour – 7 x 10½in.
(W. H. Lane & Son) **$422 £250**

SIR NOEL COWARD – Jamaican Road and two figures – signed – oil on board – 10 x 8in.
(Christie's) **$5,874 £3,300**

GARSTON COX – "Springtime", stream in a Cornish valley in West Penwith – signed – oil on canvas – 27 x 35in.
(W. H. Lane & Son) **$4,901 £2,900**

FRANK CADOGAN COWPER – Our Lady of the fruits of the Earth – signed and dated – 40 x 30in.
(Christie's) **$96,250 £55,000**

GARSTON COX – Carn Brea, Cornwall, a view of Cornish Engine Houses – signed – oil on canvas – 29 x 37in.
(W. H. Lane & Son) **$5,504 £3,200**

WILLIAM COX — Cornish fishing boats arriving in a Cornish harbour with a village and church beyond — signed — oil on canvas — 23½ x 19½in.
(W. H. Lane & Son)   **$2,236 £1,300**

ROBERT C. CRAWFORD — Portrait of a girl, seated half length, with a cape around her shoulders — signed and dated — on canvas laid down on board — 23¾ x 18in.
(Christie's)   **$666   £385**

JOOS VAN CRAESBEECK, Manner of — Boors carousing — on panel — 8 x 6½in.
(Christie's)   **$3,045 £1,760**

GIUSEPPE MARIA CRESPI, LO SPAGNUOLO, Follower of — The personification of Summer: and the personification of Autumn — 37½ x 29in.
(Christie's)   **Two $4,567 £2,640**

CRESWICK

THOMAS CRESWICK – A wooded river landscape
– oil on panel – circular – 6in. diam.
(Christie's) **$608 £352**

WILLIAM CROSBY – A small boy in a red velvet
suit accompanied by his dog – signed and dated –
oil on canvas – 41½ x 31½in.
(Anderson & Garland) **$3,927 £2,100**

GEORGES CROEGAERT – The bouquet – signed
– on panel – 55 x 39.7cm.
(Christie's) **$17,325 £9,900**

HENRI-EDMOND CROSS – La Seine devant le
Trocadero – signed – on paper – 18 x 25cm.
(Christie's) **$17,028 £9,900**

HENRI EDMOND CROSS – Le Tamaris – signed – oil on canvas – 46 x 55 cm.
(Christie's) $170,280 £99,000

M. CROUSE – "Springtime", cattle drinking at the water's edge in a Surrey meadow
– signed and dated – oil on canvas – 19 x 29½in.
(W. H. Lane & Son) $1,554 £920

CRUIKSHANK

ISAAC CRUIKSHANK, Attributed to — Presentation of colours — signed and inscribed — pencil, pen and black and grey ink and watercolour — 24 x 33cm.
(Christie's) **$1,309 £770**

JOHANN MONGELS CULVERHOUSE — The vegetable market at night — signed and dated — oil on canvas — 24 x 20in.
(Robt. W. Skinner Inc.) **$9,000 £5,113**

VERA CUMMINGS — Portrait of a young Maori woman — signed — on canvas — 10 x 8in.
(Christie's) **$822 £462**

VERA CUMMINGS – A Maori Chieftainess –
signed and indistinctly dated – 14 x 12in.
(Christie's) **$1,860 £1,045**

CHARLES COURTNEY CURRAN – Pastoral
Scene With Cows And Figures – signed, inscribed
and dated 1900 – oil on canvas – 12 x 18in.
(Robt. W. Skinner Inc.) **$1,300 £787**

CHARLES COURTNEY CURRAN – Pink Parasol
– signed and dated 1927, and inscribed on the
reverse – oil on canvas – 25½ x 30½in.
(Christie's) **$24,200 £14,928**

CHARLES COURTNEY CURRAN – Pink Clouds
– signed and dated 1937 – oil on canvas – 20¼ x
24¼in.
(Christie's) **$6,050 £3,732**

JOHN STEUART CURRY – Self-Portrait – signed
and dated – oil on canvas laid down on board –
76.7 x 63.9cm.
(Christie's) **$28,600 £15,376**

STANLEY CURSITER – A still life of red and
yellow roses – signed and dated – oil on canvas
– 39.5 x 49.5cm.
(Phillips) **$7,273 £4,180**

CURTIS

JAMES WALTHAM CURTIS – On the road –
signed – on canvas – 16 x 27¼in.
(Christie's)   **$11,748   £6,600**

JAMES WALTHAM CURTIS – Watts River,
Healesville – signed – oil on canvas – 51 x 80cm.
(Australian Art Auctions)   **$5,963   £3,240**

ABRAHAM VAN CUYLENBORCH, Circle of –
The Holy Family – signed with monogram –
oil on canvas – 50.5 x 43.5cm.
(Phillips)   **$1,848   £1,050**

CARL OTTO CZESCHKA – Greek Warriors setting
out to Battle – oil on canvas – 25 x 62.5cm.
(Christie's)   **$3,027   £1,760**

ELEANOR PARKE CUSTIS – Arab scene – signed – watercolour and gouache on paper –
22 x 17¾in.
(Christie's)   **$990   £543**

SUSAN ISOBEL DACRE – Portrait of the
daughters of Lawrence Pilkington – signed and
dated – oil on canvas – 44 x 40in.
(Christie's)   **$8,223   £4,620**

RICHARD DADD – Portrait of a young man, bust length, wearing a tam o'shanter and plaid – signed and dated – pencil and watercolour heightened with white on grey paper – 18.5 x 14cm.
(Christie's) **$2,618 £1,540**

HANS DAHL – The rivals – signed and inscribed – 29 x 44½in.
(Christie's) **$34,595** **£18,700**

HANS DAHL – The Goat Girl – signed – 26¼ x 39½in.
(Christie's) **$22,385** **£12,100**

MIODRAG DJURIC DADO – Le Conseille Crespell – inscribed – oil on canvas – 51 x 38in.
(Christie's) **$14,168 £7,700**

AUGUSTE DAINI – Entertaining the Cardinal – signed – oil on canvas – 20 x 33in.
(Christie's) **$3,718 £2,200**

DAINTREY

ADRIAN DAINTREY – The Blue Motor Boat –
signed and dated – oil on board – 8¾ x 16½in.
(Christie's)   **$1,762   £990**

EDOUARDO DALBANO – The evening stroll,
Venice – signed – oil on canvas – 10 x 13¼in.
(Christie's)   **$20,240 £11,000**

SALVADOR DALI – La Sorciere et la Belle
Miroir – signed and dated – on paper –
50.8 x 41cm.
(Christie's)   **$52,976   £30,800**

SALVADOR DALI – Tristan and Isolde – signed and dated – oil on canvas – 25¼ x 31in.
(Christie's)
$462,000 £272,626

SALVADOR DALI – Femme Assise – signed
– Charcoal on paper – 9¾ x 7½in.
(Christie's) **$7,568** **£4,400**

DALMATION SCHOOL, 17th century – The
Madonna and Child – oil on panel, gold ground –
28 x 22cm.
(Phillips) **$4,576 £2,600**

SALVADOR DALI – Le Sentiment de la Vitesse
– signed and dated – oil on canvas – 13 x 9½in.
(Christie's) **$394,680 £214,500**

PIERRE EMMANUEL DAMOYE – Arbres
fruitiers en Bord de Mer – signed and dated –
oil on canvas – 50.7 x 73.5cm.
(Christie's) **$4,620 £2,640**

JAMES FRANCIS DANBY – A shore scene with
fisherfolk – signed – oil on canvas – 10½ x 17in.
(Lawrence Fine Arts) **$3,220 £1,760**

DANISH SCHOOL

DANISH SCHOOL, 19th Century – A still life of flowers in a vase upon a stone ledge – oil on canvas – 50 x 40cm.
(Phillips)   **$1,232   £700**

CHARLES FRANCOIS DAUBIGNY – Bords de la Seine a Herblay – indistinctly signed – oil on panel – 15 x 27in.
(Christie's)   **$16,192   £8,800**

ARTHUR E. DAVIES – Long Stratton village, Norfolk – signed – watercolour – 11 x 16in.
(G. A. Key)   **$1,870 £1,000**

ARTHUR E. DAVIES – Bawburgh Mill – signed – watercolour – 11 x 15in.
(G. A. Key)   **$1,729 £925**

NORMAN PRESCOTT DAVIES – The organ grinder – signed – oil on canvas – 20 x 27¼in.
(Robt. W. Skinner Inc.)   **$2,500 £1,420**

JOSEPH BERNARD DAVIS – On the Norfolk Broads – women and children on a path – signed – 10½ x 15½in.
(W. H. Lane & Son)   **$384   £210**

MONTAGUE DAWSON – Clipper ship Fanny
Forrester – signed – oil on canvas – 24 x 36in.
(Du Mouchelles) **$27,500 £14,550**

L. DAVIS – The shuttlecock player – signed and
dated – 18 x 14in.
(Christie's) **$3,916 £2,200**

FRANCIS DAY – The Bathers – signed – oil on
canvas – 35.3 x 45.7cm.
(Robt. W. Skinner Inc.) **$425** **£251**

CHARLES FREDERICK DAWSON – Head and
shoulder portrait of a young woman with plait –
monogrammed to verso – oil on canvas –
17 x 13½in.
(W. H. Lane & Son) **$388 £230**

W. P. DAY – An Arab market – signed –
46 x 55.3cm.
(Christie's) **$1,174** **£660**

EDWARD DAYES – A Capriccio of a Doric
Temple in a garden with a potted plant under
glass dome and a watering syringe – pencil, grey
and blue wash – 5 x 7¾in.
(Christie's)   **$1,215 £715**

SONIA DELAUNAY – Composition – signed –
gouache over green ink – 25½ x 19in.
(Christie's)   **$18,287 £10,450**

EDWARD DEANES – The end of the day – signed
and dated – 28 x 42in.
(Christie's)   **$9,790   £5,500**

JOSEPH DECKER – A kitten at play – signed
and inscribed – on panel – 6¼ x 8¼in.
(Christie's)   **$1,776**   **£1,045**

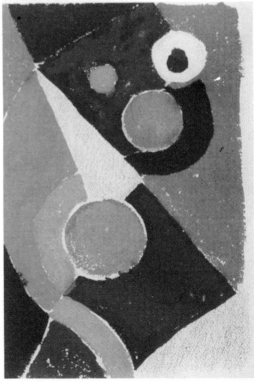

SONIA DELAUNAY – Rhythme Colore – signed
and dated – gouache and charcoal on paper –
15 x 11in.
(Christie's)   **$13,513 £7,150**

MAURICE DELCOURT – Le Depart pour le Bal
– signed and dated – oil on canvas – 55.5 x 46.5cm.
(Christie's) **$1,828 £1,045**

CHARLES EDOUARD DELORT – A voluptuous
smoke – signed and dated – oil on panel –
10½ x 8½in.
(Christie's) **$19,228 £10,450**

DELFT SCHOOL, 18th century – Two peasants
dancing a jig – oil on panel – 9¾ x 7½in.
(Phillips) **$968 £550**

PAUL DELVAUX – 'La Comedie du Soir' or Les
Belles de Nuit' – signed and dated – oil on canvas
– 39¼ x 39¼in.
(Christie's) **$605,000 £357,010**

DENCKER

AUGUST VILHELM DENCKER – A forest in
Spring – signed and dated – 39¾ x 53in.
(Christie's) **$748** **£440**

MAURICE DENIS – Jeune Femme Assise – signed
with monogram – oil on panel – 22.6 x 26.1cm.
(Christie's) **$11,550 £6,600**

MAURICE DENIS – Marine – signed with monogram – oil on canvas – 30.2 x 42cm.
(Christie's) **$9,240 £5,280**

MAURICE DENIS – Marthe au Bain – signed with
monogram – oil on canvas – 61 x 46.1cm
(Christie's) **$12,474 £6,600**

ANDRE DERAIN – Le Paon – gouache, watercolour and white chalk on paper – 38.1 x 53cm.
(Christie's) **$5,821 £3,080**

ANDRE DERAIN – La Place de l'Eglise de Saint
Maximin - signed – oil on canvas – 13¼ x 16½in.
(Christie's) **$27,027 £14,300**

ANDRE DERAIN – Portrait de Paula Osuska –
signed – oil on panel – 73.7 x 58,8cm.
(Christie's) **$30,800 £17,600**

GEORGES D'ESPAGNAT – Deux jeunes Filles
ceuillant des Roses – signed – oil on canvas –
135 x 94cm.
(Christie's) **$40,450 £22,000**

D'ESPAGNAT

GEORGES D'ESPAGNAT – Les Enfants au Bord du Lac – signed with initials – oil on board – 15¼ x 24¼in.
(Christie's) **$15,214 £8,050**

GIAQINTO DIANA – The vision of St Benedict – oil on canvas – 25 x 20¼in.
(Phillips) **$3,580 £2,000**

GEORGES DESVALLIERES – Aphrodite – signed and dated – on panel – 41 x 22.5cm.
(Christie's) **$50,050** **£28,600**

THOMAS FRANCIS DICKSEE – Running home – signed – 45 x 32½in.
(Christie's) **$4,895 £2,750**

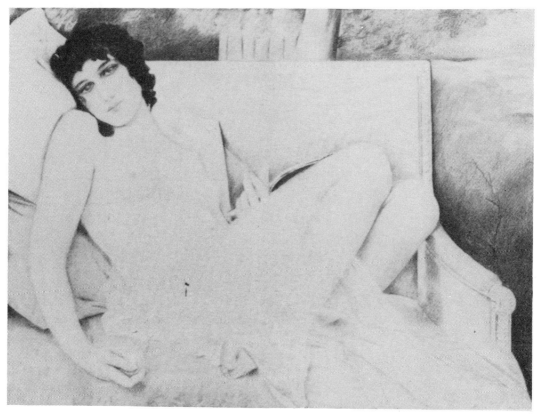

ERHARD AMANDUS DIER − A nude reclining on
a sofa − signed with initials and dated − coloured
chalks − 23¾ x 34in.
(Christie's)   **$5,667   £3,080**

DENIS DIGHTON − Reculver Abbey − signed and
dated − watercolour − 41.5 x 55.5cm.
(Phillips)   **Two**   **$4,416 £2,400**

ANDRE DIGNIMONT − Scene de Bar − signed −
gouache and pencil on paper − 60 x 53.7cm.
(Christie's)   **$3,657 £2,090**

DINGLI

EDWARD CARUANA DINGLI — Maltese fish market — signed — watercolour — 12 x 18in.
(W. H. Lane & Son) **$760 £450**

FRANCIS STILLWELL DIXON — Manchester, VT — signed — oil on panel — 8¼ x 10¼in.
(Robt. W. Skinner Inc.) **$900** **£532**

SARKIS DIRANIAN — The flower sellers — signed — oil on canvas — 46.5 x 33.5cm.
(Christie's) **$10,120 £5,500**

WALT DISNEY STUDIOS — Tinker Bell — Authenticity label from Walt Disney Productions on the reverse — gouache on celluloid — 5 x 7in.
(Bruce D. Collins) **$660** **£349**

O. R. DOGARTH — Roses, chrysanthemums, lilies, tulips, hyacinth and other flowers in a glass vase on a ledge — one of a pair — signed — oil on panel — 23¼ x 20in.
(Christie's)   **Two**   **$20,240**   **£11,000**

WILLIAM CHARLES THOMAS DOBSON — The Golden Age — signed and dated — 57 x 36in.
(Christie's)   **$23,100**   **£13,200**

STEVAN DOHANOS — Avocados — signed and dated — gouache, watercolour and pencil on paper — 10¼ x 14in.
(Christie's)   **$990**   **£543**

DOMERGUE

JEAN GABRIEL DOMERGUE – Nu en plein Air
– signed – oil on canvas – 31¾ x 25½in.
(Christie's)   **$7,484   £3,960**

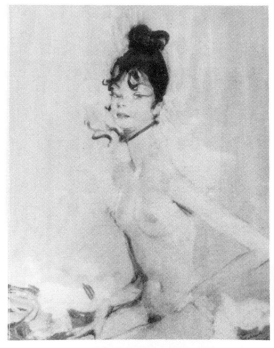

JEAN GABRIEL DOMERGUE – Jeune Fille
assise – Gitane – signed – oil on board –
55 x 45.7cm.
(Christie's)   **$7,315   £4,180**

PIETER CORNELIS DOMMERSEN – A Coastal
View With Fishing Vessels In A Choppy Sea –
signed and dated 1885 – on panel – 10¾ x 15in.
(Christie's)   **$3,267   £1,980**

WILLIAM RAYMOND DOMMERSEN – The
market place, Limburg, Holland – signed –
20 x 30in.
(Christie's)   **$3,740   £2,200**

JOHN MILNE DONALD – Beached boats at low
tide – signed and dated – oil on canvas –
56 x 89cm.
(Phillips)   **$11,484 £6,600**

146

KEES VAN DONGEN – Danseuse Orientale – La
Belle Fatima – signed – oil on canvas –
25¾ x 22in.
(Christie's)   **$545,490**   **£319,000**

KEES VAN DONGEN – Le Caire – signed – oil
on canvas – 99 x 80.5cm.
(Christie's)   **$263,120   £143,000**

KEES VAN DONGEN – Les Danseuses; Revel et
Coco – signed – oil on canvas – 36¼ x 28¾in.
(Christie's)   **$978,120**   **£572,000**

KEES VAN DONGEN – Vase de Fleurs dans un
Vase bleu – signed – oil on canvas – 40 x 32in.
(Christie's)   **$161,920   £88,000**

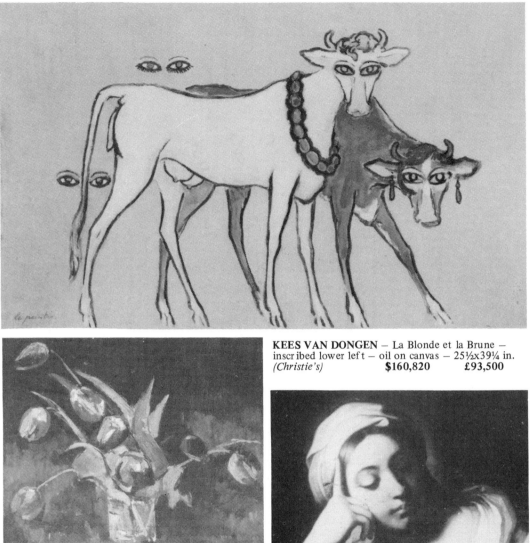

KEES VAN DONGEN — La Blonde et la Brune —
inscribed lower left — oil on canvas — 25½x39¼ in.
(Christie's) **$160,820 £93,500**

KEES VAN DONGEN — Tulipes dans un Vase —
signed — oil on canvas — 50.2 x 61.4 cm.
(Christie's) **$94,600 £55,000**

JAMES M. DONNELL — A town in winter — one
of a pair — signed and dated — pencil and watercolour — 13½ x 17½in.
(Christie's) **Two $548 £308**

GIROLAMO DONNINI — The Virgin at devotion
— oval — oil on canvas — 98 x 72.5cm.
(Phillips) **$1,750 £1,000**

GUSTAVE DORE – Portrait of Adelina Patti, head and shoulders – signed – oil on canvas – oval – 25¾ x 21¼in.
(Christie's)   **$13,763 £7,480**

PATRICK DOWNIE – Ducks and ducklings – signed – on board – 9 x 12in.
(Christie's)   **$2,937 £1,650**

JOHN DOWNMAN – Portrait of a lady, identified as Eliza Were Holdsworth, seated, half-length, in profile to the left – signed and dated – stump and watercolour heightened with white, on Whatman paper – 12 x 9¾in.
(Christie's)   **$2,057 £1,210**

DRAPER

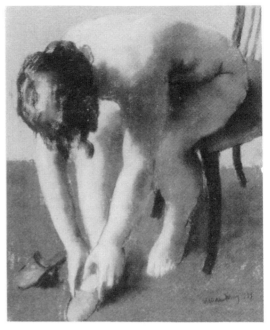

WILLIAM DRING — The Red Slippers —
signed and dated — pastel and charcoal —
14½ x 11½in.
(Christie's)　　　　**$5,138**　　　　**£2,970**

HERBERT JAMES DRAPER — A female nude —
signed and inscribed — charcoal with chalk on grey
paper — 21¼ x 13in.
(Lawrence Fine Arts)　**$9,895**　　　　**£5,720**

CLEMENT DREW — Squarerigger in a gale — oil on
academy board — 11 x 15½in.
(Bruce D. Collins)　　**$770**　　　　**£407**

JEAN DUBUFFET — Annale VI — signed and
dated — black felt marker and paper collage on
paper — 51.2 x 34.9cm.
(Christie's)　　　　**$26,741 £14,300**

JEAN DUBUFFET – Deux Tetes D'Arabes –
signed and dated – watercolour on paper –
10½ x 20in.
(Christie's)   **$45,408**   **£26,400**

WILLIAM DUFFIELD – A pineapple and grapes
in a basket with plums and peaches on a draped
table – signed and dated – oval – 82.5 x 72.7cm.
(Christie's)   **$33,286 £18,700**

ERNEST DUEZ – La Promenade au Bord de Mer,
presume Sarah Bernhardt – signed – pastel on
paper – 26 x 39cm.
(Christie's)   **$6,054**   **£3,520**

MARY ELIZABETH DUFFIELD – Flowers –
signed – pencil and watercolour – 7 x 13in.
(Christie's)   **$756**   **£440**

MARY ELIZABETH DUFFIELD – A still life
of mixed summer flowers – signed – watercolour
– 12½ x 15½in.
(Lawrence Fine Arts)   **$1,522**   **£880**

CHARLES DUFRESNE – Femme nue – signed –
pen and ink on paper – 39.1 x 29.6cm.
(Christie's)   **$210**   **£120**

DUFY

JEAN DUFY – Le Cirque – signed – oil on canvas – 21¾ x 8¼in.
(Christie's) **$24,288 £13,200**

JEAN DUFY – Vue d'Edinburgh – signed – oil on canvas – 46 x 55cm.
(Christie's) **$22,137 £12,650**

JEAN DUFY – La Seine avec Montmartre et Le Sacre Coeur, Paris – signed – oil on canvas – 50 x 61cm.
(Christie's) **$44,528 £24,200**

RAOUL DUFY – Hommage a Sisley; Les Regates, Henley – signed – water colour on paper – 19¾ x 25½in.
(Christie's) **$132,440** **£77,000**

RAOUL DUFY – Les Bains Marie-Christine, Trouville – signed – oil on canvas – 46 x 55cm.
(Christie's) **$225,720** **£132,000**

THOMAS CANTRELL DUGDALE – Portrait of Sir Winston Churchill – signed – 29¼ x 24¾in.
(Christie's) **$3,532 £2,090**

ALFRED DUKE – Fireside Friends – signed – watercolour – 7½ x 10in.
(Christie's)   **$1,513**   **£880**

THOMAS CANTRELL DUGDALE – Reclining Nude – signed – oil on canvas – 24 x 20in.
(Christie's)   **$1,174**   **£660**

THOMAS CANTRELL DUGDALE – Female Nude – signed – oil on canvas – 35½ x 30¼in.
(Christie's)   **$14,685**   **£8,250**

DANIEL DUMONSTIER, Studio of – Portrait of Madame De Bar, bust length – inscribed – oil on panel – 12¼ x 9in.
(Phillips)   **$9,308**   **£5,200**

RONALD OSSORY DUNLOP – Farmyard Among Trees – signed – oil on canvas – 16 x 20in. *(Christie's)* **$979** **£550**

A. DUNINGTON – Calves by cottages – signed – 30 x 20in.
(Christie's) **$1,370 £770**

HARVEY T. DUNN – The Gambler – oil on canvas – 96.9 x 81.9cm.
(Christie's) **$6,600** **£3,548**

BERNARD DUNSTAN – Nude After Shower,
Sisterton – signed – oil on canvas laid on board
– 13 x 10in.
(Christie's) **$3,720 £2,090**

BERNARD DUNSTAN – Portrait of Brenda –
signed with initials – oil on panel – 8 x 5½in.
(Christie's) **$1,762 £990**

BERNARD DUNSTAN – Christie's, Sunny
Morning – signed – oil on board – 12¼ x 10¼in.
(Christie's) **$6,265 £3,520**

WILLIAM HERBERT 'BUCK' DUNTON – Bronc
Rider – signed and dated – oil on canvas –
29¼ x 19in.
(Christie's) **$41,800 £22,473**

DUNTZE

JOHANNES BERTHOLOMAUS DUNTZE (1823-1895) - A winter river landscape with figures skating on the ice, by a village - signed and dated 1887, 24 x 37in. *(Christie's)* **$12,716 £7,480**

DUTCH SCHOOL – A floral group – oil on canvas – 18¼ x 14½in.
(Anderson & Garland) **$1,440** £800

DUTCH SCHOOL – The cleric – oil on canvas – 12 x 8in.
(Christie's) **$483 £286**

FRANZ DVORAK – Purity and passion – signed –
20 x 25½in.
(Christie's) **$22,440** **£13,200**

JOSEPH LAURENTIUS DYCKMANS – The fair
drover – signed and dated – oil on panel –
24.5 x 29.5 cm.
(Christie's) **$10,524 £5,720**

H. ANTHONY DYER – A corner of an old Italian
farm, Sorrento – signed – watercolour – 30 x 22in.
(Bruce D. Collins) **$990** **£523**

MARCEL DYF – Les Deux Soeurs – signed – oil on canvas – 60 x 73cm.
(Christie's)   **$22,627 £12,100**

MARCEL DYF – Moulin en Hollande – signed –
oil on canvas – 18 x 21¾in.
(Christie's)   **$21,175 £12,100**

MARCEL DYF – Eglise et Village en L'Ile de
France – signed – oil on canvas – 18½ x 21½in.
(Christie's)   **$8,316 £4,400**

MARCEL DYF – Femme decolletee – signed –
oil on canvas – 54.6 x 46.1cm.
(Christie's) **$15,400 £8,800**

MARCEL DYF – Jeune Femme au Bouquet –
signed – oil on canvas – 23½ x 28¾in.
(Christie's) **$13,475 £7,700**

MARCEL DYF – Matin Brumeux a L'Isle – signed
– oil on canvas – 38.1 x 46.1cm.
(Christie's) **$20,790 £11,000**

MARCEL DYF – Girl in a pink dress – signed –
15½ x 11½in.
(Christie's) **$836 £495**

JOAN EARDLEY – Head of a Boy – oil on board
– 10¼ x 8¼in.
(Christie's) **$1,427 £825**

HENRY EARP – A Sussex village – signed –
9½ x 13½in.
(Christie's)   **$1,208**   **£715**

SIR ALFRED EAST – Reflections – flowering
shrubs on a lakeside – signed and dated – watercolour – 10½ x 14in.
(W. H. Lane & Son)   **$512 £280**

FRANK SAMUEL EASTMAN – Cradle song –
signed and dated – watercolour – 13¼ x 17¼in.
(Christie's)   **$1,859 £1,100**

FRANK SAMUEL EASTMAN – Portrait of Peter
Eastman as a young boy – 20½ x 14½in.
(Christie's)   **$483**   **£286**

FRANK SAMUEL EASTMAN – Portrait of Mary
Eastman – signed and dated – 39 x 50in.
(Christie's)   **$892**   **£528**

FRANK SAMUEL EASTMAN – Queen of Hearts
(the artist's daughter Mary) – signed and dated –
48 x 36in.
(Christie's) **$2,230 £1,320**

FRANK SAMUEL EASTMAN – "Joy" –
43 x 30in.
(Christie's) **$2,044 £1,210**

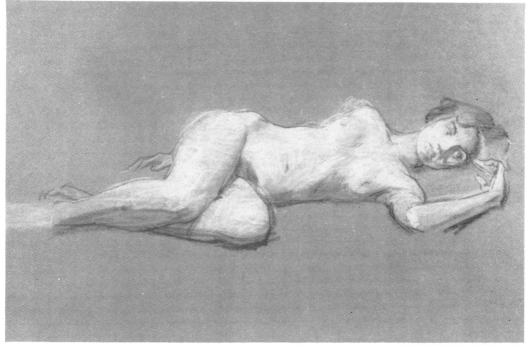

FRANK SAMUEL EASTMAN – One of a large folio of chalk life drawings
(Christie's) **Folio** **$780 £462**

EASTMAN

MARY EASTMAN – Portrait of Frank Samuel
Eastman at his easel – on panel – 13½ x 11in.
(Christie's) **$706** **£418**

CHRISTOFFER WILHELM ECKERSBERG –
Christ and the woman taken in adultery, John 8.
v. 2-11 – signed and dated – 51 x 44¾in.
(Christie's) **$28,875** **£16,500**

E. ECTUANY – The bull fight – signed – 15½ x 19in. *(Christie's)* **$3,850 £2,200**

SOREN EDSBERG – Swans on a lake – signed –
23½ x 35½in.
(Christie's)   **$3,366**   **£1,980**

ALBERT EDELFELT – Pa havet (At sea) –
signed – 23 x 20cm.
(Christie's)   **$91,575**   **£49,500**

LIONEL EDWARDS – Comandeer by Combat ex
Estage – signed, inscribed and dated – oil on
canvas – 49 x 59cm.
(Phillips)   **$12,441 £7,150**

ALBERT EDELFELT – A cavalier – signed and
dated – watercolour heightened with white –
21 x 13in.
(Christie's)   **$38,665**   **£20,900**

LIONEL EDWARDS – A Conference of the
Powers, Quantock Staghounds – signed and
indistinctly dated – oil on canvas – 20 x 24in.
(Christie's)   **$35,244 £19,800**

EDWARDS

LIONEL EDWARDS — "The Bridge, Claybrook Mill", extensive wintry rural landscape with a huntsman on a bay hunter — signed and dated — watercolour heightened with body colour — 34 x 49.5cm.
(Henry Spencer)   **$11,594 £6,200**

ALBIN EGGER-LEINZ — Der Macher — signed — oil on canvas — 62.3 x 56.8cm.
(Christie's)   **$76,912 £41,800**

DIETZ EDZARD — Suzanne Eisendieck au Parasol — signed, dated and inscribed — oil on canvas — 46 x 38.1cm.
(Christie's)   **$7,068   £3,740**

JACOB EICHHOLTZ — Mrs Pierre Louis Laguerenne — oil on canvas — 30 x 25in.
(Christie's)   **$2,200   £1,182**

FRANZ EICHHORST – Christmas Eve in the town hall of Schwalm – signed and dated – oil on canvas – 48 x 72in.
(Christie's) **$16,192 £8,800**

CONRAD EILERS – A wooded landscape with a girl and geese by a stream – signed – 29 x 25½in.
(Christie's) **$2,992 £1,760**

LOUIS MICHEL EILSHEMIUS – Nude bather – signed – oil on board – 33.3 x 46.7cm.
(Christie's) **$1,650 £906**

SUZANNE EISENDIECK – Roses dans un Verre – signed – oil on canvas – 23.8 x 16.2cm.
(Christie's) **$1,001 £572**

PETER ELLENSHAW – Seascape – oil on canvas – 25 x 50in.
(Du Mouchelles) **$3,000 £1,587**

OTTMAR ELLIGER, The Younger – Salome dancing before Herod – and companion – on canvas – 55.5 x 67.5cm.
(Christie's) **$13,725 £7,500**

ELLIOTT

FRED ELLIOTT – Off South Head – signed –
watercolour – 46 x 76cm.
(Australian Art Auctions)   **$1,704 £926**

PIERRE HENRI THEODORE TETAR VAN ELVEN
– Furnishings for a palazzo – signed and inscribed
– pencil and watercolour heightened with varnish
and white – 10¼ x 14¼in.
(Christie's)   **$446 £264**

LIONEL ELLIS – The race – signed – on board –
25 x 30in.
(Christie's)   **$2,602 £1,540**

HENRY HETHERINGTON EMMERSON – A
horse and cart at a ford – signed and dated –
7½ x 12¼in.
(Anderson & Garland)   **$1,626 £940**

ARTHUR JOHN ELSLEY – Out of reach – signed
and dated – oil on canvas – 36 x 25¼in.
(Christie's)   **$101,200 £55,000**

AXEL ENDER – A moment's rest – signed –
29¾ x 20¼in.
(Christie's)   **$12,210 £6,600**

ENGLISH SCHOOL

ENGLISH SCHOOL, circa 1890 – Cornstooks in a Summer Landscape – signed indistinctly – watercolour – 12 x 19¼in.
(Phillips) **$929** **£550**

ENGLISH SCHOOL, Circa 1890 – The Mid-day Promenade – oil on card – 9½ x 13½in.
(Hy. Duke & Son) **$422 £240**

AXEL ENDER – Making hay – signed – 33½ x 22¾in.
(Christie's) **$14,245** **£7,700**

THOMAS ENDER – Bad Ischl – signed – oil on canvas – 20½ x 28½in.
(Christie's) **$28,336 £15,400**

ENGLISH SCHOOL – A group portrait of four children, two standing full length, one seated and one mounted on a pony, the three little girls in blue, white and red dresses, the little boy in a dark green coat and a white collar, in a landscape – 56 x 43¼in.
(Christie's) **$13,244 £7,700**

ENGLISH SCHOOL

ENGLISH SCHOOL – A Trompe L'Oeil with Newspapers, Letters, playing Cards and a copy of *Cain* by Lord Byron – pen and grey ink and watercolour – 41.5 x 43cm.
(Christie's)   **$1,683**   **£990**

ENGLISH SCHOOL, MID NINETEENTH CENTURY – Feeding the parrot – 14½ x 19½in.
(Christie's)   **$1,513   £880**

ENGLISH SCHOOL – Portrait of Frances Howard, Countess of Essex, standing full length in a burgundy and orange jewel embroidered dress with lace ruff and gold embroidered lace bonnet – on panel – 18 x 10¾in.
(Christie's)   **$1,892   £1,100**

ENGLISH SCHOOL – Exeter from Pyne Hill – signed with monogram W.S.S. – watercolour – 24 x 36¼in.
(Lawrence Fine Arts)   **$2,516 £1,375**

ENGLISH SCHOOL – Portrait of Sir William Hawkesworth, Bart., bust length, in armour – – oval – 29½ x 24in.
(Christie's)   **$2,838   £1,650**

ENGLISH SCHOOL, circa 1878 – Blowing bubbles
– indistinctly signed and dated – 28 x 36in.
(Christie's)   **$3,132 £1,760**

MARY ENSOR – Langdale and Trout fishing
in Lakeland – a pair – one signed – 11½ x 18in.
(Prudential)   **$935**   **£500**

ENGLISH SCHOOL, 19th Century – Cattle in a
river landscape with a town beyond – oil on board
– 24 x 36in.
(Christie's)   **$1,332   £770**

RUDOLF EPP – The sleeping babe – signed –
35.9 x 41.3cm.
(Christie's)   **$11,935   £6,820**

JOHN JOSEPH ENNEKING – New England village in autumn twilight – signed – oil on board –
4¾ x 7in.
(Robt. W. Skinner Inc.)   **$1,500   £852**

SIR JACOB EPSTEIN – Dahlias – signed – gouache
– 22 x 17in.
(Christie's)   **$6,968 £3,850**

ERICSON

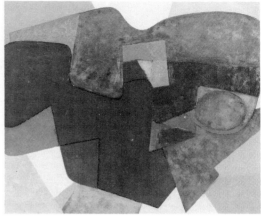

MAX ERNST – Les Papillons (Toreador) – signed
– oil on canvas – 55 x 65 cm.
(Christie's) **$357,390** **£209,000**

MAURICE ESTEVE – Manitou – signed and
dated – oil on canvas – 60 x 80 cm.
(Christie's) **$102,850 £55,000**

JOHAN ERIK ERICSON – The promenade, Haut
Meudon – signed – on panel – 54.7 x 44.7 cm.
(Christie's) **$14,652** **£7,920**

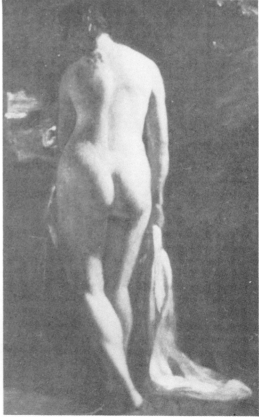

MAX ERNST – Fruhling – oil on canvas –
22¼ x 20in.
(Christie's) **$206,910** **£121,000**

WILLIAM ETTY – A female bather – oil on
canvas – 21 x 16½in.
(Lawrence Fine Arts) **$1,141** **£660**

WILLIAM ETTY, Attributed to – Portrait of a
lady, said to be Julia Friedman, head and shoulders – inscribed – 6¼ x 5in.
(Christie's)   **$929   £550**

RICHARD EURICH – Haworth, Yorkshire –
signed and dated – oil on board – 11½ x 14in.
(Christie's)   **$3,916   £2,200**

RICHARD EURICH – The Tall Ships, Southamp-
ton – signed and dated – oil on board –
30 x 46in.
(Lawrence Fine Arts)   **$4,757   £2,750**

RICHARD EURICH – The Great Tanker –
signed and dated – oil on canvas – 30¼ x 39¾in.
(Christie's)   **$8,811   £4,950**

RICHARD EURICH – Tanker in the Solent –
signed and dated – oil on canvas – 10 x 13¾in.
(Christie's)   **$1,958   £1,100**

RICHARD EURICH – The Lighthouse – signed
and dated – oil on board – 16 x 20in.
(Christie's)   **$6,853   £3,850**

FABIEN

HENRI FABIEN – Mrs Tait McKenzie – signed
and dated – oil on canvasboard – 45.4 x 60.3cm.
(Christie's) **$990 £543**

THOMAS FAED – Mother and child – signed –
charcoal and crayon – 11½ x 9in.
(W. H. Lane & Son) **$310 £180**

EMILE FABRY – Le Poete – signed, dated and
inscribed – pastel on paper – 54.5 x 19.7cm.
(Christie's) **$32,164 £18,700**

*** FAED – A Victorian drawing room – signed
and dated – 11¾ x 9¼in.
(Anderson & Garland) **$865 £500**

BETTY FAGAN – The Doctor's Visit – signed –
25 x 21in.
(Lawrence Fine Arts) **$3,044** **£1,760**

GEORG RICHARD FALKENBERG – In the garden
– signed and dated – 55 x 34½in.
(Christie's) **$21,175** **£12,100**

A. FAIRFAX – Thrush's Nest and Apple Blossoms – signed – watercolour and bodycolour –
12½ x 17½in.
(Phillips) **$1,352** **£800**

ANIELLO FALCONE, Attributed to – A band of
travelling peasants approaching an ambush in a river
valley – oil on canvas – 25 x 30in.
(Phillips) **$3,872 £2,200**

ENRICO FANFANI – A young beauty – signed –
oil on board – 8 x 5½in.
(Christie's) **$1,264 £748**

ALICE FANNER – Yachts in a stiff breeze –
signed – 25 x 30in.
(Christie's)   **$2,974 £1,760**

HENRI FANTIN-LATOUR – Nature morte aux
Roses blanches – signed and dated – oil on canvas
– 38.1 x 46cm.
(Christie's)   **$489,060   £286,000**

HENRI FANTIN-LATOUR – Etude d'apres Michel-
Ange – pencil on tracing paper – 9.2 x 14.3cm.
(Christie's)   **$831   £440**

L. FARASYN, After SIR PETER PAUL RUBENS
– The Holy Family – signed and dated –
96.8 x 72cm.
(Christie's)   **$3,616 £2,090**

STEFANO FARNETI – The scholar – signed –
oil on canvas – 27 x 18¾in.
(Christie's)   **$28,336 £15,400**

JOHN FARQUHARSON – Evening twilight Valency Valley, Boscastle, North Cornwall – signed and dated – watercolour – 9½ x 15½in.
(W. H. Lane & Son) **$540 £320**

PAOLO FARINATI, Circle of – Christ receiving succour from an angel – oil on copper – 25 x 19.5cm.
(Phillips) **$792** **£450**

ROBERT FARRAN – Coastal scene with girl and other fisherfolk leading donkey up cliff path – signed and dated – oil on canvas – 36 x 28in.
(Russell Baldwin & Bright) **$1,690 £1,000**

JOSEPH FASSBENDER – Gelbes Bild – signed and dated – oil on paper mounted on board – 24 x 34in.
(Christie's) **$7,568 £4,400**

GUY-PIERRE FAUCONNET – The sleeping Shepherd – signed – oil on canvas – 37½ x 50½in.
(Christie's) **$17,974 £10,450**

HILDA FEARON – The white parasol – signed and dated – oil on canvas – 30 x 24in.
(Anderson & Garland) **$33,345 £19,500**

FEDDEN

MARY FEDDEN — The teapot — signed and
dated — oil on canvas — 12 x 16in.
(Christie's) **$2,588 £1,430**

RICHARD FEHDMER — Returning home —
signed and dated — 26 x 37in.
(Christie's) **$9,134 £5,280**

PAUL FELGENTREFF, Circle of — The Love Letter — indistinctly signed — oil on canvas —
27 x 35in.
(Christie's) **$1,487 £880**

SERGE FERAT — Harlequin cubiste — signed and
dated — watercolour and pencil with collage on
paper — 29 x 20cm.
(Christie's) **$10,285 £5,500**

CIRRO FERRI, Circle of — St. Cecilia with SS
Clare & Agnes — oil on canvas — 45.5 x 35cm.
(Phillips) **$1,700 £950**

RAINER FETTING – Mann u Axt-Frau I –
signed and dated – acrylic on canvas –
78¾ x 78¾in.
(Christie's) **$24,596** **£14,300**

HARRY FIDDLER – Rustic figures before a
cottage – signed – 18¼ x 13in.
(W. H. Lane & Son) **$915** **£500**

CAROLINE FEUILLAS-CREUSY – Portrait of a
lady in a white dress, reading a music score –
signed – oil on canvas – 39½ x 32in.
(Christie's) **$6,072** **£3,300**

HARRY FIDLER – Cows on a country lane –
signed – 9¾ x 12in.
(Christie's) **$650** **£385**

HARRY FIDLER – Harrowing – signed – oil
on canvas – 8¼ x 10in.
(Christie's) **$4,699** **£2,640**

ISABEL JANE FIELD – Lake landscape, South Island – signed and dated – watercolour heightened with white – 14½ x 25¼in.
(Christie's) **$4,307 £2,420**

H. FIEG – The morning ride – signed – on panel – 36 x 25.1cm.
(Christie's) **$1,046 £605**

ANTHONY VAN DYKE COPLEY FIELDING – A view of Stirling – a family group in the foreground – signed – watercolour – 15.5 x 23cm.
(Henry Spencer) **$1,245 £720**

EMIL FILLA – Still life with Lute – signed '46 – oil on canvas – 97 x 130cm. *(Christie's)* **$22,704 £13,200**

SIR LUKE FILDES, Attributed to – Bust length portrait of a young lady, seated – oil on canvas – 61 x 51cm.
(Henry Spencer) **$1,410** **£750**

LEONOR FINI – Jeune Fille en Robe verte – signed – oil on canvas – 32 x 26¾in.
(Christie's) **$70,840 £38,500**

LEONOR FINI – Composition with Figures on a Terrace – signed and dated – oil on canvas – 39¼ x 32in.
(Christie's) **$154,000** **£90,875**

LEONOR FINI – Tete de Femme – watercolour and pen and ink on paper – 27.9 x 20.1cm.
(Christie's) **$1,663 £880**

FINI

LEONOR FINI – Green Sphinx – Spring – signed
– watercolour, pen and black ink on paper –
11½ x 8¼in.
(Christie's)   **$4,400**   **£2,596**

EMIL FIRMOTH – The purple shawl – signed –
on panel – 35½ x 29½in.
(Christie's)   **$1,337 £715**

CARL H. FISCHER – Cornflowers, daisies, and
other flowers in a vase by a kettle on a ledge –
signed – 70 x 100cm.
(Christie's)   **$3,459**   **£1,870**

HERBERT FINN – Lincoln Cathedral – signed
and dated – pencil and watercolour –
28 x 10½in.
(Christie's)   **$529**   **£308**

ALVAN FISHER – Under the bridge – signed and
dated – oil on canvas – 30 x 25in.
(Robt. W. Skinner Inc.)   **$24,000 £13,636**

PAUL FISCHER – The Royal Danish Lifeguards
marching through Ostergade, Copenhagen – signed
– 39½ x 39½in.
(Christie's)   **$56,980**   **£30,800**

PAUL FISCHER – The artist's wife Dagny and their
son Sigurd – signed and dated – 21¼ x 16½in.
(Christie's)   **$30,525**   **£16,500**

PAUL FISCHER – On the beach – signed –
15½ x 21in.
(Christie's)   **$16,280**   **£8,800**

FISCHER

PAUL FISCHER – A Royal life guard on duty outside the Royal Palace Amalienborg, Copenhagen – signed – on panel – 9¾ x 12¾in.
(Christie's) **$12,210 £6,600**

WILLIAM MARK FISHER – Cottage on a River Bank – oil on canvas – 21 x 32in.
(Christie's) **$5,874 £3,300**

FLEMISH SCHOOL, 17th century – The Christ child with St John – oil on panel – 39.5 x 53cm.
(Phillips) **$840 £480**

FLEMISH SCHOOL – Landscape with figures resting beside a house, a sailing vessel and mountains and trees – oil on oak panel – 20 x 24cm.
(Henry Spencer) **$439** **£260**

BLANDFORD FLETCHER, Manner of – Children on the Shore – oil on canvas – 11 x 15in.
(Christie's) **$12,727** **£7,150**

WILLIAM BLANDFORD FLETCHER – Fishing boars at low tide in a Cornish harbour – signed – oil on canvas – 16 x 18in.
(W. H. Lane & Son) **$6,364 £3,700**

J. VIVIEN DE FLEURY – The Fendertaal Tyrol – signed and dated – 20 x 30in.
(Christie's) **$2,459** **£1,430**

WILLIAM RUSSELL FLINT – Rosa and Marisa – signed – proof – limited edition of 700.
(Anderson & Garland) **$1,496 £800**

SIR WILLIAM RUSSELL FLINT – Reclining nude – signed – coloured chalk – 8½ x 12¼in.
(Anderson & Garland) **$7,020** **£3,900**

FLINT

SIR WILLIAM RUSSELL FLINT – Wind – signed – watercolour – 10¼ x 14¾in.
(Christie's)   **$10,181   £5,720**

SIR WILLIAM RUSSELL FLINT – Three Groups, Viviers, Rhone – signed and dated – watercolour.
(Christie's)   **$74,404   £41,800**

SIR WILLIAM RUSSELL FLINT – The Well Within the Wall, Montclar – signed – watercolour – 19 x 26¼in.
(Christie's)   **$39,160   £22,000**

SIR WILLIAM RUSSELL FLINT – River side garden – signed – watercolour – 9 x 14in.
(W. H. Lane & Son)   **$1,605 £950**

SIR WILLIAM RUSSELL FLINT – Homage to Demeter, Provence – signed – oil on canvas – 36 x 61½in.
(Christie's)   **$88,110 £49,500**

SIR WILLIAM RUSSELL FLINT – Miranda: Study
for Woman from Megara – signed – coloured chalk
– 10 x 15in.
(Anderson & Garland) **$7,020**   **£3,900**

SIR WILLIAM RUSSELL FLINT – In the Valley
of the Dronne, Perigord – signed – watercolour –
7½ x 10½in.
(Christie's)   **$4,307   £2,420**

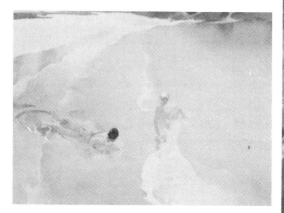

SIR WILLIAM RUSSELL FLINT – Two
Splashes – signed – watercolour –
24.6 x 30cm.
(Christie's)   **$33,286   £18,700**

FRANS FLORIS, Circle of – Scenes from the Old
Testament – oil on panel – 55 x 44cm.
(Phillips)   **$2,200   £1,250**

ERNESTO FONTANA – A beauty – signed –
33 x 26in.
(Christie's)   **$3,179   £1,870**

FONTANA

LUCIO FONTANA – Concetto Spaziale – signed – water-based paint on canvas – 28¾ x 36¼in. *(Christie's)* **$170,000** **£99,000**

F. FOOTTIT – Hide and seek – signed – oil on canvas – 16½ x 27¼in. *(Christie's)* **$1,236** **£715**

JEAN LOUIS FORAIN – Le Desespoir – signed – watercolour and black crayon on paper – 8¾ x 10in. *(Christie's)* **$808** **£462**

JEAN LOUIS FORAIN – Doux Pays – signed – pen and brown ink on paper – 30.5 x 23.8cm. *(Christie's)* **$1,193** **£682**

ELIZABETH ADELA FORBES – By the pond – signed watercolour and bodycolour – 17 x 11½in. *(Christie's)* **$6,265** **£3,520**

CHARLES RAMUS FORREST – Bridge of Oudanulla, Bengal – inscribed – pencil and watercolour – 26.6 x 44.7cm.
(Christie's)   **$1,272**   **£715**

GEORGE FORSTER – Fruit Still Life – signed and dated – oil on panel – 41 x 52.7cm.
(Christie's)   **$8,800**   **£4,731**

ELIZABETH ADELA STANHOPE FORBES – The Old Mill, Penryn – signed with monogram – on panel – 10½ x 6½in.
(Christie's)   **$743**   **£440**

ERNEST FORBES – The Rose Garden – signed and dated – oil on board – 20 x 27in.
(Christie's)   **$1,958**   **£1,100**

WILLIAM BANKS FORTESCUE – Portrait of an old fisherwoman in bonnet and shawl – monogrammed and dated – watercolour – 10¾ x 8¾in.
(W. H. Lane & Son)   **$366**   **£200**

FORUP

MYLES BIRKET FOSTER – Beach at Bonchurch
with children playing in a boat – signed monogram
– watercolour – 8 x 11in.
(Chrystals)   **$14,960**   **£8,000**

CARL CHRISTIAN FORUP – In the orchard –
signed – 23½ x 21¼in.
(Christie's)   **$6,512**   **£3,520**

TSUGUJI FOUJITA – Les Musiciens – signed –
thinned oil on canvas – 46.1 x 55.3cm.
(Christie's)   **$188,100**   **£110,000**

TSUGUJI FOUJITA — Kiki de Montparnasse — signed and dated — oil on canvas — 21¼ x 25½in.
(Christie's) **$357,390 £209,000**

TSUGUJI FOUJITA — La Porte de Vouves —
signed — oil on canvas — 15 x 18¼in.
(Christie's) **$86,625 £49,500**

ALEXIS JEAN FOURNIER — My studio — So.
Lee — signed and inscribed — oil on panel — 5x8in.
(Robt. W. Skinner Inc.) **$800 £454**

FOX

HENRY CHARLES FOX — Cows watering —
one of a pair — signed and dated — 14½ x 21½in.
(Prudential)   **Two**   **$2,681 £1,550**

FRANCOIS LOUIS FRANCAIS — Vue de Cannes
prise de l'ile St. Honorat — signed and dated —
oil on canvas — 39 x 55½in.
(Christie's)   **$50,600 £27,500**

EURILDA LOOMIS FRANCE — Still life with
grapes and oranges — signed — oil on canvas —
34 x 22in.
(Christie's)   **$1,540   £846**

ESTEBAN FRANCES — Fantastic Masks on blue —
watercolour and thinned oil on paper — 22 x 28in.
(Christie's)   **$5,348   £2,860**

ESTEBAN FRANCES — Fantastic Masks on green
— watercolour and thinned oil on paper — 22 x 28in.
(Christie's)   **$2,674   £1,430**

EDWARD J. FRANCIS — Victorian family portrait
group — signed and dated — 76 x 130cm.
(Henry Spencer)   **$1,295 £700**

JOHN F. FRANCIS – Apples and Chestnuts –
signed and dated – oil on canvas – 26.5 x 34.3cm.
(Christie's) **$13,200** **£7,096**

SAM FRANCIS – Untitled – watercolour on
paper – 22¾ x 30¾in.
(Christie's) **$68,112** **£39,600**

G. FRANCOLINI – A clever move – signed –
19¼ x 23¼in.
(Christie's) **$1,439** **£770**

HIERONYMUS FRANCKEN – Portrait of an archi-
tect standing, three-quarter length, in an interior –
signed with monogram – oil on panel –
107 x 75.5cm.
(Phillips) **$47,520** **£27,000**

LUIS FRANCS – A Moroccan – signed and
inscribed – pencil and watercolour –
18¾ x 13in.
(Christie's) **$799** **£462**

FRASER

DONALD HAMILTON FRASER − Jetty,
Capernaum − signed − oil on paper − 22 x 16in.
(Christie's) **$2,349 £1,320**

ALEXANDER FRAZER − The hornets' nest −
signed and dated − oil on panel − 39.5 x 32cm.
(Phillips) **$7,273 £4,180**

FRENCH SCHOOL, Early 19th century − Portrait
of a lady, seated three-quarter length holding her
child, roses and freesias in a glass vase and a letter
on a table at her side − 38 x 31in.
(Christie's) **$3,496 £1,870**

CHARLES FRECHOU − Harvesters in the Roman Campagna − signed and dated − 42 x 63in.
(Christie's) **$16,175 £9,350**

FRENCH SCHOOL, Early 19th century — Putti and maidens disporting in a woodland - oil on canvas — 17 x 13in.
(Christie's) **$1,078 £638**

FRENCH SCHOOL, Early 19th century — Portrait of a gentleman, seated three-quarter length, his daughter seated on his lap holding a stem of pansies and her doll — 38 x 31in.
(Christie's) **$4,525 £2,420**

WASHINGTON F. FRIEND — Quebec from the Fall of Montmorency — signed and dated — watercolour heightened with white — 23¼ x 36½in.
(Christie's) **$11,748 £6,600**

HARRY FRIER — Quay Street, The Harbour, Minehead — signed and dated — watercolour — 7 x 10½in.
(Greenslades) **$385 £220**

EMILE OTHON FRIESZ — Paysage provencal — signed — oil on canvas — 32.2 x 42.2cm.
(Christie's) **$12,512 £7,150**

FRIESZ

INNES FRIPP — The fishing party — signed and dated — 20 x 24in.
(Christie's)   **$1,566**   **£880**

EMILE OTHON FRIESZ — Scene de Foret — signed — oil on canvas — 81 x 65cm.
(Christie's)   **$10,395** **£5,500**

F. C. FRISCH — At the forge — signed — oil on canvas — 10 x 14in.
(Christie's)   **$929**   **£550**

EMILE OTHON FRIESZ — Jeune Femme nue regardant dans une Glace — signed — pastel on paper — 17.2 x 11.7cm.
(Christie's)   **$873**   **£462**

WILLIAM POWELL FRITH — 'Sir Roger de Coverley And The Beautiful Widow' — signed and dated 1887 — on canvas — 34 x 43½in.
(Phillips)   **$14,960** **£8,500**

LUCY MARGUERITE FROBISHER – Bathing
belles – signed – 19 x 25in.
(Christie's)   **$929**   **£550**

A. FROHR – A Continental flower market –
signed and dated – oil on canvas – 25¼ x 22in.
(Anderson & Garland)   **$576**   **£320**

WILLIAM EDWARD FROST – Venus disarming
Cupid – signed and dated – oil on canvas –
35 x 29in.
(Christie's)   **$14,168 £7,700**

FURINI

FRANCESCO FURINI, Manner of – The discovery of Callisto – 22 x 43¾in.
(Christie's)   **$2,474 £1,430**

JANE GAGE – A new coat of paint – signed – Oil on board – 24 x 30in.
(Bruce D. Collins)   **$247**   **£130**

GIUSEPPE GABANI – The meet – signed and inscribed – oil on canvas – 27 x 52½in.
(Christie's)   **$34,408 £18,700**

LOUIS GAIDAN – Sous les Pins a Carqueiranne – signed – oil on canvas – 110.5 x 150.8cm.
(Christie's)   **$32,725 £18,700**

PIETRO GABRINI – The walnut gatherers – signed and dated – watercolour – 21¼ x 13¾in.
(Christie's)   **$1,337 £715**

WILLIAM GALE – The song of Miriam the Prophetess – signed with monogram – 42 x 90in.
(Christie's)   **$7,832 £4,400**

EMILE GALEY? – The Meet – indistinctly signed
and dated – oil on canvas – 28 x 39½in.
(Christie's) **$2,044 £1,210**

EUGENE GALIEN-LALOUE – L'ancien Trocadero,
Paris – signed – bodycolour – 8 x 16¼in.
(Christie's) **$18,216 £9,900**

FRANCOIS GALL – L'Artiste sur la Plage –
signed and inscribed – oil on board –
15½ x 11¾in.
(Christie's) **$2,494 £1,320**

EUGENE GALIEN-LALOUE – L'Arc de
Triomphe, Paris – signed – black chalk and body-
colour – 203 x 332mm.
(Christie's) **$14,168 £7,700**

GALL

FRANCOIS GALL – Le Parc – signed and inscribed – mixed media on paper – 6¼ x 7½in.
(Christie's) **$374 £198**

M. DE GARAY – A maiden with her goat – signed – pencil and watercolour – 11½ x 7¾in.
(Christie's) **$418 £242**

AKSELI GALLEN-KALLELA – An Italian beauty – signed – 17 x 13¾in.
(Christie's) **$44,770 £24,200**

EMIL GANSO – Girl in Old Fashioned Chaise – Signed – pencil on paper – 17½ x 14½in.
(Robt. W. Skinner Inc.) **$600 £340**

DANIEL GARBER – Portrait of a woman – signed – charcoal on paper – 62.2 x 46cm.
(Christie's) **$1,045 £574**

FREDERICK GARLING – Sydney Cove – pencil and watercolour – 31.4 x 46.3cm.
(Christie's) $17,622 £9,900

DANIEL GARDNER – A portrait of Mrs Paul Prickett (Sarah), daughter of Robert Hunt of Send, Surrey – gouache heightened with pastel and pencil – 33 x 21¼in.
(Anderson & Garland) **$23,040** **£12,800**

LEON GASPARD – Souks in Tunis – signed and dated – oil on canvas laid down on board – 30.8 x 34.1cm.
(Christie's) **$15,400** **£8,279**

HENRY GARLAND – Trust – signed – 14 x 18in.
(Christie's) **$14,685 £8,250**

LEON GASPARD – Forest – signed – oil on board – 31.8 x 37.7cm.
(Christie's) **$4,950** **£2,661**

GASPARD

LEON GASPARD – Gate to Gobi, Peking –
signed – oil on canvas laid down on board –
32.1 x 38.1cm.
(Christie's) **$14,300** **£7,688**

HENRY MARTIN GASSER – Service station;
and Portrait of Mrs Gasser – two paintings – signed – one oil on masonite, the other oil on board
– 9 x 12in. and smaller.
(Christie's) **$935** **£513**

HENRY MARTIN GASSER – Railroad tracks and
telephone poles – signed – watercolour, charcoal
and pencil on paper – 15 x 24in.
(Christie's) **$1,650** **£906**

IGNAZ MARCEL GAUGENGIGL – The Hat –
signed and inscribed – oil on panel –
25.1 x 17.5cm.
(Christie's) **$13,200** **£7,096**

PAUL GAUGUIN – Portrait d'Enfant: Tete de Jean
Gauguin – watercolour, red chalk, pen and ink and
pencil on paper – 11.8 x 11.8cm.
(Christie's) **$39,083 £20,900**

WILLIAM GILBERT GAUL – New Jersey farmhouse – signed – oil on canvas – 14 x 20in.
(Christie's) **$3,300 £1,813**

EDWARD GAY – Wooded river landscape –
signed – on canvas – 61.2 x 76.4cm.
(Christie's) **$1,664 £935**

LUCIEN GENIN – La Place de Triomphe –
signed – gouache on paper – 50 x 61.4cm.
(Robt. W. Skinner Inc.) **$500 £295**

GOLTZIUS GELDORP, Follower of – Portrait of
an elderly woman, head and shoulders, in a lace
cap and ruff – 18 x 15½in.
(Christie's) **$1,808 £1,045**

GENNARI

JEAN GERIN – Portrait of a lady, small bust length, wearing an elaborate feathered hat – signed and dated – 18¼ x 14½in.
(Christie's) **$1,713 £990**

BENEDETTO GENNARI, Circle of – St John the Baptist – oil on canvas – 50 x 37½in.
(Phillips) **$1,253 £700**

CHARLES MARCH GERE – A harbour at dusk – signed – watercolour and pastel – 13½ x 19½in.
(Lawrence Fine Arts) **$951 £550**

GERMAN SCHOOL − One of a set of four genre scenes − oil on metal − 3½ x 2½in.
(Michael J. Bowman)   **$686   £365**

GERMAN SCHOOL, 20th century − Still Life with Wild Flowers − signed 'Kaiser' − oil on canvas − 24¾ x 21½in.
(Robt. W. Skinner Inc.)   **$700 £397**

GERMAN SCHOOL, 18th century − A fiddler playing to Boers seated before an inn; and the companion − oil on panel − 5¼ x 4¼in.
(Phillips)   **$2,112 £1,200**

GERMAN SCHOOL

GERMAN SCHOOL, 16th century − Portrait of a man wearing a red hat and fur cape − oil on panel − 29.5 x 20cm.
(Phillips) **$5,280 £3,000**

GERMAN SCHOOL, circa 1880 − Playing with a kitten − oil on canvas − 17½ x 14in.
(Lawrence Fine Arts) **$1,332** **£770**

MARK GERTLER − The Sonata − signed on reverse − oil on canvas − 29 x 37in.
(Christie's) **$47,784 £26,400**

MARCUS GHEERHAERTS, Circle of – Portrait of
a lady, three-quarter length – oil on panel –
44 x 34¼in.
(Phillips)   **$5,012   £2,800**

E. GIACHI – A fair beauty – signed – oil on canvas – 13 x 9½in.
(Christie's)   **$446   £264**

NIKO HADJIKIRIAKOS GHIKA – Leaves –
signed and dated – oil on canvas – 24 x 20in.
(Christie's)   **$20,240 £11,000**

CORRADO GIAQUINTO, Attributed to –
Voluptas – oil on canvas – 33.5 x 27cm.
(Phillips)   **$2,816   £1,600**

GIBB

ROBERT GIBB — The Artist's Wife — signed and dated — oil on canvas — 50 x 37in.
(Christie's)   **$4,307   £2,420**

WILLIAM WALLACE GILCHRIST, Jr — Portrait of the Artist's Daughter — artist's estate stamp on verso — oil on canvas — 213 x 117cm.
(Robt. W. Skinner Inc.) **$7,000   £4,142**

WILLIAM WALLACE GILCHRIST, Jr — Quahog Bay, Maine — signed — watercolour with pencil and gouache on paper — 49.9 x 33.7cm.
(Robt. W. Skinner Inc.)   **$500   £284**

EDMUND GILL — A rocky scene, with waterfall — signed and dated —16 x 24in.
(Christie's)   **$1,527   £858**

SIR WILLIAM GEORGE GILLIES – Cartmel
Priory – signed – oil on canvas – 53 x 83cm.
(Phillips) **$12,441 £7,150**

JOHN WILLIAM GILROY – A young fish-seller –
signed – oil on board – 19¼ x 15½in.
(Anderson & Garland) **$1,675 £980**

HAROLD GILMAN – Portrait of Douglas Fox
Pitt – oil on canvas – 36 x 24in.
(Christie's) **$31,856 £17,600**

JOHN WILLIAM GILROY – Steam trawlers on the
Tyne – signed – oil on board – 11¼ x 15¾in.
(Anderson & Garland) **$1,197 £700**

JOHN WILLIAM GILROY – A girl washing her
brother's face at a fireside – signed – oil on canvas
– 19½ x 15½in.
(Anderson & Garland) **$5,709 £3,300**

GILROY

JOHN WILLIAM GILROY – Whitby Harbour –
signed – oil on canvas – 13 x 16¾in.
(Anderson & Garland) **$726 £420**

J. W. GILROY – Yellow roses in a blue vase – signed
– 14½ x 14½in.
(Anderson & Garland) **$900** **£500**

CHARLES GINNER – The backs of gardens,
Oxted, Surrey – inscribed – oil on board –
8 x 7in.
(Christie's) **$12,941 £7,150**

BELISARIA GIOJA – L'harem – signed and inscribed – watercolour – 20¼ x 30½in.
(Christie's) **$17,660 £10,450**

VICTOR GILSOUL – Nature morte aux Pommes
– signed – oil on panel – 26.7 x 36.5cm.
(Christie's) **$1,143** **£605**

EDOURDO GIOJA – Michaelmas daisies – signed
and inscribed – oil on canvas – 19¼ x 23¼in.
(Christie's) **$856** **£495**

ITALO GIORDANI — Una Veduta Lacuste —
signed — oil on canvas — 36 x 48in.
(Christie's)   **$1,247   £660**

LUCA GIORDANO, Studio of — The Massacre of
the Innocents — oil on canvas — 184 x 254cm.
(Phillips)   **$10,850   £6,200**

LUCA GIORDANO, Studio of (called FA PRESTO)
— Moses striking the rock — 60 x 80in.
(Christie's)   **$24,739 £14,300**

VINCENZO GIOVANNINI — The Pope leaving
Rome — signed and dated — oil on canvas —
19 x 38in.
(Christie's)   **$14,168   £7,700**

MARIE FRANCOIS FIRMIN GIRARD — Le marche aux fleurs, Paris — signed — 18 x 24in.
(Christie's)   **$77,000 £44,000**

GIRARDOT

ERNEST GUSTAVE GIRARDOT – A Declaration in the Olden Time – an XVIII century gallant playing a lute, kneeling at the feet of his young lady – oil on canvas   64 x 76cm.
(Henry Spencer)   **$3,196**   **£1,700**

OSWALD VON GLEHN – The Lovers; Boreas and Orithyia – signed with monogram – oil on canvas – 24¾ x 63in.
(Christie's)   **$28,380   £16,500**

WILFRID GABRIEL DE GLEHN – The Winged Boy – signed – oil on canvas – 25 x 30in.
(Christie's)   **$82,236   £46,200**

WILLIAM J. GLACKENS – Blue Vase and Spring Flowers – signed with initials – oil on canvas – 66 x 34.7cm.
(Christie's)   **$25,300   £13,602**

WILFRID GABRIEL DE GLEHN – The Seine at Vieny Port – signed – watercolour, bodycolour and pencil – 14¾ x 19¼in.
(Christie's)   **$4,699   £2,640**

ALBERT GLEIZES – L'Oiseau – signed and dated – gouache on paper – 21 x 31.5 cm.
(Christie's) **$13,370 £7,150**

ALFRED AUGUSTUS GLENDENING – Bramber Castle, Sussex – signed and dated – oil on canvas – 30 x 50in.
(Christie's) **$64,768 £35,200**

ALFRED AUGUSTUS GLENDENING JNR – The cottage garden – signed and dated – 24 x 16in.
(Christie's) **$10,950 £6,050**

ALFRED AUGUSTUS GLENDENING, Jr. – The apple picker – signed with monogram and dated – 40½ x 25½in.
(Christie's) **$11,748 £6,600**

ALLERLEY GLOSSOP – Cape Sunset and five others – signed with initials – on panels – 14.9 x 21.2 cm.
(Christie's) **(Six) $587 £330**

GOBAUT

GASPARD GOBAUT — Combat pres Tlemcen du Gdl Cavaconne contre Moomumud ben Abdoola — signed, inscribed and dated — pencil and watercolour heightened with white — 15.2 x 23.3cm.
(Phillips) $743 £440

GERRIT HENDRIK GOBELL — A winter landscape with skaters on a frozen river, passing a village — signed — oil on panel — 42 x 59cm.
(Phillips) $3,168 £1,800

J. BEDDOE GODDARD — Evening in the marshes near Parkstone — signed and dated — pencil and watercolour — 18 x 27in.
(Christie's) $1,046 £605

JULIUS GODET — An extensive mountainous river landscape, North Wales — signed and dated — 23½ x 35½in.
(Christie's) $780 £462

JOHN WILLIAM GODWARD — The Muse Erato at her lyre — signed and dated — 28¾ x 32½in.
(Christie's) $32,725 £18,700

MARY GODWIN — Woman seated in an interior — oil on canvas — 27 x 20½in.
(Christie's) $2,190 £1,210

EDOUARD GOERG – Cueillette de Fleurs dans l'Esterel – signed – oil on canvas – 26 x 21½in.
(Christie's) **$12,512 £7,150**

THOMAS SWORD GOOD – The egg seller – on panel – 10½ x 8in.
(Christie's) **$2,153 £1,210**

NATALIE GONTCHAROVA – Femme au Chat – coloured crayons on paper – 13 x 9½in.
(Christie's) **$623 £330**

FREDERICK GOODALL – "The Wayside Musicians", figures resting on the road with a distant view of an Eastern town – signed – oil on canvas – 27 x 22in.
(W. H. Lane & Son) **$2,197 £1,300**

GOODWIN

ARTHUR C. GOODWIN — Storm King Highway — signed and inscribed — pastel on tan paper — 20 x 24in.
(Robt. W. Skinner Inc.)　　**$1,300**　　**£738**

CONSTANTIN GORBATOFF — View of Capri — signed — watercolour and gouache on paper — 13¾ x 18¼in.
(Christie's)　　　　**$2,887　£1,650**

WILLIAM HENRY GORE — The Reaper — signed — pencil and water colour — 4¼ x 6¾in.
(Christie's)　　**$1,135**　　**£660**

CONSTANTIN GORBATOFF — Le Port de Capri — signed — oil on canvas — 40 x 50cm.
(Christie's)　　　　**$6,237　£3,300**　　1165

THOMAS COOPER GOTCH – Half portrait of
Maria Sainsbury Tuke in dark dress with white
collar – oil on canvas – 23 x 19¼in.
(W. H. Lane & Son) **$3,660 £2,000**

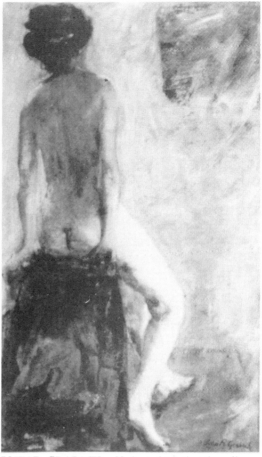

JOHN R. GRABACH – Nude study – signed – oil
on canvas – 58.4 x 35.9cm.
(Christie's) **$2,200 £1,208**

THOMAS COOPER GOTCH – Young child in a
cape – initialled – pencil drawing – 12 x 8¾in.
(W. H. Lane & Son) **$1,014 £600**

PAUL GRABWINKLER – Nude with Monkey –
signed and inscribed – coloured crayons on paper –
41 x 40.5cm.
(Christie's) **$9,081 £5,280**

PAUL GRAF – Feeding the swans – signed –
25¼ x 30¾in.
(Christie's)   **$20,350**   **£11,000**

ANTON GRAFF – Portrait of an elegant gentleman – oil on canvas – 84.5 x 67cm.
(Phillips)   **$5,370**   **£3,000**

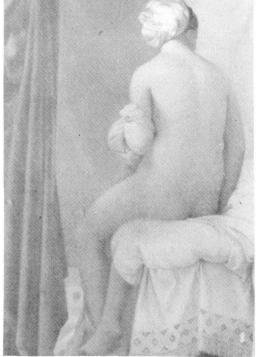

**G. GRAFTON, After Jean Auguste Dominique
Ingres** – The bather of Valpincon – signed, in-
scribed and dated – oil on canvas – 31½ x 21¼in.
(Christie's)   **$929**   **£550**

DUNCAN GRANT – The Glass – signed with
initials – oil on canvas – 10 x 14in.
(Christie's) **$25,883 £14,300**

DUNCAN GRANT – Still Life – signed – watercolour – 21½ x 15¼in.
(Lawrence Fine Arts) **$6,660** **£3,850**

ORAZIO GRAVENBROECK – Ships sailing before
a waterside palace at sunset – oil on canvas –
23½ x 32¼in.
(Phillips) **$5,280 £3,000**

DUNCAN GRANT – Man sleeping – signed – oil
on canvas – 18 x 24in.
(Christie's) **$7,565 £4,180**

GRAY

CEDRIC GRAY – Pastoral river landscapes at dusk; and Dawn – both signed and dated – oil on canvas – 10 x 18in.
(Christie's) Two $1,294 £748

EDMUND WILLIAM GRAECEN – Girl with Parasol – signed – oil on canvas – 75.7 x 76.3cm.
(Christie's) $48,400 £26,021

EDMUND WILLIAM GREACEN – The Parasol – signed – oil on canvas – 65 x 54cm.
(Christie's) $16,500 £8,870

WILLIAM GREASON – Lowtide – signed – oil on cardboard – 32.7 x 26cm.
(Robt. W. Skinner Inc.) $650 £384

ROLAND GREEN – Mute Swans over the Fens – signed – watercolour and bodycolour – 14½ x 21¾in.
(Phillips) $811 £480

FRANK GRESLEY – Women and girls paddling in a stream before a bridge – signed – watercolour – 7 x 10in.
(W. H. Lane & Son) $1,462 £850

FRANK GRESLEY — Haymaking — figures and cart before trees — watercolour — 11 x 7½in.
(W. H. Lane & Son) **$845 £500**

— Noon, St Ives Cornwall — watercolour and bodycolour — 14 x 18in.
(Christie's) **$418** **£242**

JEAN-BAPTISTE GREUZE, After — A mother and son in a kitchen, feeding a dog — 19¾ x 15½in.
(Christie's) **$1,713 £990**

JAMES STEPHEN GRESLEY — A group of three children walking alongside a fast flowing river with rocky tree lined banks — signed and dated — watercolour heightened with body colour — 48.5 x 74.5cm.
(Henry Spencer) **$1,496 £800**

CHARLES MacIVER GRIERSON — Afternoon Tea — a young lady reading, sitting beside a table — signed — watercolour — 27 x 38cm.
(Henry Spencer) **$2,197** **£1,300**

GRIMSHAW

ATKINSON GRIMSHAW – In the glowing gold of autumn – signed and dated – oil on canvas – 20 x 30in.
(Christie's) **$48,576 £26,400**

LOUIS H. GRIMSHAW – Sunderland Harbour in the moonlight – signed and dated – oil on canvas – 11¾ x 17¾in.
(Anderson & Garland) **$2,249 £1,300**

JOHN ATKINSON GRIMSHAW – Old houses near Adel Leeds by moonlight – signed and dated – on board – 11½ x 9½in.
(Christie's) **$10,406 £6,050**

JUAN GRIS – La Jarre – signed and dated – oil on canvas – 18 x 21½in.
(Christie's) **$291,555 £170,500**

JOHN ATKINSON GRIMSHAW – Clydeside, Glasgow – Quayside view, boats, horse drawn carriages and shop fronts – signed and dated – 59 x 89cm.
(Henry Spencer) **$31,265 £18,500**

FRANCOIS ADOLPHE GRISON – Kitchen chaos – signed – oil on canvas – 35 x 45½in.
(Christie's) **$26,312 £14,300**

GRISOT – Studying Form – signed –
21 x 17¼in.
(Anderson & Garland) **$828** **£460**

GEORGE GROSZ – Sitzender weiblicher Akt –
signed and dated – on paper – 30½ x 24¾in.
(Christie's) **$14,190** **£8,250**

CHARLES ROGER ('RED') GROOMS – Slushing
– signed and dated – colour lithograph on Arches
Cover paper – 22 x 28in.
(Robt. W. Skinner Inc.) **$750** **£443**

WILLIAM GROPPER – Sweat Shop – signed –
oil on canvas – 18 x 30in.
(Christie's) **$11,000** **£5,913**

GEORGE GROSZ – Strassenszene – signed –
brush and indian ink on paper – 31 x 23.5cm.
(Christie's) **$6,737 £3,850**

GRUPPE

CHARLES P. GRUPPE – Sailboats on land –
signed – oil on canvas – 12½ x 19½in.
(Christie's)   **$1,430**   **£785**

CHARLES PAUL GRUPPE – Dutch canal scene –
signed – oil on canvas – 18 x 22in.
(Christie's)   **$1,430**   **£785**

EMILE A. GRUPPE – Low tide, East Gloucester –
signed – oil on canvas – 20 x 24in.
(Bruce D. Collins)   **$3,300**   **£1,746**

EMILE A. GRUPPE – Rocky coastal scene with
breaking waves – oil on canvas – impressionistic
palette technique – 24 x 29in.
(Du Mouchelles)   **$1,750**   **£1,035**

ADRIAEN DE GRYFF – A peacock, a cockerel
and chickens in a parkland – oil on copper – oval
– 6¾ x 5½in.
(Phillips)   **$880**   **£500**

FRANCESCO GUARDI, Manner of – Elegant
figures – oil on canvas, unstretched – 25 x 29.5 cm.
(Phillips)   **$1,320**   **£750**

FRANCESCO GUARDI, Follower of − A view of Santa Maria Della Salute and the Point of the Dogana from the Riva Del Grano − 30 x 45½in.
(Christie's) **$47,575 £27,500**

EUGENE JOHAN JOSEPH VON GUERARD − Australian landscapes − folio − 18½ x 25in. overall.
(Christie's) **$13,706 £7,700**

HANS FREDRIK GUDE − Sailing vessels and fishing boats in a calm sea, Christiania fjord − signed and dated − 16¾ x 21¾in.
(Christie's) **$26,455 £14,300**

ARMAND GUILLAUMIN − Le Plateau du Pont Charraut; Crozant − signed − oil on canvas − 24 x 36¼in.
(Christie's) **$49,192 £28,600**

HANS FREDRIK GUDE − By the lake − signed and dated − 22¾ x 37¾in.
(Christie's) **$52,910 £28,600**

GUILLAUMIN

ARMAND GUILLAUMIN – Chemin en Bord de
Mer – signed – oil on canvas – 18 x 21¾ in.
(Christie's)   **$56,760**   **£33,000**

HERBERT JACOB GUTE – Easy Does It – signed
– egg tempera on board – 25¾ x 19in.
(Robt. W. Skinner Inc.) **$950**   **£562**

RENATO GUTTUSO – Nudo in Piedi – signed and
indistinctly inscribed – gouache, brush and black
ink on paper laid down on canvas – 71 x 50cm.
(Christie's)   **$2,117 £1,210**

JEAN BAPTISTE LOUIS GUY – A mid-day encounter – signed and dated – 17¼ x 26in.
(Christie's)   **$4,862 £2,860**

CORNELIS CORNELISZ-VAN HAARLEM, Circle of – The Resurrection – on panel – 16½ x 9½in.
(Christie's) **$685 £396**

JACOB PHILIP HACKAERT – The Temple of Hercules at Cori – signed, inscribed and dated – gouache – 348 x 470mm.
(Christie's) **$13,725 £7,500**

SIR ARTHUR HACKER – 'And there was a great cry in Egypt' – signed and dated – oil on canvas – 35½ x 59¾in.
(Christie's) **$22,704 £13,200**

CECIL VAN HAANEN – The masked ball – stamped with the Nachlass mark – on panel – 13 x 9in.
(Christie's) **$654 £385**

JACOB HACKAERT, Circle of – Peasants conversing on a hillside above the Bay of Naples – oil on canvas – 24 x 33½in.
(Phillips) **$7,920 £4,500**

ELSA HAEMGEN-DINGKUTEN – Mutter und Kind – signed – oil on panel – 28 x 21¼in.
(Christie's) **$1,732 £990**

HAGBORG

AUGUST HAGBORG – Mussel gatherers, Brittany – signed – 100 x 81cm.
(Christie's) $50,875 £27,500

WILLIAM HAHN – Portrait of a lady, bust length, in a black dress with a black velvet choker – signed, inscribed and dated – on canvas – 22½ x 17in.
(Christie's) $744 £418

CLIFFORD HALL – Three Clowns – signed and dated – watercolour – 14¼ x 9¾in.
(Christie's) $608 £352

CLIFFORD HALL – The Clown (Fred Knowles)
– signed and dated – oil on canvas – 24¼ x 20½in.
(Christie's)   **$2,741   £1,540**

DIRCK HALS, Circle of – A Merry Company –
oil on panel – 31.5 x 50.5cm.
(Phillips)   **$13,200   £7,500**

FRANS HALS, Follower of – A portrait of a girl,
small bust length, in a red dress and white collar –
signed with monogram – 12¼ x 10in.
(Christie's)   **$1,141 £660**

HALS

HARMEN HALS – A peasant woman seated in a window niche holding a glass – oil on panel – 13¼ x 10¾in.
(Phillips)   **$1,496**   **£850**

MARIUS HAMANN – Interior with woman reading – signed – 24 x 29in.
(Christie's)   **$2,057**   **£1,210**

JAY HAMBIDGE – Schoolgirls' Outing – signed – watercolour with pencil and gouache on paper – 90.7 x 55cm.
(Robt. W. Skinner Inc.)   **$1,000**   **£591**

HELEN HAMILTON – Connecticut Farms – signed – oil on board – 8 x 10in.
(Bruce D. Collins)   **$110**   **£58**

VILHELM HAMMERSHOI – Portrait of Ida Ilsted, aged 21, seated three-quarter length – 49½ x 39¼in.
(Christie's)   **$101,750**   **£55,000**

VILHELM HAMMERSHOI – Christiansborg Palace from the Marmorbroen bridge – 117 x 139cm.
(Christie's)   **$407,000**   **£220,000**

ARTHUR KNIGHTON HAMMOND – Still Life
with Mixed Flowers – signed – oil on panel –
30 x 25in.
(Christie's) **$3,426** **£1,925**

ARTHUR HENRY KNIGHTON HAMMOND –
Portrait of a lady in a red suit – signed – water-
colour – 62.2 x 43.7cm.
(Woolley & Wallis) **$553** **£320**

ARTHUR KNIGHTON HAMMOND – The Beach
at Dieppe – signed – watercolour, bodycolour and
pencil – 18 x 23½in.
(Christie's) **$1,566** **£880**

ARTHUR KNIGHTON HAMMOND – Brighton, Sussex, 22nd May 1933 – signed – watercolour and pencil – 19¼ x 24½in.
(Christie's)   **$881   £495**

WALTER SIGMUND HAMPEL – The Vision – oil on panel – 26¾ x 33in.
(Christie's)   **$30,272   £17,600**

H. HAMMOND – On the Kent Coast – one of a pair – 11 x 17in.
(Prudential)   **Two $1,297 £750**

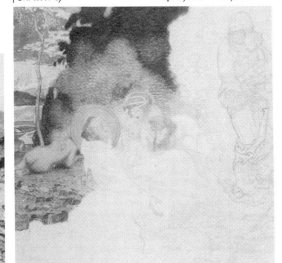

WALTER SIGMUND HAMPEL – The Temptation of St. Anthony – signed – watercolour, pencil, pen and black ink heightened with gold on paper – 34 x 31.5cm.
(Christie's)   **$12,298 £7,150**

H. HAMMOND – "Going fishing" and "Bringing home the sheaves" – both signed – 11 x 17in.
(Prudential)   **$2,249 £1,300**

WILLIAM LEE-HANKEY – Getting ready –
signed – oil on canvas – 25 x 29in.
(Christie's) **$18,601** **£10,450**

WILLIAM LEE-HANKEY – Le Repos – signed
– watercolour – 15 x 22in.
(Christie's) **$8,223** **£4,620**

WILLIAM LEE-HANKEY – The Inn at Avebury
– signed – oil on canvas – 24½ x 29in.
(Christie's) **$15,664** **£8,800**

WILLIAM LEE-HANKEY, Attributed to – French
street scene – on panel – 20 x 25in.
(Christie's) **$1,394** **£825**

WILLIAM LEE-HANKEY – The Cottagers –
signed – watercolour and bodycolour –
14¼ x 17¼in.
(Christie's) **$5,678** **£3,190**

WILLIAM LEE-HANKEY – Red haired girl –
signed – watercolour and bodycolour – 12 x 10in.
(Christie's) **$1,860** **£1,045**

HANSEN

HEINRICH HANSEN — The fishmarket in Florence — signed with initials and dated — 11 x 9in.
(Christie's)   **$8,976**   **£5,280**

ADOLPH HEINRICH HANSEN — Amalienborg Palace, Copenhagen — signed with initials — 19½ x 16in.
(Christie's)   **$935**   **£550**

GEORGE HARCOURT — Meriel, Cynthia and George (Perkins) — signed and dated — 71¾ x 90½in.
(Christie's)   **$38,500**   **£22,000**

MELBOURNE H. HARDWICK — A lady by the sea — signed — watercolour and pencil heightened with gouache — 19½ x 13in.
(Christie's)   **$1,650**   **£906**

MELBOURNE H. HARDWICK — The Favourite Toy — signed — watercolour with gouache on paper — 57.7 x 42.2cm.
(Robt. W. Skinner Inc.) **$650**   **£384**

THOMAS BUSH HARDY — Off Calais — signed and dated — 23½ x 32in.
(Christie's)   **$2,741**   **£1,540**

EVELYN HARKE — Horses ploughing — signed and dated — 12 x 16in.
(Prudential)   **$897**   **£480**

ALEXEI ALEXEIWITSCH HARLAMOFF — The pink bonnet — signed — oil on canvas — 22 x 17in.
(Christie's)   **$60,720 £33,000**

HARMAR

FAIRLIE HARMAR – Interior of Ramridge
House – oil on canvas – 21 x 25in.
(Christie's)   **$8,223   £4,620**

EDWARD STEEL HARPER – Homer Water,
Somerset – signed with monogram and dated –
oil on board – 18 x 30in.
(Christie's)   **$2,153   £1,210**

EDWIN HARRIS – "The Evening Story", a young
girl seated at a table reading to her grandmother by
lamp light – signed – oil on canvas – 36 x 28in.
(W. H. Lane & Son)   **$14,365   £8,500**

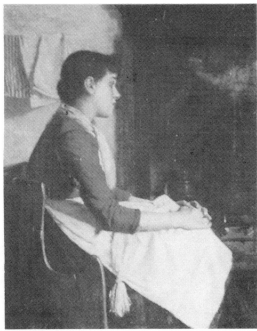

THOMAS HARPER – Tynemouth Priory from
South Shields – signed and dated – 14 x 20¾in.
(Anderson & Garland) **$2,250   £1,250**

EDWIN HARRIS – By the fireside – signed – oil
on canvas laid down on board – 19¾ x 15¾in.
(Christie's)   **$7,832   £4,400**

JOHN CYRIL HARRISON – Two mallard drakes and a hen taking flight – signed – watercolour – 46.5 x 32.5cm.
(Henry Spencer)   **$1,557**   **£900**

JOHN CYRIL HARRISON – Geese in flight over north Norfolk coast – signed – watercolour – 9 x 12in.
(G. A. Key)   **$3,272 £1,750**

HAROLD HARVEY – "A summer evening", Evelyn seated on the wall of Vivian House with St Peter's Church, Newlyn, below – signed and dated – oil on canvas – 24 x 20in.
(W. H. Lane & Son)   **$26,660 £15,500**

C. BERTRAM HARTMAN – Two Natures – signed and dated – oil on canvas – 29½ x 38½in.
(Christie's)   **$62,436 £36,300**

GUNTHER HARTWICK – Winter's Pleasures – oil on canvas – 76.2 x 107cm.
(Christie's)   **$9,350**   **£5,026**

HAROLD HARVEY – Ash trees at Drift, near Penzance, Cornwall – signed and dated – oil on canvas – 20 x 24in.
(W. H. Lane & Son)   **$12,810 £7,000**

HAROLD HARVEY – Man with a woman in a cart – signed and dated – oil on canvas – 21¾ x 27in.
(Christie's) **$12,922 £7,260**

J. R. HARVEY – Country scene with cattle grazing – a pair – oil on board – 11 x 12in.
(Fellows & Sons) **$845 £500**

KIYOSHI HASEGAWA – Village provencal – signed – watercolour and crayon on paper – 27.5 x 40.5cm.
(Christie's) $6,737 £3,850

WILLIAM M. HAY – A funny story – signed and dated – 23¾ x 19¾in.
(Christie's) $16,643 £9,350

JOHANN HAUSER – Nackte Frau mit rotem Haar – signed – coloured pencil on card – 73 x 102cm.
(Christie's) $16,456 £8,800

JOHN HAUSER – The Flight – signed and dated – oil on panel – 24.7 x 35.7cm.
(Christie's) $6,600 £3,548

WILLIAM M. HAY – A young beauty – signed – on board – oval – 11½in. x 9½in.
(Christie's) $832 £484

HENRI HAYDEN – Paysage – signed and dated – oil on canvas – 65.1 x 91.7cm.
(Christie's) **$34,303 £18,150**

HENRI HAYDEN – La Marine a St Jean – signed and dated – gouache and black ink on paper laid down on card – 13 x 20¼in.
(Christie's) **$3,080 £1,760**

HENRI HAYDEN – Auverne – signed and dated – oil on canvas – 60 x 73cm.
(Christie's) **$13,860 £7,920**

HENRI HAYDEN – Nature Morte a la Pipe et au Journal – signed – oil and sand on canvas – 18 x 25½in.
(Christie's) **$23,655 £12,650**

HENRI HAYDEN – Nature morte a la Theiere et a la Cafetiere – signed and dated – oil on canvas – 21½ x 28¾in.
(Christie's) **$5,390 £3,080**

CLAUDE HAYES – The Shepherdess – signed – oil on board – 14 x 12in.
(Christie's) **$2,349 £1,320**

JAMES HAYLLAR – Portrait of a young boy, quarter length, playing with toys – oil on panel – circular – 6½ x 6in.
(Christie's) **$666** **£385**

JOHN HAYES – Portrait of Robert Biddulph Phillips, seated half length, in a black coat and stock, a crimson curtain background - 13½ x 11½in.
(Christie's) **$1,040** **£605**

WILLIAM HAYES – A blue crown'd Parakeet from the Sandwich Islands – inscribed – pen and grey ink and watercolour – 13¼ x 9½in. – and a watercolour of a parrot.
(Christie's) **$1,402 £825**

JAMES HAYLLAR – Miss Lily's first flirtation – signed and dated – 36 x 28in.
(Christie's) **$27,874 £15,400**

JAMES HAYLLAR – May day – signed – oil
on canvas – 40 x 60in.
(Christie's)   **$32,384 £17,600**

FRANCIS HAYMAN – Adam and Eve in the
Garden of Eden – pen and brown ink, brown
wash, heightened with white – 10 x 17cm.
(Christie's)   **$748   £440**

ALFRED HAYWARD – Evening in the garden
– signed and dated – oil on canvas – 18 x 24in.
(Christie's)   **$7,440   £4,180**

GEORGE A. HAYS – Woonsocket Hill / A Summer
Morning – signed – oil on canvas – 63.2 x 75.1cm.
(Robt. W. Skinner Inc.) **$950**   **£562**

GARNET HAZARD – The last autumn colour –
signed – oil on canvas – 23 x 32in.
(Bruce D. Collins)   **$990**   **£523**

MARTIN JOHNSON HEADE – Orchids and Hummingbird – signed and dated – 15½ x 20in.
(Christie's) $550,000   £295,698

MARTIN JOHNSON HEADE – Magnolias on Light Blue Velvet – signed – oil on canvas – 15 x 24in.
(Christie's) $264,000   £141,935

THOMAS HEAPHY –Portrait of a lady, full length, in a white dress on a woodland path – one of a pair – pencil and watercolour – 21½ x 16¼in.
(Christie's)   Two $1,122   £660

MARTIN JOHNSON HEADE – Still Life with Glass of Roses – signed and dated – oil on canvas – 17 x 14½in.
(Christie's) $30,800   £16,559

ERICH HECKEL – Krankes Madchen — woodcut on paper – 7½ x 5½in.
(Robt. W. Skinner Inc.) $225   £133

ERICH HECKEL – Frauen am Ufer – signed and
dated - on paper – 21 x 26¾in.
(Christie's) **$17,028** **£9,900**

RALPH HEDLEY – The Cellarman – signed –
oil on canvas – 31½ x 29¼in.
(Anderson & Garland) **$4,680** **£2,600**

ERICH HECKEL – Gelbe und blaue Bluten, *recto
and verso* -- signed, dated and inscribed –
22½ x 16¾in.
(Christie's) **$14,399 £7,700**

RALPH HEDLEY – Passengers in an omnibus –
signed – oil on canvas – 15¼ x 19¼in.
(Anderson & Garland) **$4,860** **£2,700**

RALPH HEDLEY – Setting the mill to windward
– signed with initials and dated – pastel –
22 x 17½in.
(Anderson & Garland) **$991 £580**

RALPH HEDLEY – Mrs Elliot in her garden – signed and dated – oil on canvas – 17¼ x 13½in.
(Anderson & Garland) **$3,740 £2,000**

RALPH HEDLEY – A woman seated by a range – signed – oil on panel – 16 x 12in.
(Anderson & Garland) **$761 £440**

RALPH HEDLEY – Hylton – inscribed on reverse – oil on canvas – 17½ x 13¼in.
(Anderson & Garland) **$2,250** **£1,250**

RALPH HEDLEY – A tinker's caravan – inscribed on label on reverse – oil on canvas – 13¾ x 18in.
(Anderson & Garland) **$6,840** **£3,800**

EGBERT VAN HEEMSKERK, Attributed to – A dwarf on a village street – on panel – 22.9 x 19.4cm.
(Christie's) **$856 £495**

HENDRIK JAN HEIN – Dead game and fruit on a
table – signed – 29 x 26in.
(Christie's) **$9,625** **£5,500**

JOHAN VAN HELL – Heringsverkaufer – signed
and dated – watercolour and pencil on paper –
19½ x 17¼in.
(Christie's) **$9,873** **£5,280**

THOMAS THEODORE HEINE-The Evening Walk (Abend spaziergang) - oil on copper-
oval-23¼ x 31½in. *(Christie's)* **$37,840** **£22,000**

HELGE HELME – Harvest time – signed –
78.5 x 100.3cm.
(Christie's)   **$2,035**   **£1,100**

PAUL CESAR HELLEU – A portrait study of
Ellen the artist's eldest daughter – signed – black,
red and white chalks – 16½ x 21in.
(Christie's)   **$16,596 £9,020**

PAUL CESAR HELLEU – Madame Helleu at her
bureau in the drawing room of the artist's studio –
signed – 30½ x 22¾in.
(Christie's)   **$1,358,000**   **£776,000**

PAUL CESAR HELLEU – Portrait of a Woman in
a feathered hat – signed – etching and drypoint on
paper – 37.2 x 26.7cm.
(Robt. W. Skinner Inc.) **$1,300**   **£769**

PAUL CESAR HELLEU – On deck – signed –
oil on canvas – 32 x 23½in.
(Christie's)   **$101,200 £55,000**

WILLIAM HEMSLEY — Sunday in the nineteenth century — signed — on panel — 8¼ x 10½in.
(Christie's) **$1,860 £1,045**

BERNARD BENEDICT HEMY — North Shields Harbour — signed — oil on canvas — 23½ x 35¾in.
(Anderson & Garland) **$3,979 £2,300**

BERNARD BENEDICT HEMY — A jetty, North Shields — signed — 13½ x 19½in.
(Anderson & Garland) **$935 £500**

WILLIAM HEMSLEY — The naughty boy — signed and dated — on panel — 8½ x 6½in.
(Christie's) **$1,393 £770**

BERNARD BENEDICT HEMY — A collier and a tug on the Tyne — signed — 19½ x 29¼in.
(Anderson & Garland) **$864 £480**

CHARLES NAPIER HEMY — Shipping in Harbour — signed with initials — 30 x 25in.
(Chrystals) **$5,096 £2,800**

THOMAS MARIE MADAWASKA HEMY – A barge builder's yard on the banks of the Tyne – signed and dated – 12¼ x 21¼in.
(Anderson & Garland)   **$2,898 £1,550**

CARSTEN HENRICHSEN – A wooded landscape with deer – signed – 37 x 52½in.
(Christie's)   **$1,870   £1,100**

JOSEPH MORRIS HENDERSON – Waves breaking on the Ayrshire coast – signed – oil on canvas – 45 x 75cm.
(Phillips)   **$5,359 £3,080**

JEAN JACQUES HENNER – A reclining nude – oil on canvas – 27 x 50in.
(Christie's)   **$13,763 £7,480**

PAUL HENRY – Irish cottages beside track – signed – oil painting – 7½ x 10½in.
(Hobbs & Chambers)   **$6,480   £3,600**

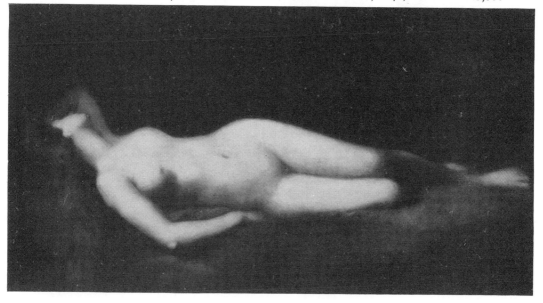

HEPPLE

NORMAN HEPPLE – Silhouettes in Queen
Victoria Street – signed and dated – oil on canvas
– 20 x 16in.
(Christie's) **$4,307 £2,420**

WILSON HEPPLE – A tabby kitten playing with
a rose – signed and dated – 10 x 15in.
(Anderson & Garland) **$2,992 £1,750**

WILSON HEPPLE – Two tabby kittens playing
with a butterfly – signed and dated – 9¼ x 12½in.
(Anderson & Garland) **$2,057 £1,100**

AUGUSTE HERBIN – Nature morte aux Fruits
– signed – watercolour on paper – 30½ x 22in.
(Christie's) **$13,090 £7,480**

SIR HUBERT VON HERKOMER – Still life of a
porcelain figure, oriental vases and bowls – signed
and dated – pencil and watercolour – 41.3 x 51.8cm.
(Christie's) **$532 £308**

FRIEDRICH HERLEN – Saints Matthew, James and Peter standing behind a stone gallery – oil on panel – 22¾ x 30¾in.
(Phillips) **$5,280 £3,000**

LEON PIERRE HERPIN – A coastal landscape with beached fishing boats and a lighthouse – signed and dated – 15 x 18in.
(Christie's) **$3,740 £2,200**

JOSEF HERMAN – Meeting of neighbours – oil on board – 26 x 36in.
(Christie's) **$11,946 £6,600**

C. K. HERRICK – Feeding the chickens – signed and dated – oil on canvas – 12 x 18in.
(Bruce D. Collins) **$825 £436**

OLOF HERMELIN – A wooded river landscape with a woman on a bridge – signed and dated – on metal – 60.7 x 41cm.
(Christie's) **$7,122 £3,850**

JOHN FREDERICK HERRING JNR, Follower of A harnessed chestnut cob outside a stable; and A bay hunter watering from a trough – 13¾ x 17½in.
(Christie's) **Two $1,046 £605**

JOHN FREDERICK HERRING, Senior – The Moroccan Groom – signed and dated – oil on canvas – 17½ x 23½in.
(Anderson & Garland) **$104,400** **£58,000**

EDMOND-AMEDEE HEUZE – La Plage a Cap Benat – signed – oil on canvas – 53.7 x 64.8cm.
(Christie's) **$1,732** **£990**

HERMAN HERZOG – The Matterhorn, Switzerland – signed – oil on canvas – 30 x 40in.
(Christie's) **$33,000** **£17,741**

ARTHUR HEYER – Curiosity – signed – 26¾ x 21½in.
(Christie's) **$785** **£462**

HERMAN HERZOG – Crashing stream – signed – oil on canvas laid down on masonite – 16 x 20in.
(Christie's) **$5,500 £3,021**

ARTHUR HEYER – A proud mother – signed – 23 x 31in.
(Christie's) **$3,366** **£1,980**

ALDRO THOMPSON HIBBARD – The covered
bridge, Swiftwater NH – signed – oil on canvas-
board – 45.4 x 61cm.
(Robt. W. Skinner Inc.) **$3,600 £2,045**

GEORGE ELGAR HICKS – Evening tales – signed
and dated – on board – 7¾ x 9¾in.
(Christie's) **$6,853 £3,850**

ALDRO THOMPSON HIBBARD – Winter Brook
– signed – oil on artist board – 44.8 x 61cm.
(Robt. W. Skinner Inc.) **$1,700** **£1,005**

FRANK HIDER – "The Sunset Hour", Chapel
Porth, St Agnes Head – figure on a beach with
shipping off shore – signed – oil on canvas –
14 x 18in.
(W. H. Lane & Son) **$877 £510**

ALDRO THOMPSON HIBBARD – Mt Mansfield
Stowe Vermont – signed – oil on canvas laid down
on board – 18 x 20¾in.
(Christie's) **$4,400 £2,417**

CAMILLE HILAIRE – Pesage a la Touques – signed
– oil on canvas – 73.3 x 92.4cm.
(Christie's) **$5,821 £3,080**

HILDER

ROWLAND HILDER – Oast Houses, Kent –
signed – watercolour – 8 x 12in.
(Christie's)   **$1,409   £792**

HENRIK HILLBOM – Brook in Winter – signed
and dated – oil on canvas – 63.2 x 76.2cm.
(Robt. W. Skinner Inc.) **$425**   **£251**

THOMAS HILL, Attributed to – Yosemite Valley
with Bridal Veil Falls – unsigned – oil on canvas –
43 x 54in.
(Robt. W. Skinner Inc.)   **$4,250 £2,414**

HENRICK HILLBOM – A ferry on the Hudson
river – signed and dated – 14 x 18in.
(Christie's)   **$6,512**   **£3,520**

ROBERT HILLINGFORD – The bibliophile –
signed with monogram – 10¼ x 8in.
(Christie's)   **$783   £440**

ROBERT ALEXANDER HILLINGFORD –
Napoleon on the flight from Leipzig; and An
engagement between English Artillery and French
Cavalry – both signed – on panel – 8 x 12in.
(Christie's)   **$6,265 £3,520**

ROGER HILTON – September 1953 – dated – oil on canvas – 18½ x 36½in.
(Christie's) $20,905 £11,550

ROBERT ALEXANDER HILLINGFORD – The departure of the Coldstream Guards for Egypt – signed – 36 x 24in.
(Christie's) **$7,315** **£4,180**

THEODORE HINES – "Medmenham Abbey on Thames", depicts house in background, swans in foreground – signed – oil on canvas – 20 x 30in.
(Du Mouchelles) **$2,200 £1,164**

LAURA COOMBS HILLS – Gelley Flowers No.29 – signed – pastel on board – 21½ x 18in.
(Robt. W. Skinner Inc.) **$19,000 £10,795**

HIRAKAWA – Passage de l'Atles, Paris – signed and dated – oil on canvas – 21¾ x 25½in.
(Christie's) **$5,197 £2,970**

HITCHENS

IVON HITCHENS – After a bathe, No. 2 –
signed, inscribed and dated – oil on canvas –
18 x 36in.
(Christie's) **$28,869 £15,950**

IVON HITCHENS – Blue and yellow – signed –
oil on canvas – 20 x 30in.
(Christie's) **$17,919 £9,900**

DAVID HOCKNEY – Untitled – signed and dated
– on paper – 14½ x 10¼in.
(Christie's) **$41,624 £24,200**

DANIEL HOCK – Portrait of a lady – signed and
dated – 18 x 12½in.
(Woolley & Wallis) **$1,903 £1,100**

JOHN EVAN HODGSON – Extensive river landscape with haymaking scene in distance – signed –
oil on canvas – 35 x 26in.
(G. A. Key) **$1,636 £875**

FRANZ HOEPFNER – Figures sitting on a river bank in a wooded landscape – signed – on panel – 17.8 x 16.9cm.
(Christie's)   **$1,776**   **£1,045**

KARL HOFER – Bildnis – signed and dated – oil on canvas – 35½ x 25in.
(Christie's)   **$34,408**   **£18,700**

KARL HOFER – Mondmann – signed and dated – oil on canvas – 79 x 53cm.
(Christie's)   **$31,762 £18,150**

CHARLES C. J. HOFFBAUER – On the beach – signed and dated – oil on canvas – 25¼ x 32in.
(Robt. W. Skinner Inc.)   **$130,000 £73,863**

HOFFMANN

CARL HEINRICK HOFFMANN – The New Wine – Wine cellar with serving girl seated, holding a wine bottle, two gallants before her – signed and dated oil on canvas - 64 x 84.5cm.
(Henry Spencer) **$3,114** **£1,800**

P. L. HOHNSTEDT – Bend in the river – signed – oil on board – 9 x 9½in.
(Bruce D. Collins) **$99** **£52**

GEORGES HOFFMAN – L'Apres-midi sur la Plage de Carolles – signed – oil on canvas – 38.5 x 46cm.
(Christie's) **$10,587 £6,050**

FRANCIS MABEL HOLLAMS – A huntsman in a pink coat, mounted on a bay hunter – signed with initials, oil on panel – 9½ x 13½in.
(Christie's) **$1,141** **£660**

JOSEF WAGNER HOHENBERG – The notary – signed – 27½ x 35½in.
(Christie's) **$5,984** **£3,520**

JOHN HOLLAND – Douglas Bay Hotel and Onchan Head – signed – 29 x 39in.
(Chrystals) **$3,366** **£1,800**

W. P. HOLLYER – Morning in the Highlands – Two ewes, ram, lambs, on a mountain side – signed – oil on canvas – 49 x 74cm.
(Henry Spencer)   **$1,989**   **£1,150**

GUSTAV HOLMBOM – A winter landscape – signed with initials and dated – oil on canvas – 25¾ x 36¼in.
(Christie's)   **$836**   **£495**

CARL HOLSOE – A lady in an interior – signed – oil on canvas – 19 x 15¾in.
(Christie's)   **$76,912 £41,800**

GEORGE AUGUSTUS HOLMES – The foxglove – signed – oil on canvas – 28 x 17in.
(Hy. Duke & Son)   **$5,984 £3,400**

CARL HOLSOE – A lady looking in a mirror by an open door – signed – 31¾ x 26¼in.
(Christie's)   **$122,100**   **£66,000**

HOLSOE

CARL HOLSOE – An interior – signed – oil on canvas – 17 x 18½in.
(Christie's) **$48,576 £26,400**

WINSLOW HOMER – Fishing Schooner, Nassau – signed and inscribed – watercolour, gouache and pencil on paper – 36.9 x 53.6cm.
(Christie's) **$660,000 £354,838**

CARL HOLSOE – An interior with a woman peeling vegetables – signed – 65.5 x 55.5cm.
(Christie's) **$28,490 £15,400**

WINSLOW HOMER – A Garden in Nassau – signed and dated – watercolour, gouache and pencil on paper – 36.8 x 53cm.
(Christie's) **$660,000 £354,838**

JOSEF HOLSTAYN – A still life of roses, poppies and other flowers in a basket on a ledge – signed and inscribed – oil on canvas – 30 x 23¾in.
(Christie's) **$8,096 £4,400**

M. HONEY (?) – A barn interior with sheep, a turkey and cat and a peasant girl feeding chickens – signed – oil on panel – 16 x 12½in.
(Christie's) **$856 £495**

GERRIT VAN HONTHORST, Circle of — Portrait of the Duke of Buckingham, long bust length, wearing a ceremonial green sash — oil on canvas — 28½ x 23½in.
(Phillips) **$4,400 £2,500**

BERNARD DE HOOG — Playmates — signed — 17 x 21in.
(Chrystals) **$4,862 £2,600**

BERNARD DE HOOG — Feeding baby — signed — 31¾ x 34in.
(Christie's) **$15,895 £9,350**

BERNARD DE HOOG — A mother's duty — signed — 20 x 17¼in.
(Christie's) **$7,480 £4,400**

ROBERT HOPE — Girl choosing Silks — signed — oil on canvas — 17 x 15¼in.
(Christie's) **$3,044 £1,760**

ARTHUR HOPKINS — The Tryst — signed and
inscribed — watercolour and bodycolour —
11 x 8¼in.
(Phillips)   **$3,718**   **£2,200**

JAN JOSEF HOREMANS — A musical party
around a table — signed — oil on canvas —
15½ x 12½in.
(Phillips)   **$4,475   £2,500**

JAN JOSEF HOREMANS, the Younger — Elegant
figures seated amongst Classical ruins, taking re-
freshments — oil on canvas — 22 x 33in.
(Phillips)   **$5,632   £3,200**

J. HOPPNER — A portrait of Richard Colley Wesley,
Marquess Wellesly, brother of the Duke of Welling-
ton — oil on canvas — 29½ x 24½in.
(Anderson & Garland)   **$4,860**   **£2,600**

JAN JOSEF HOREMANS THE YOUNGER —
Putti disporting with hunting dogs in a landscape:
An overdoor — signed — 33 x 64½in.
(Christie's)   **$2,474   £1,430**

JAN JOSEF HOREMANS THE YOUNGER — A satyr spying on the sleeping Diana — 18¾ x 23in. *(Christie's)* **$2,284 £1,320**

EDWARD ATKINSON HORNEL — Amongst the bluebells — oil on canvas — 63 x 76cm. *(Phillips)* **$13,398 £7,700**

EDWARD ATKINSON HORNEL — The Geisha Girl — oil on canvas laid down — 46 x 36cm. *(Phillips)* **$11,484 £6,600**

261

EDWARD ATKINSON HORNEL – Primroses –
signed and dated – oil on canvas – 50 x 40cm.
(Phillips) **$36,366 £20,900**

EDWARD ATKINSON HORNEL – Foxgloves in
a wood – oil on canvas – 150 x 120cm.
(Phillips) **$42,108 £24,200**

EDWARD ATKINSON HORNEL – At Appleblossom time – signed and dated – oil on canvas
– 19¾ x 15½in.
(Anderson & Garland) **$16,245 £9,500**

EDWARD ATKINSON HORNEL – Hide and seek
– signed and dated – oil on canvas – 90 x 76cm.
(Phillips) **$20,097 £11,550**

EDWARD ARKINSON HORNEL – The butterfly – signed and dated – oil on canvas – 50 x 60cm.
(Phillips)   **$21,054 £12,100**

EDWARD ATKINSON HORNEL – Three dancing Japanese girls – oil on canvas – 63 x 76cm.
(Phillips)   **$11,484 £6,600**

EDWARD ATKINSON HORNEL – The bluebell wood – oil on canvas – 112 x 91.5cm.
(Phillips)   **$26,796 £15,400**

WALTER HORROWING — A bay stallion in a loose box — signed and dated — oil on canvas — 23 x 28 in.
(Christie's)   **$1,046   £605**

WALTER CHARLES HORSLEY — There is no God but God — signed and dated — oil on canvas — 42½ x 62 in.
(Christie's)   **$44,528 £24,200**

BARTHOLOMEUS JOHANNES VAN HOVE — The Binnenhof or Court of Justice, The Hague — signed — on panel — 15½ in x 19½ in.
(Christie's)   **$12,512   £7,150**

JOHN BARR CLARKE HOYTE — Timber cutter in a forest scene — signed — water colour — 50 x 68 cm.
(Australian Art Auctions)   **$6,389 £3,472**

SERGE HRUBY — Geisha — signed and dated — 35¾ x 16¼ in.
(Christie's)   **$2,992   £1,760**

WILLIAM HUGGINS – Head of a lion – on panel
– 19.7 x 17.5cm.
(Christie's) **$3,916 £2,200**

TALBOT HUGHES – The retrieved hat – signed
– oil on canvas – 36 x 28in.
(Du Mouchelles) **$6,500 £3,439**

WILLIAM HUGHES – Grapes, an apple and a bird's
nest on a mossy bank – signed and dated – on
board – 10 x 14in.
(Christie's) **$2,270 £1,320**

EDWARD ROBERT HUGHES – A Viking –
portrait of a young boy holding a bow, arrows and
a horn – signed – watercolour – 52 x 32cm.
(Henry Spencer) **$4,056 £2,400**

ABRAHAM HULK – An estuary scene – signed
– oil on canvas – 22¾ x 34¼in.
(Christie's) **$12,548 £6,820**

JOHN FREDERICK HULK — A barge in a Dutch canal town; and Figures and a horse and cart in a village street — both signed — oil on canvas — 18 x 14in.
(Christie's)   Two   **$6,506   £3,850**

FRIEDENSREICH HUNDERTWASSER — Winterglocke — signed and dated — watercolour on paper — 25 x 36cm.
(Christie's)   **$20,570   £11,000**

WILLIAM H. HUMPHRIS — Young lady seated in white lilac trimmed dress with black shawl — signed — watercolour — 20 x 15in.
(G. A. Key)   **$691   £370**

A HUNT — A fishing boat and a barge near a Dutch town — signed and dated — oil on canvas — 20x30in.
(Anderson & Garland)   **$1,384   £800**

CHARLES HUNT Jnr – The game of draughts –
signed and dated – 24¼ x 36½in.
(Christie's) **$18,601 £10,450**

EDGAR HUNT – Poultry at a cottage door –
signed and dated – 12 x 10in.
(Christie's) **$16,923 £9,350**

EDGAR HUNT – Farmyard scene with shetland
pony, goat, cockerel and hens – signed and dated
– oil on board 30 x 40cm.
(Henry Spencer) **$16,920 £9,000**

EDGAR HUNT – Chickens and chicks feeding –
signed and dated – 11 x 15in.
(Christie's) **$17,622 £9,900**

EDGAR HUNT – A cockerel and hens, a rabbit in
a hutch nearby – signed and dated – 10 x 8in.
(Christie's) **$15,529 £8,580**

HUNT

EDGAR HUNT – A goat and chickens in a farmyard
– signed and dated – 12 x 16in.
(Christie's) **$23,496 £13,200**

LESLIE HUNTER – Venice – signed – oil on
board – 13 x 21cm.
(Phillips) **$24,882 £14,300**

WILLIAM HENRY HUNT – An old Sea Dog --
signed – pencil and watercolour – 39.5 x 27cm.
(Christie's) **$2,838 £1,650**

DANIEL HUNTINGTON – Greek girl with leky-
thos – signed and dated – oil on canvas – 30x25in.
(Robt. W. Skinner Inc.) **$1,600 £909**

LESLIE HUNTER – A still life of fruit and flowers
– signed – oil on canvas – 41 x 51cm.
(Phillips) **$26,796 £15,400**

LOUIS BOSWORTH HURT – Autumn Glory –
signed – oil on board – 33 x 48cm.
(Phillips) **$3,253 £1,870**

LOUIS BOSWORTH HURT – Highland cattle in a
mountain landscape – signed – 35½ x 29½in.
(Christie's) **$29,370 £16,500**

ROBERT GEMMELL HUTCHISON – Washing
day – oil on board – signed – 39 x 29cm.
(Phillips) **$23,925 £13,750**

ROBERT GEMMELL HUTCHISON – On the creel – signed – oil on panel – 22 x 30cm.
(Phillips) **$34,452 £19,800**

ROBERT GEMMELL HUTCHISON – A cup of tea – signed – oil on canvas – 62 x 76cm.
(Phillips) **$20,097 £11,550**

ROBERT GEMMELL HUTCHISON – The young caddy – signed – oil on board – 23 x 30cm.
(Phillips) **$19,140 £11,000**

THOMAS SWIFT HUTTON – Loch Sligachan, Isle of Skye – signed – 19 x 28¾in.
(Anderson & Garland) **$3,114 £1,800**

THOMAS SWIFT HUTTON – Richmond Castle – signed – watercolour – 13¾ x20in.
(Anderson & Garland) **$1,333 £780**

FRANK HYDE – Calling the tune – signed – 31¼ x 46½in.
(Christie's) **$3,524 £1,980**

LAURENT DE LA HYRE, Follower of – Diana and Actaeon – on copper – 16½ x 11¾in.
(Christie's) **$1,332 £770**

LOUIS ICART – 'Mr L'Amour' – signed – pastel and black chalk on paper – 50.8 x 42.2cm.
(Christie's)   **$1,540   £880**

PETER ILSTED – A woman seated in an interior – signed with monogram – on panel – 13¾ x 10¾in.
(Christie's)   **$71,225   £38,500**

PETER ILSTED – A young girl reading a letter at a window – signed with monogram and dated – 12 x 9½in.
(Christie's)   **$15,262   £8,250**

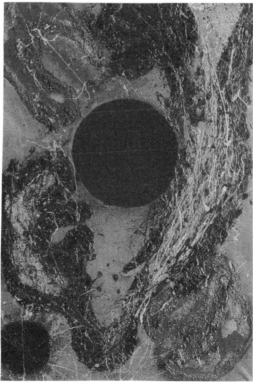

TOSHIMATAU IMAI – Soleil Levant (La Journee) – signed and dated – on canvas – 77 x 51in.
(Christie's)   **$32,164   £18,700**

271

GUGLIELMO INNOCENTI – The puppet –
signed and dated – on panel – 16½ x 21¼in.
(Christie's)   **$12,155**   **£7,150**

ITALIAN SCHOOL, 16th century – The Last
Judgement – oil on panel – 131.5 x 92cm.
(Phillips)   **$2,275** **£1,300**

KYOHEI INUKAI – Portrait of a Woman – signed
and dated – oil on canvas – 60 x 48in.
(Christie's)   **$18,700**   **£10,053**

ITALIAN SCHOOL – Laggo Maggiore –
inscribed – pencil and watercolour heightened with
white – 10½ x 26¼in.
(Christie's)   **$863 £462**

ITALIAN SCHOOL, 16th Century – Portrait of
Nicolas Macavelli, in profile – inscribed – oil on
panel – 50.5 x 39.5cm.
(Phillips)   **$1,267**   **£720**

ITALIAN SCHOOL, 18th century − The Piazza Navona, Rome − 19 x 28¾in.
(Christie's) **$5,899 £3,410**

ITALIAN SCHOOL, 19th century − The Bridge of Sighs, Venice − 10 x 7¾in.
(Christie's) **$2,057 £1,100**

ITALIAN SCHOOL − Diana and her nymphs − 31 x 41in.
(Christie's) **$2,416 £1,430**

ITALIAN SCHOOL − The chair ride − indistinctly signed − pencil and watercolour − 11 x 17in.
(Christie's) **$456 £264**

ITALIAN SCHOOL − The flower seller − indistinctly signed and dated − 42.5 x 34cm.
(Christie's) **$2,093 £1,210**

ITALIAN SCHOOL

ITALIAN SCHOOL, late 19th century – Flower sellers at the foot of the Spanish steps, Rome – 50.5 x 40cm..
(Christie's)   **$935**   **£550**

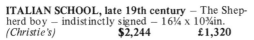

ITALIAN SCHOOL, late 19th century – The Shepherd boy – indistinctly signed – 16¼ x 10¾in.
(Christie's)   **$2,244**   **£1,320**

ITALIAN SCHOOL, Early 19th century – A rocky coastal landscape with figures on a beach – indistinctly signed – 36 x 47cm.
(Christie's)   **$5,610**   **£3,300**

FOUSSA ITAYA – Jeune Fille et Chien – signed and inscribed – oil on prepared canvas – 27x22cm.
(Christie's)   **$7,700 £4,400**

FOUSSA ITAYA – Chiens – signed, dated and inscribed – oil on prepared canvas – 11¼ x 18½in.
(Christie's) **$7,315 £4,180**

SAMUEL JACKSON – Clifton Gorge, Bristol – watercolour – 21 x 31in.
(Woolley & Wallis) **$865** **£500**

ANTONIO JACOBSEN – El Siglo – signed, dated and inscribed – oil on board – 40.3 x 70.5cm.
(Christie's) **$6,050 £3,324**

PAUL JACOULET – Bergers des Hautes Montagnes, Coree – signed – colour woodcut on wove paper – 15½ x 11¾in.
(Robt. W. Skinner Inc.) **$350** **£207**

JACQUE

JACQUE – Return of the flock – signed – oil on canvas – 26 x 37in.
(Du Mouchelles)   **$2,000 £1,183**

DAVID JAGGER – Head of a negress, in profile – 22½ x 14½in.
(Christie's)   **$706 £418**

WILLIAM JAMES, Circle of – Figures before St Mark's Square, Venice – oil on canvas – 15 x 26in.
(Phillips)   **$3,520 £2,000**

V. JANSSENS – Still lives of grapes, apples, peaches and other fruit on tables – both signed – 25½ x 21¼in.
(Christie's)   **$9,450   £5,400**

LUCIEN JAUNAS – Femme cousant au Bord de la Mer – signed – oil on paper laid down on canvas – 46 x 61.5cm.
(Christie's) **$4,620 £2,640**

ALEXEJ JAWLENSKY – Abstrakter Kopf – signed and dated – oil on board – 17¾ x 12¾in.
(Christie's) **$235,125 £137,500**

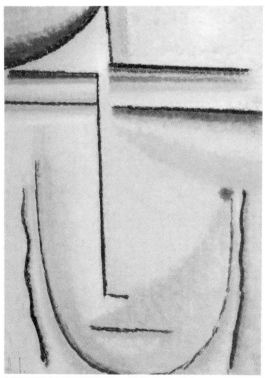

ALEXEJ JAWLENSKY – Hellgrunes Schauen – signed, inscribed and dated – oil on board – 39.8 x 30.8cm.
(Christie's) **$188,100 £110,000**

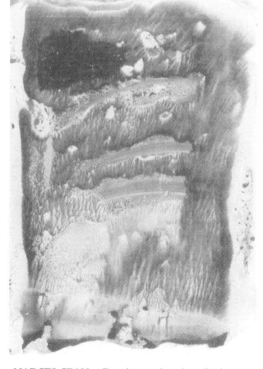

MARCEL JEAN – Decalcomanie – inscribed on the reverse – black gouache *decalcomanie* on paper – 32.6 x 25cm.
(Christie's) **$2,420 £1,428**

AMAN-JEAN

EDMOND AMAN-JEAN — La Robe rose — signed
— pastel — 38¼ x 29in.
(Christie's)   **$160,820 £93,500**

EDMOND AMAN-JEAN — Au Bal masque — signed
— pastel on paper — 22 x 18½in.
(Christie's)   **$18,920 £11,000**

EDUARD JEANMAIRE, Attributed to — Pond scene
with a duck and ducklings, a cockerel and two hens —
signed — oil on panel — 29 x 39cm.
(Henry Spencer)   **$1,176**   **£680**

ANDREAS JEKLIN — Lake Leman with les Dents
de Morcles — signed and dated — 18¼ x 29½in.
(Christie's)   **$2,992**   **£1,760**

ANDREAS JEKLIN — Lake Leman with the Dent
du Midi — signed and dated — 18¼ x 29½in.
(Christie's)   **$2,618**   **£1,540**

JOHAN LAURENTS JENSEN – Roses in a basket on a marble ledge – signed and dated – on panel – 12¼ x 17in.
(Christie's)   **$20,350**   **£11,000**

JENO JENDRASSIK – Close companions – signed and dated – 46 x 33¼in.
(Christie's)   **$9,240**   **£5,280**

JOHAN LAURENTS JENSEN – Tulips and Hyacinths in a vase – signed and dated – 14½ x 11¼in.
(Christie's)   **$22,385**   **£12,100**

CHRISTIAN ALBRECHT JENSEN – Portrait of a lady, bust length, in a black dress – signed and dated – 23.5 x 18.8cm.
(Christie's)   **$7,122**   **£3,850**

JOHAN LAURENTS JENSEN, Follower of – Mixed flowers in a basket on a ledge – 30 x 40in.
(Christie's)   **$1,903 £1,100**

JOHAN LAURENTS JENSEN — Roses in a vase —
signed — on panel — 35.5 x 46cm.
(Christie's) **$20,350** **£11,000**

HOLGER HVIDTFELDT JERICHAU — Hotel
Grotte Bleu, Capri — signed and inscribed —
55 x 100cm.
(Christie's) **$14,025** **£8,250**

OLOF AUGUST ANDREAS JERNBERG — A
river landscape with a steamboat — signed, inscribed and dated — 36 x 55.5cm.
(Christie's) **$3,663** **£1,980**

ANNA MARIA ELISABETH JERICHAU-
BAUMANN — Portrait of a girl, seated three-quarter
length, in a red bonnet, reading at a table — signed
and dated — 44¾ x 31¾in.
(Christie's) **$5,698** **£3,080**

OLOF AUGUST ANDREAS JERNBERG — An
extensive summer landscape — signed — on board —
12½ x 17¾in.
(Christie's) **$4,477** **£2,420**

HENRY LE JEUNE – Boys fishing – signed with
monogram – on board – 7 x 9in.
(Christie's) **$1,762   £990**

HENRY LE JEUNE – Removing the thorn –
signed with monogram – 14 x 10¾in.
(Christie's) **$7,440   £4,180**

ROBERT JOBLING – Fisher life at Cullercoats –
signed and dated – oil on canvas – 29½ x 21½in.
(Anderson & Garland) **$7,182   £4,200**

JAMES LE JEUNE – Piazza de Duomo, S. Ragusa,
Sicily – signed – oil on canvas – 20 x 24in.
(Christie's) **$1,762   £990**

ROBERT JOBLING – Crossing the brook –
signed – watercolour – 10 x 8¼in.
(Anderson & Garland) **$684 £400**

ROBERT JOBLING – Fisherfolk on a quay – signed – oil on panel – 10 x 14in.
(Anderson & Garland)   **$2,681 £1,550**

ROBERT JOBLING – Cullercoats Bay – signed and dated – oil on canvas – 29½ x 21½in.
(Anderson & Garland)   **$10,380 £6,000**

ROBERT JOBLING – There she blows – signed and dated – oil on canvas – 11½ x 15½in.
(Anderson & Garland)   **$1,159 £620**

ROBERT JOBLING – Fishing Harbour, North Shields – signed, inscribed and dated – watercolour – 9½ x 15¼in.
(Anderson & Garland)   **$1,197 £700**

CARL JOHANSSON – Spring – signed and dated –
38½ x 57½in.
(Christie's)   **$40,700**   **£22,000**

AUGUSTUS JOHN – Head of Dorelia – signed
– red chalk – 9 x 7½in.
(Christie's)   **$23,892 £13,200**

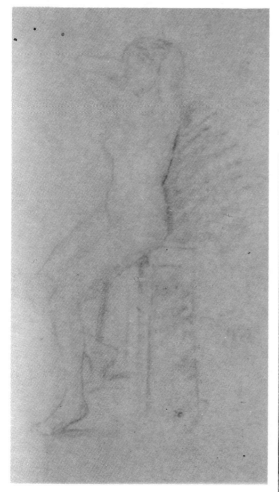

AUGUSTUS JOHN – Seated Female Nude –
signed – pencil on tan paper – 32.1 x 20cm.
(Robt. W. Skinner Inc.)   **$250 £142**

GWEN JOHN – Vieille dans un Tramway – signed
– watercolour and pencil – 6½ x 5in.
(Christie's)   **$15,928 £8,800**

AKSEL KARL JORGENSEN – Christiansborg
Palace, Copenhagen – signed and dated –
34 x 36¼in.
(Christie's)　　　**$3,663**　　　**£1,980**

MARTIN GWILT JOLLEY – Figures in Rose Lane
of Digey, St Ives – signed – oil on board –
17 x 8½in.
(W. H. Lane & Son)　　　**$1,464　£800**

EUGEEN JOORS – A basket of pears with chestnuts – signed and dated – 22 x 32in.
(Christie's)　　　**$5,610**　　　**£3,300**

ASGER JORN – Birds – signed – watercolour,
gouache and pencil on paper – 21¼ x 17¾in.
(Christie's)　　　**$26,488　£15,400**

ASGER JORN – Loch Ness – signed – oil on canvas – 18¼ x 21¾in.
(Christie's)   **$37,026 £19,800**

ASGER JORN – U.F.O. (Unidentified Flying Object) – signed, inscribed and dated – oil on canvas – 18¼ x 21¾in.
(Christie's)   **$55,539 £29,700**

FREDERIK HENDRIK KAEMMERER – A Spanish beauty – signed – 10 x 6¼in.
(Christie's)   **$3,740**   **£2,200**

GEORGES JOUBIN – Bateaux de Peche a St Jean de Luz – signed – oil on panel – 25½ x 21¼in.
(Christie's)   **$2,502 £1,430**

GOTTFRID KALLSTENIUS – The sun setting behind a forest – signed and dated – 25¾ x 32in.
(Christie's)   **$4,070**   **£2,200**

KALLSTENIUS

GOTTFRID KALLSTENIUS – The pine forest –
signed – 36¼ x 33in.
(Christie's)   **$6,105**   **£3,300**

GOTTFRID KALLSTENIUS – A wooded landscape,
evening – signed with initials – 17¾ x 22in.
(Christie's)   **$7,733**   **£4,180**

WASSILY KANDINSKY – Kleine Welten XI –
signed – etching on hand-made paper –
23.5 x 19.3cm.
(Robt. W. Skinner Inc.) **$3,500**   **£2,071**

JOHAN MARI TEN KATE – Children playing on
a frozen lake in a winter landscape – signed – oil
on canvas – 26 x 40in.
(Christie's)   **$40,480 £22,000**

HERMAN FREDERICK CAREL TEN KATE –
The card game – signed and dated – oil on panel
– 16 x 20in.
(Robt. W. Skinner Inc.)   **$4,500 £2,556**

WASSILY KANDINSKY – Composition – signed
and dated – gouache on paper – 18 x 11¾in.
(Christie's)   **$79,464**   **£46,200**

HERMAN FREDERIK CAREL TEN KATE –
Figures in an inn – signed and dated – on panel –
7½ x 10in.
(Christie's) **$3,235 £1,870**

HERMAN TEN KATE – Reading the news –
signed – on panel – 6¾ x 9¼in.
(Christie's) **$3,366** **£1,980**

MANE-KATZ – Bateaux pres du Phare – signed
and dated – gouache on paper – 48 x 63.8cm.
(Christie's) **$6,237** **£3,300**

MANE KATZ – Le jeune Juif et son Pere –
signed and dated – oil on canvas – 50¼ x 31½in.
(Christie's) **$80,960 £44,000**

LEE LUFKIN KAULA –"Blue and gold"/Portrait
of a young woman – signed – oil on canvas –
29 x 29in.
(Robt. W. Skinner Inc.) **$8,000 £4,545**

JAMES KAY – A busy Parisian boulevard –
signed – oil on canvas – 54 x 80cm.
(Phillips) **$34,452 £19,800**

ARNE KAVLI – Portrait of Johanne Heiberg,
seated half length – signed – 67.6 x 55cm.
(Christie's) **$10,582** **£5,720**

JAMES KAY – A bustling river scene – signed
– oil on panel – 24 x 34cm.
(Phillips) **$5,742 £3,300**

ARNE KAVLI – A seated woman with an orange
parasol – signed and dated – 31½ x 31½in.
(Christie's) **$24,420** **£13,200**

JULES VAN KEIRSBLICK – A helping hand –
signed – 26¾ x 37½in.
(Christie's) **$4,114** **£2,420**

SIR GERALD KELLY — Portrait of Miss Olive
Groves as Clarissa in 'Lionel and Clarissa' at The
Lyric Theatre Hammersmith — signed — 28 x 22in.
(Woolley & Wallis) **$2,595** **£1,500**

ELIZABETH KEITH — Tokyo and New Year's
Lanterns Evening, Malacca — Edition 100 —
colour woodcuts on laid paper —
37.5 x 25.1cm. and 42.6 x 28.9cm.
(Robt. W. Skinner Inc.)
Two **$425** **£251**

ELIZABETH KEITH — Kamakura Summer Reflections and Street Scene with Bridge over Narrow
River — Edition 100 — both signed — colour
woodcuts on laid paper — 9½ x 14¾in. and
11 x 15¾in.
(Robt. W. Skinner Inc.)
Two **$650** **£384**

SIR GERALD KELLY — The Market, Burma —
oil on panel — 14½ x 11¼in.
(Christie's) **$2,545** **£1,430**

SIR GERALD KELLY – Sun D'Angkor II –
signed and inscribed – oil on board – 20 x 16in.
(Christie's)   **$3,328   £1,870**

MATTHEW KENDRICK – SS Indian Empire leaving
Galway – 28 x 59in.
(Chrystals)   **$11,220   £6,000**

JAN THOMAS VAN KESSEL, Circle of – Archers
before an inn – oil on panel – 11¾ x 15in.
(Phillips)   **$2,685   £1,500**

ROBERT KEMM – The guitar player – signed –
oil on panel – 17½ x 13½in.
(Prudential)   **$2,941   £1,700**

FERNAND KHNOPFF – La Tiare d'Argent –
signed – pastel on paper – 24.5 cm. diameter.
(Christie's)   **$321,640   £187,000**

FERNAND KHNOPFF — Portrait de jeune Femme
— oil on canvas laid down on board — 14 x 11cm.
(Christie's)   **$30,272   £17,600**

FERNAND KHNOPFF — La Meduse endormie —
signed — pastel on paper — 29.5 x 13.2cm.
(Christie's)   **$227,040 £132,000**

GEORGE GOODWIN KILBURNE — A Woman in
Italian Costume, spinning — signed and dated —
watercolour — 10½ x 7in.
(Phillips)   **$1,690**   **£1,000**

KLITZ

PETER KLITZ – A village in a winter landscape – signed and dated – 16 x 22½in.
(Christie's)   **$1,402**   £825

WILLIAM GUNNING KING – Feeding time – signed and dated – 15 x 19in.
(Christie's)   **$706**   **£418**

DONG M. KINGMAN – A Festival in Chinatown – signed – watercolour on paper – 25½ x 39½in.
(Robt. W. Skinner Inc.) **$3,700**   **£2,189**

HENRY JOHN YEEND-KING – Hanging out the washing – signed – 20½ x 24in.
(Christie's)   **$4,699** **£2,640**

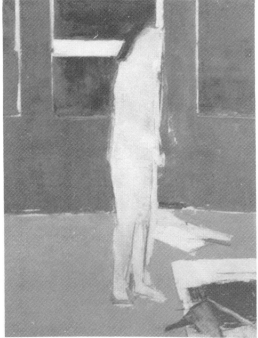

HENRY JOHN YEEND KING – The Water Meadow – signed – pencil and watercolour – 24.6 x 34.6cm.
(Christie's)   **$1,324**   £770

PETER KINLEY – Red interior – signed – oil on canvas – 72 x 54in.
(Christie's)   **$3,584 £1,980**

MOISE KISLING — Fleurs dans un Vase vert —
signed — oil on canvas — 24¾ x 21¼in.
(Christie's) **$179,740** **£104,500**

ERNST LUDWIG KIRCHNER — Steinbruch bei
Wildboden — signed — oil on canvas —
47 x 35½in.
(Christie's) **$216,315** **£126,500**

GEORGY DMITRIYEVICH KISEVALTER —
Traurig — oil on canvas — signed and dated —
100 x 130cm.
(Hauswedell & Nolte) **$4,365 £2,538**

MOISE KISLING — Nu allonge — signed — oil on
canvas — 27.5 x 41cm.
(Christie's) **$71,995** **£38,500**

MOISE KISLING — Pavots dans un Vase bleu —
signed — oil on canvas — 41 x 33 cm.
(Christie's) **$122,980** **£71,500**

JOSEPH MILNER KITE – Portrait of a lady in a feathered hat – signed – 29 x 24in.
(Christie's) **$1,766 £1,045**

LODEWYK-JOHANNES KLEYN, Follower of –
A coastal landscape with beached fishing boats –
signed – oil on canvas – 20 x 25cm.
(Christie's) **$1,766 £1,045**

LOUIS KLINGENDER – A boar hunt in winter –
signed – oil on canvas – 170 x 240cm.
(Christie's) **$19,228 £10,450**

PAUL KLEE – Anatomie der Aphrodite – signed,
dated, numbered and inscribed – gouache and
watercolour on chalk ground on paper – 22 x 13.5cm.
(Christie's) **$154,275 £82,500**

LOUIS KLINGENDER – The Kill – signed and
dated – oil on canvas – 43¼ x 59in.
(Christie's) **$10,120 £5,500**

GUSTAV KLIMT – Damenportrat – inscribed – pencil on paper – 20¼ x 14¼in.
(Christie's) **$6,160 £3,520**

DAME LAURA KNIGHT – Madame Tchernichev – signed and dated – oil on canvas – 32 x 27in.
(Christie's) **$12,139 £6,820**

SIR GODFREY KNELLER, Circle of – Portrait of a nobleman, standing full length – oil on canvas – 92½ x 58in.
(Lawrence Fine Arts) **$4,186 £2,420**

A. ROWLAND KNIGHT – A pair of retrievers – signed – oil on canvas – 14 x 19½in.
(Prudential) **$657 £380**

DAME LAURA KNIGHT – Restoration, Derby House Roof – signed – oil on canvas – 40 x 30in.
(Christie's) **$15,272 £8,580**

KNIGHT

DAME LAURA KNIGHT – A Ballet Dancer –
signed – oil on canvas – 23 x 17½in.
(Christie's)   **$32,307**   **£18,150**

DAME LAURA KNIGHT – Chinese Acrobats –
signed with initials and dated – watercolour and
soft pencil – 14½ x 10½in.
(Christie's)   **$12,727**   **£7,150**

DAME LAURA KNIGHT – At the circus – signed
– watercolour and charcoal – 14 x 10in.
(Christie's)   **$10,224** **£6,050**

DAME LAURA KNIGHT – Gemini – signed –
black and white aquatint – 12 x 10in.
(G. A. Key)   **$523 £280**

DAME LAURA KNIGHT – Peach Blossom –
signed – oil on canvas – 30 x 24in.
(Christie's)　　　　　$15,664　£8,800

DAME LAURA KNIGHT – A cloudy day, Gypsy
Encampment – signed – watercolour, bodycolour
and pencil – 15 x 21in.
(Christie's)　　　$9,790　£5,500

LOUIS ASTON KNIGHT – Venice – signed –
oil on canvas – 45¾ x 34¾in.
(Christie's)　　　$14,300　　£7,688

JAN KNIKKER – Street Scene, Paris – signed –
oil on panel – 23.4 x 36.2cm.
(Christie's)　　　$1,058　£605

JOHN WILLIAM BUXTON KNIGHT – Outside the
'Old Plantation Tavern' – signed and dated –
21½ x 15½in.
(Christie's)　　$2,270　£1,320

AUGUST KNIP – A King Charles spaniel –
signed – canvas laid down on panel –
16.3cm. diam.
(Christie's)　　　$3,366　　£1,980

GEORGE SHERIDAN KNOWLES – English
country garden scene with mother and child –
signed – watercolour – 19½ x 14in.
(Morphets)   **$7,240 £4,000**

SUSAN RICKER KNOX – Mountainscape –
signed – watercolour on paper – 8½ x 11in.
(Bruce D. Collins)   **$165**   **£87**

GEORGE SHERIDAN KNOWLES – Choir practice
– signed and dated – 76.5 x 63.7cm.
(Christie's)   **$3,916 £2,200**

PETRA KOCH – Dandelions, poppies, and other
wild flowers in a beaker vase – signed – bodycolour – 24 x 14in.
(Christie's)   **$2,645**   **£1,430**

MARINUS ADRIANUS KOEKKOEK, Follower of
– Peasants with a sledge and horses in a winter land-
scape – signed – oil on copper – 11 x 15¾in.
(Christie's) **$892 £528**

OSCAR KOELLINKER – Paysage suisse au
Printemps – signed – oil on panel – 12¾ x 16in.
(Christie's) **$2,310 £1,320**

WALTER KOENIGER – Winter thaw – signed –
oil on canvas – 20 x 24in.
(Christie's) **$1,320 £725**

NINA KOGAN – Composition – signed – watercolour on paper – 50.5 x 33cm.
(Christie's) **$19,541 £10,450**

OSKAR KOKOSCHKA – Christ on the Cross –
signed and dated – watercolour on paper –
75.6 x 50.5cm.
(Christie's) **$2,117 £1,210**

WILHELM KOLLER – Faust and Mephistopheles
waiting for Gretchen at the cathedral door –
signed and dated – on panel – 29¼ x 39½in.
(Christie's) **$9,625 £5,500**

DIRK KONING — Cubist Still Life — signed and
dated — oil on canvas — 66.5 x 77.5cm.
(Christie's)   **$2,494   £1,320**

PETER KRAEMER — The Gambler — one of a
pair — signed — pencil and watercolour with
touches of white heightening — 17.1 x 11.7cm.
(Christie's)   **Two**   **$608 £352**

MICA KONO — La Seductrice — signed in Japanese
and dated — oil on board — 26.5 x 21.5cm.
(Christie's)   **$3,326   £1,760**

E. D. KOSSVTH — Portrait of the Baroness Von
Hutton — signed and dated — oil on silk —
circular — 22in. diam.
(G. A. Key)   **$561 £300**

JACOB KRAMER — Half length portrait of the
Madonna and Child — signed — oil on canvas —
64.5 x 50cm.
(Henry Spencer)   **$2,281**   **£1,350**

NILS KREUGER — A horseman seen from behind — authenticated by artist's daughter — on panel — 49.5 x 61.2cm.
(Christie's)   **$4,680**   **£2,530**

LEON KROLL — Isabel and Marie Claude — oil on paper laid down on paper — 58 x 37cm.
(Christie's)   **$8,000**   **£4,301**

CHRISTIAN KROHG — Portrait of a lady, half-length; and Portrait of a gentleman, half-length — signed — 24 x 19¾in.
(Christie's)   **Two**   **$3,740**   **£2,200**

MAX KUEHNE – Racing Sloops – signed – oil on canvas – 30 x 40in.
(Bruce D. Collins) **$8,250** **£4,365**

WALT KUHN – Magnolias and Jonquils – signed and dated – watercolour and gouache on board – 21¾ x 27½in.
(Christie's) **$15,400** **£8,279**

PEDER SEVERIN KROYER – Portrait of Dr W. Azis, standing three-quarter length – signed and dated – coloured chalks on brown paper – 39 x 23in.
(Christie's) **$16,280** **£8,800**

WALT KUHN – The Performer – signed and dated – oil on canvas – 102.2 x 76.5cm.
(Christie's) **$50,600** **£27,204**

ALFRED KUBIN – Einbrecher I – signed – watercolour and pen and ink on paper – 25.4 x 32.7cm.
(Christie's) **$4,158** **£2,200**

WILHELM KUHNERT – A Hyena with its prey – signed and dated – on board – 16½in. x 22in.
(Christie's) **$4,620** **£2,640**

WILHELM JUHNERT – A lion and a lioness in the Savannah – signed and dated – oil on canvas – 30 x 46in.
(Christie's)

$141,680 £77,000

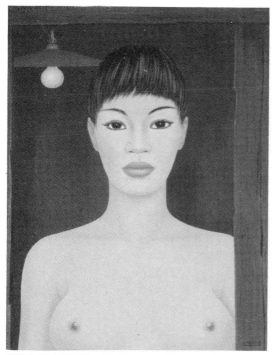

FELIX LABISSE – Le Tresor de Tijuca – signed – oil on canvas – 61.5 x 50cm.
(Christie's) **$18,711 £9,900**

EDWARD LADELL – A still life of assorted fruit, walnuts and glass of wine on a marble ledge – signed with monogram – oil on canvas – 43 x 36cm.
(Phillips) **$63,162 £36,300**

LADELL

EDWARD LADELL — Prawns, a peeled lemon and
a glass of white wine on a draped ledge — signed
— 11½ x 9in.
(Christie's)   **$14,335**   **£7,920**

FELIX LABISSE — Icare et Dedale — signed —
oil on canvas — 25½ x 31¼in.
(Christie's)   **$19,228 £10,450**

EDWIN LADELL — The Mathematical Bridge,
Cambridge — oil on canvas — 20 x 24in.
(Christie's)   **$2,153 £1,210**

GUSTAV LAEVERENZ – Tea time – signed –
on panel – 13¾ x 19in.
(Christie's) **$13,090** **£7,480**

HENRY LAMB – Hatches on the River Ebble,
near Salisbury – signed and dated – oil on panel
– 15 x 18in.
(Lawrence Fine Arts) **$4,227 £2,310**

HENRY LAMB – Cottages at Coombe Bissett –
signed and dated – oil on canvas – 12¾ x 20in.
(Lawrence Fine Arts) **$5,233 £2,860**

GEORGE COCHRAN LAMBDIN – Still Life with
Roses – signed and dated – oil on canvas –
41.2 x 30.8cm.
(Robt. W. Skinner Inc.) **$15,000** **£8,875**

JAN BAPTIST LAMBRECHTS – A couple drinking
at a table in an interior – bears monogram – oil on
panel – 5¼ x 4¼in.
(Phillips) **$1,936 £1,100**

LAMEN

JASPER VAN DER LAMEN, Attributed to —
Diana hunting in a forest — oil on copper —
10¼ x 15in.
(Phillips)   **$2,992 £1,700**

WILLIAM B. LAMOND — Chickens in a farmyard
— signed — oil on canvas — 24 x 30cm.
(Phillips)   **$4,593 £2,640**

PERCY LANCASTER — The cottage gate — signed
with monogram — 10½ x 9½in.
(Anderson & Garland)   **$1,072 £620**

RONALD LAMPITT — A Village under Snow —
signed — watercolour — 10¼ x 13½in.
(Christie's)   **$1,617**   **£935**

PERCY LANCASTER — A breeze on the Uplands
signed - 13½ x 19¼in.
(Anderson & Garland) **$3,960**   **£2,200**

LOUIS LANG — Chinese Amah and Child — signed
and dated — oil on board — 14 x 10in.
(Christie's)   **$1,320   £725**

WALTER LANGLEY – Three figures in a boat under sail – signed and dated – charcoal drawing – 13½ x 11in.
(W. H. Lane & Son)   **$743   £440**

WALTER LANGLEY – A street in Newlyn – signed – oil on panel – 11 x 8in.
(Christie's)   **$7,832   £4,400**

WALTER LANGLEY – The Waif – signed and dated – watercolour – 26 x 34½in.
(Christie's)   **$88,110   £49,500**

LANGLOIS

MARK LANGLOIS – Into battle – signed –
21 x 16in.
(Christie's) **$1,664 £935**

MARK W. LANGLOIS – The frustrated artist –
signed – 21 x 17in.
(Christie's) **$1,762 £990**

MARK W. LANGLOIS – The prompter – signed
with initials – 30.5 x 25.8cm.
(Christie's) **$2,153 £1,210**

ANDRE LANSKOY – Refuge d'un Gepe – signed
– oil on canvas – 100 x 65cm.
(Christie's) **$18,920 £11,000**

ANDRE LANSKOY – Composition – signed – oil on canvas – 23½ x 29in.
(Christie's)   **$18,920**   **£11,000**

PIERRE LANSKOY – Composition Abstraite – signed – gouache on board – 4½ x 8½in.
(Christie's)   **$3,850 £2,200**

FERNAND LANTOINE – Au bord de la Seine – signed and dated – oil on canvas board – 23½ x 31¾in.
(Christie's)   **$10,395**   **£5,500**

GEORGINA LARA – Country folk outside a thatched house; and Horses drinking from a trough outside an inn – 46.1 x 35.9 cm.
(Christie's)   **$3,982**   **£2,200**

GEORGINA LARA, Attributed to — A busy village street — oil on canvas — 9½ x 13¾in.
(Hy. Duke & Son) **$2,288 £1,300**

GEORGINA LARA, Attributed to — Figures unloading hay in a farmyard landscape — 13½ x 15in.
(Christie's) **$1,272 £715**

MIKHAIL LARIONOV — La Coquette de Provence — signed — oil on canvas — 81 x 65 cm.
(Christie's) **$32,164 £18,700**

CARL LARSSON – Appelblom (Appleblossom)
– signed with initials and dated – watercolour –
24½ x 14in.
(Christie's)   **$244,200**   **£132,000**

CARL LARSSON – Varflod (Springflood) –
signed with monogram and dated – watercolour –
37¾ x 25¼ in.
(Christie's)   **$244,200**   **£132,000**

CARL LARSSON – My wife (Karin in the studio)
– signed with monogram and dated – watercolour
– 73.5 x 51.7cm.
(Christie's)   **$488,400**   **£264,000**

CARL LARSSON – En gard (A farmstead, Bingsjo)
– signed and dated – watercolour – 48 x 63.2cm.
(Christie's)   **$244,200**   **£132,000**

ROLAND LARY – Pluto and Bruno – signed and
dated – 35 x 46½in.
(Christie's)   **$3,702 £1,980**

LATAPIE

LOUIS LATAPIE — Nature morte aux Fruits —
signed — oil on canvas — 49.9 x 32.1cm.
(Christie's)   **$1,155 £660**

GASTON DE LATOUCHE — Les Amants et les
Cygnes; La Promenade d'Automne — signed and
dated — pastel on paper — 29¼ x 23¾in.
(Christie's)   **$66,220 £38,500**

HENRI FANTIN LATOUR — Marine (Effet du
Matin) — signed — oil on canvas — 6¼ x 9in.
(Christie's)   **$17,028**   **£9,900**

MARIE LAURENCIN — Deux Femmes — signed
— oil on canvas — 32 x 25½in.
(Christie's)   **$378,400 £220,000**

MARIE LAURENCIN — Tete de Marc Vanclair —
signed, dated and inscribed — oil on panel —
27.2 x 21.8 cm.
(Christie's)   **$37,840**   **£22,000**

MARIE LAURENCIN – Danseuses – signed and
dated – oil on canvas – 21 x 25¼in.
(Christie's) **$395,010** **£231,000**

MARIE LAURENCIN – Jeunes Femmes a la
Guitare et aux Flutes – signed and dated – oil on
canvas – 32 x 39¾in.
(Christie's) **$902,880** **£528,000**

MARIE LAURENCIN – Deux jeunes Filles –
signed – oil on canvas – 18¼ x 15in.
(Christie's) **$172,040 £93,500**

JOHN LAVALLE – The Kill – signed and inscribed – oil on Masonite – 6¼ x 8¼in.
(Robt. W. Skinner Inc.) **$425** **£251**

AUGUST LAUX – Raspberries – signed – oil on canvas – 11¼ x 14¼in.
(Christie's) **$1,430** **£785**

AUGUST LAUX – Chickens feeding – signed – oil on panel – 6 x 9in.
(Du Mouchelles) **$1,300 £687**

JOHN LAVALLE – Castellane – signed, dated and inscribed – watercolour and pencil on paper – 17¾ x 14in.
(Robt. W. Skinner Inc.) **$400** **£236**

SIR JOHN LAVERY – Farm cottages in County Kilkenny, Ireland – signed – watercolour – 11½ x 18½in.
(W. H. Lane & Son) **$507 £300**

C. LAWRENCE – The goose girl – a girl driving geese on a path before a cottage – signed – oil on canvas – 11 x 18in.
(W. H. Lane & Son) **$658 £360**

F. J. LAWRENCE – Large family portrait, mother with babe in arms and boy by her side, seated beside a stone wall – signed and dated – oil on canvas – 43 x 41in.
(G. A. Key) **$3,179 £1,700**

ALFRED KINGSLEY LAWRENCE – A standing nude – signed and dated – charcoal and pastel – 26 x 14½in.
(Anderson & Garland) **$1,188** **£660**

JAMES KERR LAWSON – Coastal Harbour – signed – oil on canvas – 18 x 24in.
(Christie's) **$3,524** **£1,980**

JEAN PIERRE LAYS – Roses, poppies, wall-flowers and other flowers in a vase with raspberries beside, on a wooden chest – signed – 86.4 x 58.8cm
(Christie's) $11,550   £6,600

BERNARD H. LEACH – South Downs landscape – initialled – ink and sepia wash – 3¼ x 5in.
(W. H. Lane & Son) $507 £300

BENJAMIN WILLIAM LEADER – Bridge over a mountain river – signed – oil on canvas – 89 x 72cm.
(Phillips) $3,445 £1,980

WILLIAM L'ENGLE – The Snow Fence – signed and dated – oil on canvas – 61 x 75.9cm.
(Robt. W. Skinner Inc.) $1,100   £650

BENJAMIN WILLIAMS LEADER – Near Bettwys-y-Coed, North Wales – fisherman, boy and dog seated beside a country bridge – signed and dated – oil on canvas – 18 x 23in.
(W. H. Lane & Son) $3,268 £1,900

NOEL HARRY LEAVER – A River running through a Country Town – signed – watercolour and bodycolour – 10 x 14in.
(Phillips) **$2,028** **£1,200**

HENRI LEBASQUE – Baigneuse sur la Plage – signed – watercolour and charcoal on paper – 31 x 24.5cm.
(Christie's) **$5,390 £3,080**

HENRI LEBASQUE – Femme au Puit en Provence – signed – oil on canvas – 23¼ x 28½in.
(Christie's) **$51,084** **£29,700**

HENRI LEBASQUE – Le Cannet – signed and inscribed – watercolour and pencil on paper – 30 x 34cm.
(Christie's) **$11,550 £6,600**

HENRI LEBASQUE Vase de Fleurs – signed – oil on canvas – 55.5 x 46.5 cm.
(Christie's) **$52,976** **£30,800**

LEBASQUE

HENRI LEBASQUE – Au Bord de la Mer – signed
– watercolour and soft pencil on paper –
25.4 x 35.9cm.
(Christie's) **$18,513 £9,900**

HENRI LEBASQUE – Paysage – signed – oil on
canvas – 72.5 x 54.3cm.
(Christie's) **$23,100 £13,200**

HENRI LEBASQUE – Nu allonge contre le Lit
– oil on canvas – 63.5 x 79cm.
(Christie's) **$111,320 £60,500**

ALBERT LEBOURG – Le Port d'Alger – signed
and dated – oil on canvas – 37.5 x 46.1cm.
(Christie's) **$28,798 £15,400**

ALBERT LEBOURG – Le Canal de Charenton –
signed – oil on canvas – 15¾ x 28¾in.
(Christie's) **$39,732 £23,100**

PAUL LECOMTE – A wooded landscape with a
boy by a hut – signed – 13 x 18¼in.
(Christie's) **$5,049 £2,970**

JOHN INGLE LEE — Home — signed and dated —
31½ x 21¼in.
(Christie's) **$4,503 £2,530**

JOHN LEECH — Saturday night shower — signed —
18¾ x 27¾in.
(Christie's) **$1,370 £770**

DERWENT LEES — Mediterranean Coast — signed
and dated — oil on panel — 9½ x 14in.
(Christie's) **$10,950 £6,050**

WILLIAM LEE — A farm girl and calf — signed —
16½ x 13¼in.
(Anderson & Garland) **$1,816 £1,050**

ALEXIS DE LEEUW — Homeward bound — herdsman on horseback with sheep and bullocks returning
along a snow-covered road — signed — 30 x 50in.
(W. H. Lane & Son) **$12,810 £7,000**

LEFEVRE

MARIE LEFEVRE – "Ring-a-roses" – signed –
oil on canvas – 10 x 14in.
(W. H. Lane & Son) **$845 £500**

FERNAND LEGOUT-GERARD – Scene de Port
– signed – pastel on paper – 58.8 x 71.8cm.
(Christie's) **$6,237 £3,300**

RENE LEGRAND – "En Sentinelle" – signed –
oil on canvas – 20 x 23½in.
(W. H. Lane & Son) **$4,644 £2,700**

ALPHONSE LEGROS – Peasants by a Village –
signed – etching –
(Anderson & Garland) **$198** **£110**

FREDERICK LORD LEIGHTON – A classical
beauty – oil on canvas – 17 x 13in.
(Christie's) **$105,248 £57,200**

SIR PETER LELY – Portrait of Sir Randolph (or Ranulph) Crew(e) (1558-1646), seated three-quarter length in a black coat and ruff; and Portrait of Lady Crewe, standing three-quarter length in a black dress and collar – 48 x 36½in.
(Christie's)
$5,297   £3,080

SIR PETER LELY, Circle of – Portrait of lady seated three-quarter length, wearing a brown decollete dress with slashed sleeves, leaning on a plinth, by a brown curtain – 50 x 40in.
(Christie's)   **$3,784**   **£2,200**

SIR PETER LELY, Studio of – Portrait of a lady, seated half length, in a buff coloured dress and a yellow cloak, holding a dog – 37 x 32in.
(Christie's)   **$3,784**   **£2,200**

LELY

SIR PETER LELY, Studio of — Portrait of a nobleman, standing, small three-quarter length — 50 x 40in.
(Lawrence Fine Arts) **$5,328** **£3,080**

EDWARD BLAIR LEIGHTON — God speed —
signed and dated — oil on canvas — 62 x 45¾in.
(Christie's) **$76,912 £41,800**

EDMUND BLAIR LEIGHTON — An oft told tale
— signed with initials and dated — oil on board —
14 x 10in.
(Anderson & Garland) **$5,190 £3,000**

TAMARA DE LEMPICKA — Still Life with onions
— signed — oil on canvas — 15½ x 11½in.
(Christie's) **$15,592 £8,250**

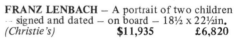

TAMARA DE LEMPICKA – Le Paysan – signed
– oil on cradled panel – 15¾ x 11¼in.
(Christie's) **$28,380** **£16,500**

ARTHUR LEMON – Cattle on a cliff top – signed
– 46 x 47½in.
(Christie's) **$706** **£418**

FRANZ LENBACH – A portrait of two children
– signed and dated – on board – 18½ x 22½in.
(Christie's) **$11,935** **£6,820**

STANISLAS LEPINE – La Seine a Paris – signed and dated '62 – oil on canvas – 17¾ x 29½in. – *(Christie's)* $56,760 £33,000

STANISLAS LEPINE – Vaches au Clair de Lune – signed – oil on canvas – 18¼ x 21¾in. *(Christie's)* $8,085 £4,620

PAULUS LESIRE – Portrait of an old man, seated half length in black tunic and a white ruff – oil on panel – 69 x 55cm. *(Phillips)* $5,370 £3,000

JEAN LEPPIEN – Composition – signed – oil on canvas – 45 x 36 cm. *(Christie's)* $11,392 £6,600

PRUDENT LOUIS LERAY, After – The Stepping Stones – 15 x 12¼in. *(Anderson & Garland)* $828 £460

GEORGE DUNLOP LESLIE — Lucy, daughter of
Charles Andrew, Esq., seated three-quarter length
in a wicker chair with her cat — signed and dated —
36 x 28in.
(Christie's)   **$10,769 £6,050**

ANDRE LEVEILLE — Le Pont Neuf, Paris —
signed — oil on canvas — 55 x 65.5cm.
(Christie's)   **$21,175 £12,100**

RICHARD HAYLEY LEVER — Haystacks-England
— signed — oil on canvas — 11 x 14in.
(Christie's)   **$1,320 £725**

THERESE LESSORE — The audience — signed
and dated — watercolour, pen and ink — 8 x 8½in.
(Christie's)   **$817 £484**

RICHARD HAYLEY LEVER — New York Harbour
— signed — oil on canvasboard — 12 x 16in.
(Christie's)   **$1,870 £1,027**

RICHARD HAYLEY LEVER — The Boathouse —
signed — watercolour — 16 x 18in.
(Du Mouchelles)   **$700 £370**

LEVER

RICHARD HAYLEY LEVER – Safe Harbor – signed – oil on canvas – 24 x 36¼in.
(Christie's)   **$28,600 £15,376**   **351 (2)**

RICHARD HAYLEY LEVER – Monhegan Island
– signed – oil on canvasboard – 25 x 30in.
(Christie's)   **$9,350**   **£5,026**

RICHARD HAYLEY LEVER – Still Life –
signed – watercolour with pencil on paper –
40.6 x 52.4cm.
(Robt. W. Skinner Inc.)   **$750 £426**

EDMUND D. LEWANDOWSKI – Grain Elevators –
signed and dated – oil on board – 19 x 24in.
(Robt. W. Skinner Inc.) **$4,250** **£2,514**

MARTIN LEWIS – Boss of the Block – etching,
aquatint and drypoint on paper – 11¼ x 7½in.
(Robt. W. Skinner Inc.) **$375** **£221**

EDMUND DARCH LEWIS – Young Boy Fishing
– signed and dated – oil on canvas – 30 x 20in.
(Christie's) **$3,740 £2,054**

LEON L'HERMITTE – A break from the
harvest – signed with initials – pastel – 13 x 11¼in.
(Christie's) **$7,816 £4,180**

L'HERMITTE

LEON AUGUSTIN LHERMITTE – Les premiers pas dans le jardin – signed – pastel – 14 x 18in.
(Christie's) **$32,384 £17,600**

ANDRE LHOTE – La Cuisine – signed – oil on board – 27 x 35cm.
(Christie's) **$9,450 £5,000**

ANDRE LHOTE – Mirmande sous la Neige – signed – oil on canvas – 19¾ x 25½in.
(Christie's) **$17,010 £9,000**

WALTER LIBBEY – Self Portrait – dated – oil on canvas – 21 x 17in.
(Christie's) **$5,500 £2,956**

ANDRE LHOTE – Viviers, Vallee du Rhone – signed – watercolour on paper – 36.8 x 55cm.
(Christie's) **$7,568 £4,400**

FRANCIS O. LIBBY – West Indian palms – signed – oil on board – 10 x 12in.
(Bruce D. Collins) **$303 £160**

328

MAX LIEBERMANN – Badende Knaben – signed
and dated –oil on canvas – 45 x 54.5 cm.
(Christie's)   **$104,060**   **£60,500**

ROBERT LIE – Ship on rough seas – signed and
dated – oil on canvas – 18 x 22in.
(Christie's)   **$1,100**   **£604**

MAX LIEBERMANN – Pferdcknecht – signed and
dated '09 – oil on canvas – 26 x 31½in.
(Christie's)   **$41,624**   **£24,200**

LILJEFORS

BRUNO LILJEFORS – A cat basking in the sun –
signed and dated – 29¼ x 24½in.
(Christie's) **$162,800** **£88,000**

BRUNO LILJEFORS – A court-yard in Grez-sur-
Loing – signed with initials and dated – water-
colour on paper laid down on board – 13 x 9½in.
(Christie's) **$24,420** **£13,200**

BRUNO LILJEFORS – A mountainous landscape
with an eagle and its prey – signed and dated –
en grisaille canvas laid down on board –
14½ x 22in.
(Christie's) **$21,367** **£11,550**

BRUNO LILJEFORS – A fox in the snow –signed and dated – 28 x 35½in.
(Christie's)   **$48,840**   **£26,400**

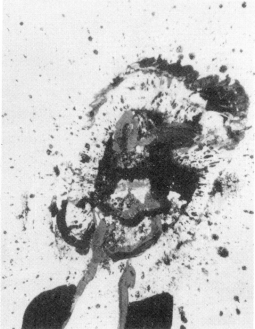

BRUNO LILJEFORS – Rav och Krakor (A fox taking a crow) – signed and dated – 20 x 25¼in.
(Christie's)   **$325,600**   **£176,000**

BENGT LINDSTROM – Tete explosante – signed – oil and wax on paper – 25 x 19in.
(Christie's)   **$1,069**   **£572**

BENGT LINDSTROM – Figure – signed – black ink, oil, gouache and wax on paper – 63.7 x 48.6cm.
(Christie's)   **$1,069**   **£572**

SVEN OTTO LINDSTROM – The harbour at Honfleur – signed and dated – 24 x 18in.
(Christie's)   **$3,866**   **£2,090**

LINTON

SIR JAMES DROMGOLE LINTON – Hero –
signed with initials – watercolour – 10in. dia.
(Phillips)   **$1,521**   **£900**

WILLIAM HENRY LIPPINCOTT – Lady with Fan
– signed and dated – oil on panel –
35.7 x 26.4 cm.
(Christie's)   **$10,450**   **£5,618**

WILLIAM EVANS LINTON – A white cob horse
– oil on board – 10 x 13in.
(W. H. Lane & Son)   **$585 £340**

LORENZO LIPPE, Follower of – A naked woman
at a casement – 83.8 x 113.3cm.
(Christie's)   **$2,474 £1,430**

PIETER LISAERT – The Annunciation – oil on
panel – 49.5 x 36cm.
(Phillips)   **$1,848**   **£1,050**

ARTHUR LISMER – Georgian Bay – signed and dated – oil on masonite – 8 x 10in.
(Robt. W. Skinner Inc.)   **$3,700 £2,102**

DOROTHEA M. LITZINGER – Blue Still Life – signed – oil on canvas – 40 x 30in.
(Robt. W. Skinner Inc.) **$3,200**   **£1,893**

WILLIAM STUART LLOYD – The bargees at sunset, near Chichester – signed and dated – 27 x 18½in.
(Prudential)   **$2,335 £1,350**

DOROTHEA M. LITZINGER – Still Life with Peonies – unsigned – oil on canvas – 40 x 50in.
(Robt. W. Skinner Inc.)   **$3,600 £2,045**

DOROTHEA M. LITZINGER – Still Life with flowers – unsigned – oil on canvas – 84.4 x 154cm.
(Robt. W. Skinner Inc.)   **$3,100 £1,761**

ANDREA LOCATELLI, Follower of – Figures in a sculpture garden – oil on canvas – 45 x 37cm.
(Phillips)   **$2,464**   **£1,400**

LODGE

GEORGE EDWARD LODGE — Pheasants flying over a Wood — signed — bodycolour — 11½ x 17½in.
(Phillips) **$6,084** **£3,600**

AUGUST LOHR — Mexican landscape — signed — 12¼ x 21½in.
(Christie's) **$4,307** **£2,420**

GUSTAVE LOISEAU — Le Pont de St Ouen, Pontoise, sous la Neige — signed — oil on canvas — 21¼ x 25¾in.
(Christie's) **$40,480 £22,000**

GUSTAVE LOISEAU — L'Eglise Saint-Medard et la Rue Mouffetard, Paris — signed — oil on canvas — 18 x 21½in.
(Christie's) **$79,464** **£46,200**

GUSTAVE LOISEAU — Barques echouees dans un Port — signed — oil on canvas — 29 x 34.5cm.
(Christie's) **$32,912** **£17,600**

LONGCHAMPS — Le Bal du 14 Juillet — signed and dated — oil on canvas — 21½ x 29in.
(Christie's) **$1,732** **£990**

JULES CESAR DENIS VAN LOO – A winter landscape with peasants on a track – signed and dated – 14¼ x 21¼in.
(Christie's)   **$4,525 £2,420**

ERNST HUGO LORENZ – An interior – signed – 31½ x 47½in.
(Christie's)   **$2,992**   **£1,760**

CHARLES FREDERICK LOWCOCK – Portrait of an elegant lady, full length in a lilac dress, in a landscape – signed – oil on board – 9 x 4in.
(Christie's)   **$380**   **£220**

CHRISTINE LOVMAND – A still life of fruit on a ledge – signed – on panel – 12½ x 16¾in.
(Christie's)   **$3,751 £2,220**

ALAN LOWNDES – Halshtown in snow – signed and dated – oil on board – 21½ x 28in.
(Christie's)   **$4,181 £2,310**

LAURENCE STEPHEN LOWRY – Waiting for an answer – signed and dated – oil on board – 10 x 6in.
(Christie's) **$22,896 £12,650**

LOUIS LOZOWICK – Through Brooklyn Bridge Cables – signed – lithograph on paper – 24.7 x 32.6cm.
(Robt. W. Skinner Inc.) **$3,750** **£2,218**

LAURENCE STEPHEN LOWRY – Private view, Manchester – signed and dated – oil on canvas – 20 x 30in.
(Christie's) **$119,460 £66,000**

MAXIMILIEN LUCE – La Rue des Abbesses – signed – oil on cradled panel – 19½ x 14¾in.
(Christie's) **$160,820** **£93,500**

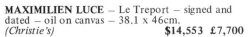

MAXIMILIEN LUCE – Le Treport – signed and dated – oil on canvas – 38.1 x 46cm.
(Christie's) **$14,553 £7,700**

MAXIMILIEN LUCE – Femme et Enfant au Jardin – signed – oil on panel – 10 x 9¾in.
(Christie's) **$17,325 £9,900**

MAXIMILIEN LUCE – Nature morte aux Fleurs dans un Vase – signed – oil on canvas – 18 x 24in.
(Christie's) **$28,798** **£15,400**

MAXIMILIEN LUCE – Le Reveur (The dreamer) – signed – brown wash over pencil on China paper – 5 x 4in.
(Robt. W. Skinner Inc.) **$175** **£99**

MAXIMILIEN LUCE – L'Usine – signed and dated – oil on canvas – 21¼ x 14¾in.
(Christie's) **$44,528 £24,200**

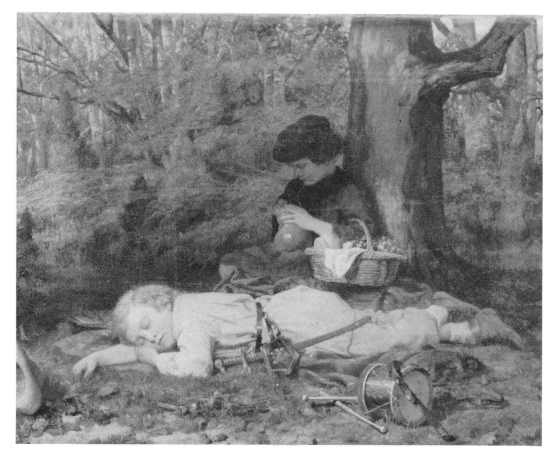

CHARLES LUCY — The Bivouac — signed with monogram and dated — oil on canvas — 19¼ x 24¾in.
(Christie's)   **$54,648**   **£29,700**

LODEWIJCK VAN LUDICK — A herdsman with
his animals beside a river in an Italianate landscape
— signed indistinctly — oil on canvas — 23¾ x 29¼in.
(Phillips)   **$2,640 £1,500**

GEORGE B. LUKS — Mahaney City, Pennsylvania
— signed — oil on canvas — 17 x 23½in.
(Bruce D. Collins)   **$7,150**   **£3,783**

GEORGE BENJAMIN LUKS – The Sick Doll –
signed – oil on canvas laid down on board –
10½ x 8½in.
(Christie's)   **$13,200**   **£7,096**

BEORGE BENJAMIN LUKS – Men on the
Beach – signed – charcoal on paper – 9 x 7in.
(Robt. W. Skinner Inc.)   **$475 £269**

AMELIE LUNDAHL – In the woods – signed –
canvas laid down on board – 12½ x 10¼in.
(Christie's)   **$132,275**   **£71,500**

EGRON SILLIF LUNDGREN – The guest –
signed with initials – pencil and watercolour –
35 x 53cm.
(Christie's)   **$1,831**   **£990**

ALESSANDRO LUPO – Il Gondoliere – signed –
22 x 25½in.
(Christie's)   **$4,525 £2,420**

E. A. LUTH – Wild flowers in a meadow – signed
and dated – 25½ x 36½in.
(Christie's)   **$6,160**   **£3,520**

**CHARLES AUGUSTUS HENRY LUTYENS, Circle
of** – Putti dancing whilst others play a tune and
eight other paintings of Putti by the same hand
– oil on canvas – 14.5 x 19cm.
(Phillips)   **Nine**   **$1,050**   **£600**

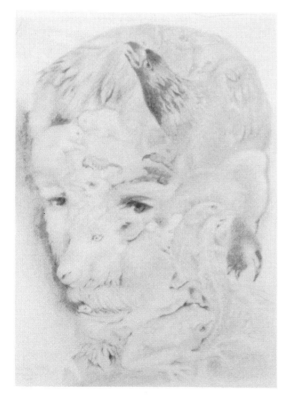

MARIETTE LYDIS – L'Homme cache –
signed, dated and inscribed – pencil on paper –
33 x 24.5cm.
(Christie's)   **$1,925 £1,100**

JAMES LYNCH – Chestnut Horse in Landscape,
Balalitra – signed and dated – gouache –
16 x 19½in.
(Christie's)   **$783   £440**

JAMES McBEY – Venice, 16 October 1925 –
signed – etching and drypoint on paper –
20.6 x 25.2cm.
(Robt. W. Skinner Inc.) **$350**   **£207**

ANDREW McCALUM – A woodland – signed –
30 x 40in.
(Christie's)   **$494   £286**

GEORGE McCONNELL – Autumn – signed –
watercolour on paper – 5 x 6in.
(Bruce D. Collins)   **$66**   **£34**

ARTHUR DAVID McCORMICK – The Envoy –
signed – 28 x 35in.
(Chrystals)   **$6,358**   **£3,400**

JOHN BLAKE McDONALD – "The Legend of
Montrose", taking shelter in the Highland croft
– signed and dated – oil on canvas – 28 x 36in.
(W. H. Lane & Son)   **$5,504 £3,200**

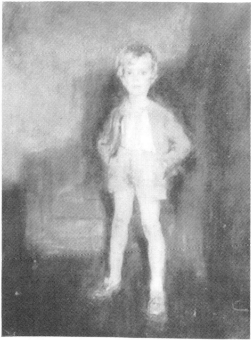

AMBROSE McEVOY – Boy in blue – signed –
31 x 25in.
(Christie's)   **$1,115   £660**

AMBROSE McEVOY – Standing female nude –
signed and inscribed – watercolour – 22 x 15¼in.
(Christie's)   **$706   £418**

HENRY RYAN MacGINNIS – West Field House –
signed – oil on canvas – 63.8 x 76cm.
(Robt. W. Skinner Inc.) **$200**   **£118**

GEORG MACCO – An Arab market street – signed
and dated – oil on canvas – 55.5 x 81.7cm.
(Christie's)   **$2,230 £1,320**

JAMES HAMILTON MACKENZIE – The
Western Sea, Iona – signed – oil on canvas –
51 x 67cm.
(Phillips)   **$13,015 £7,480**

HOWARD McLEAN – Peonies – oil on canvas –
(Christie's)   **$880   £483**

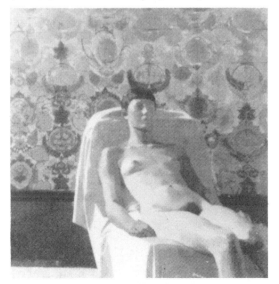

ANDREW MACLAREN – Female nude in an
interior – signed – oil on canvas – 36 x 35½in.
(Christie's)   **$995   £550**

ELYSEE MACLET – Le Moulin de Montmartre –
signed – oil on canvas – 15¾ x 22¼in.
(Christie's)   **$4,573   £2,420**

DANIEL MACLISE – May – signed – on panel
– 16 x 12½in.
(Christie's) **$8,959** **£4,950**

PERCY THOMAS MACQUOID – A bulldog and a
dachshund attacking a mannequin – signed –
watercolour – 13¾ x 19¼in.
(Anderson & Garland) **$1,710 £1,000**

PAUL MADELINE – Pins au Bord de Mer – signed
– oil on canvas – 23¼ x 28¾in.
(Christie's) **$17,325 £9,900**

ELMER LIVINGSTON MACRAE – Portrait of a
Young Child – signed and dated – pastel on grey
paper – 11 x 14in.
(Robt. W. Skinner Inc.) **$325** **£192**

PAUL MADELINE – La Cour de la Ferme –
signed and dated – oil on canvas – 18 x 21½in.
(Christie's) **$10,587 £6,050**

MAELLA

MARIANO SALVADOR DE MAELLA, Circle of
– The Coronation of the Virgin, in the company of
Saints – oil on copper, tondo – 19.5cm. diam.
(Phillips) **$560** **£320**

ALBERTO MAGNELLI – L'Uomo Ubriaco – signed
and dated – oil on canvas – 39¼ x 29½in.
(Christie's) **$94,622** **£50,600**

DOROTHEA MAETZEL-JOHANNSEN – Anne-
marie – signed with initials and dated '20 – oil
on board – 33½ x 25in.
(Christie's) **$22,704** **£13,200**

RENE MAGRITTE – Le Cicerone – signed – oil
on canvas – 25½ x 20½in.
(Christie's) **$319,770** **£187,000**

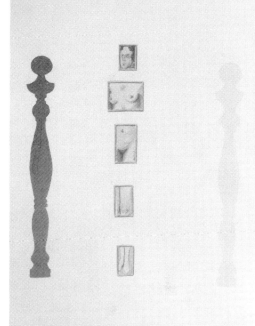

RENE MAGRITTE — La Peine perdue — signed — gouache on paper — 39 x 29cm.
(Christie's) **$143,990 £77,000**

RENE MAGRITTE — 'Nude among Pawns' — water-colour on paper — 19¾ x 14¼in.
(Christie's) **$41,800 £24,666**

RENE MAGRITTE — Le Brasier — signed, inscribed and dated — oil on canvas — 60 x 80cm.
(Christie's) **$244,530 £143,000**

MAGRITTE

RENE MAGUIRE – La Retour a la nature – signed – gouache on paper – 10¼ x 15¼in.
(Christie's)   **$83,600   £49,332**

HELEN MAGUIRE – Girls and Ponies – signed – a pair – 9 x 7¼in.
(Anderson & Garland)   **$3,330 £1,850**

HENRI MANGUIN – Le Paysage Mediterraneen
– signed – oil on canvas – 11¾ x 16in.
(Christie's)   **$34,408 £18,700**

PAUL FORDYCE MAITLAND – Barges on the
Thames – signed – on board – 12½ x 20½in.
(Christie's)   **$1,115 £660**

HENRI MANGUIN – Le Port de Rouen – signed
– oil on canvas – 17½ x 14½in.
(Christie's)   **$28,336 £15,400**

ZBIGNIEW MAKOWSKI – Untitled – signed and
dated – pen, brush and black ink on paper –
18¾ x 25¼in.
(Christie's)   **$822 £440**

CHRISTIAN MALI – Lunch-time – signed and
inscribed – oil on canvas – 12 x 27½in.
(Christie's)   **$17,204 £9,350**

ROY DE MAISTRE – Boatyard recto; Seated man
in blue verso – signed – oil on board – 25 x 30in.
(Christie's)   **$32,851 £18,150**

LOUIS CLAUDE MALLEBRANCHE – A winter
river landscape with skaters on the ice – signed –
21.5 x 40.3cm.
(Christie's)   **$2,244 £1,320**

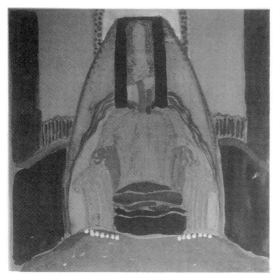

ERICH MALLINA – Throne Figure – pencil and watercolour heightened with white and gold on paper – 8½ x 8½in.
(Christie's) **$4,162** **£2,420**

EDOUARD MANET – Lola de Valence – signed – etching and aquatint on laid paper – 10¼ x 7in.
(Robt. W. Skinner Inc.) **$950** **£562**

EDOUARD MANET – Femme a la Fourrure, de profil – oil and pastel on canvas – 22 x 18½in.
(Christie's) **$1,128,600** **£660,000**

KAREL VAN MANDER, Follower of – The supper at Emmaus – on copper – 21.6 x 16.2cm.
(Christie's) **$761 £440**

EDWARD MIDDLETON MANIGAULT – Allegorical Scene – unsigned – oil on canvas – 32¼ x 50¼in.
(Robt. W. Skinner Inc.) **$5,500** **£3,254**

HARRINGTON MANN – Young Boy in an Interior – signed and dated – oil on canvas – 49 x 31in.
(Christie's)   **$10,769**   **£6,050**

WILLIAM MANNERS – Cattle with a drover crossing a bridge – signed and dated – on panel – 8¼ x 12¾in.
(Christie's)   **£685**   **£385**

WILLIAM MANNERS – The edge of the Beroh Wood; and Cottingley, Near Bingley – signed and dated – 30 x 20in.
(Christie's)   **$3,784**   **£2,200**

WILLIAM MANNERS – A river landscape with an angler – signed and dated – on panel – 8¼ x 12¾in.
(Christie's)   **$744**   **£418**

A. MARANGONI, After GIOVANNI BELLINI – An allegory of prudence – on panel – 15½ x 9½in.
(Christie's)   **$1,522**   **£880**

MARCHAND

ANDRE MARCHAND – Saulieu; Hiver – signed
– oil on panel – 8½ x 10¼in.
(Christie's)   **$4,812 £2,750**

ANDRE MARCHAND – La Lune dans la Mer,
Belle Ile – signed – oil on canvas – 25¾ x 32in.
(Christie's)   **$9,460   £5,500**

EMILE VAN MARCKE – Cattle and a drover in a
meadow – signed – oil on panel – 9½ x 14½in.
(Christie's)   **$1,152 £682**

LOUIS MARCOUSSIS – La Guitare – signed and
dated – 33 x 46 cm.
(Christie's)   **$39,732   £23,100**

MICHELE MARIESCHI, Follower of – The Grand
Canal, Venice, with the Fondaco dei Tedeschi –
oil on canvas – 24¾ x 38¼in.
(Phillips)   **$12,530 £7,000**

JEAN ALFRED MARIOTON – Picking roses –
signed – oil on canvas – 82 x 49½in.
(Christie's)   **$8,096 £4,400**

JACOB MARIS – A cottage interior with a girl
playing with a cat – signed and dated – 18 x 14in.
(Christie's)   **$21,175**   **£12,100**

FERDINAND MAROHN – Feeding Chickens –
signed – 11¼ x 9¾in.
(Anderson & Garland)   **$2,970**   **£1,650**

GEORGES PHILIBERT-CH. MARONIEZ – Mussel
gatherers at dusk – signed – 21½ x 28¼in.
(Christie's)   **$1,439 £770**

WALTER B. MARLING – "Off the Lizard,
Cornwall", rocky coastal view – oil on canvas
– 24 x 16in.
(W. H. Lane & Son)   **$405 £240**

ALBERT MARQUET – Le Pont de Poissy –
signed – oil on panel – 33.5 x 41cm.
(Christie's)   **$127,534**   **£68,200**

MARQUET

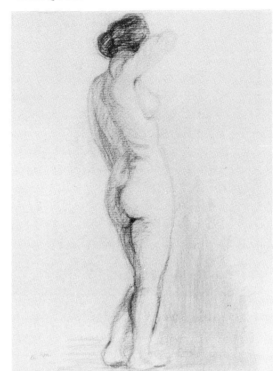

ALBERT MARQUET − Nu debout − signed −
black and white crayon on paper − 10¾ x 8in.
(Christie's)   **$1,347 £770**

REGINALD MARSH − Girl Walking − signed
− oil on panel − 10 x 8in.
(Robt. W. Skinner Inc.)   **$2,100 £1,193**

D. W. MARSHALL − Hyde Park Corner − signed,
inscribed and dated − oil on canvas − 59 x 90cm.
(Phillips)   **$2,105 £1,210**

JAMES MILLER MARSHALL − On Cromer Sands
− signed and dated − pencil and water colour −
23½ x 11½in.
(Christie's)   **$4,162**   **£2,420**

HENRI MARTIN – Vase de Fleurs – signed – oil on board – 50 x 41cm.
(Christie's) **$34,408 £18,700**

HENRI MARTIN – Jeune Femme pres du Bassin – oil on canvas – 67 x 106cm.
(Christie's) **$242,880 £132,000**

HENRI MARTIN – Le Bassin de Marquayrol – signed – oil on canvas – 81 x 65 cm.
(Christie's) **$160,820 £93,500**

HENRY MARTIN – Gentleman and child with baskets on a country path – signed – oil on canvas – 14 x 21in.
(W. H. Lane & Son) **$878 £480**

HENRI MARTIN – Le Chien – signed – oil on board – 24.2 x 15.6cm.
(Christie's) **$5,405 £2,860**

HENRY MARTIN – Newlyn slip and harbour with fishing boats at anchor – signed – oil on board – 5 x 8in.
(W. H. Lane & Son) **$1,135 £660**

MARTINES

H. MARTINES – Harvesting – signed –
17½ x 21¼in.
(Christie's) **$1,141 £660**

G. MAS – A busy Parisian street scene – signed –
oil on panel – 22 x 28cm.
(Phillips) **$2,679 £1,540**

GEORGE HEMING MASON – Evening Matlock;
the Harvest Moon – oil on canvas – 44 x 74cm.
(Christie's) **$17,974 £10,450**

JACQUELINE MARVAL – Une Nuit a Chang-
Hai – signed and titled – colour lithograph poster
on paper – 45¼ x 29½in.
(Robt. W. Skinner Inc.) **$300 £177**

AUGUSTE ANTOINE MASSE – Une compagnie
de la 2ᵉ legion, aux champs de Mars, un tour de
revue, Paris – signed and dated 1836 –
52½ x 73in.
(Christie's) **$31,790 £18,700**

ANDRE MASSON – Montserrat – signed and inscribed – pencil on paper laid down on board –
10 x 19¼in.
(Christie's) **$2,494 £1,320**

LORENZO MASUCCI, Attributed to – The Immaculate Conception – on copper – 12¾ x 9¾in.
(Phillips) **$1,700 £950**

GEORGES MATHIEU – Composition – signed and dated – gouache on red paper – 19½ x 25½in.
(Christie's) **$5,348 £2,860**

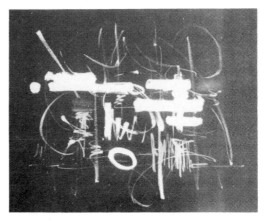

GEORGES MATHIEU – Composition – signed and dated – gouache on black paper – 20 x 26in.
(Christie's) **$5,759 £3,080**

JOHN GEORGE MATHIESON – Polmaise Woods – signed – oil on canvas – 25½ x 21½in.
(Anderson & Garland) **$3,366 £1,800**

HENRI MATISSE – Bateaux a Port – signed – oil on board – 27 x 35cm.
(Christie's) **$161,920 £88,000**

MATISSE

HENRI MATISSE – Bords de la Seine a Vetheuil
– signed – oil on canvas – 38 x 46cm.
(Christie's) **$283,360 £154,000**

MAXIME MAUFRA – Les Bords du Loir a Ponce
Sarthe – signed – oil on canvas – 21¼ x 28¾in.
(Christie's) **$17,028** **£9,900**

MAXIME MAUFRA – Les Inondations a Paris
– signed and dated – oil on canvas – 71.5x99cm.
(Christie's) **$36,432 £19,800**

ANTON MAUVE – For hire – signed – oil on
canvas – 12 x 20in.
(Christie's) **$24,288 £13,200**

ANTON MAUVE – A shepherdess leading two goats
into a shed – signed – watercolour and bodycolour
– 8 x 13½in.
(Christie's) **$7,315** **£4,180**

ALEXEI KONSTANTINOVICH MAXIMOV –
Winterspiele II – signed with initials – tempera
and oil on canvas – 120 x 100cm.
(Hauswedell & Nolte) **$4,937 £2,870**

PAUL MAZE – Summer landscape – signed –
pastel – 22 x 29½in.
(Christie's) **$836 £495**

ARTHUR JOSEPH MEADOWS – The old bridge,
Verona – signed and dated – on panel – 11¾ x 9½in.
(Christie's) **$7,440 £4,180**

PAOLO MEI – Italian lady seated on open
veranda – signed – oil on panel – 13 x 6in.
(Du Mouchelles) **$800 £475**

WILLIAM MEADOWS – The Piazzetta, Venice –
signed – canvas laid down on board – 20 x 30in.
(Christie's) **$1,468 £825**

WILHELM MELBYE – Sailing vessels in a stormy
sea – signed and dated – 16 x 27in.
(Christie's) **$5,984 £3,520**

CAMPBELL A. MELLON – Molesey Lock – oil
on panel – 12 x 16in.
(Christie's)   **$1,762   £990**

MORTIMER MENPES – A Japanese child at the
entrance to a shop – signed – watercolour and
pencil – 12.4 x 21.5cm.
(Christie's)   **$4,895   £2,750**

WILLIAM MELLOR – On the Llugwy, North
Wales – signed and inscribed – 12 x 18¼in.
(Christie's)   **$2,283   £1,320**

MARIO MERZ – Untitled – oil and enamel on
joined canvas laid down on board – 98 x 137¾in.
(Christie's)   **$70,873   £37,900**

ANTON RAPHAEL MENGS, Manner of – The
Madonna and child – 11¾ x 10in.
(Christie's)   **$1,618   £935**

W. E. METCALFE – Market Day in Belgium –
signed and dated – oil on panel – 28 x 58cm.
(Henry Spencer)   **$830   £480**

WILLIAM LEROY METCALF – Portrait of A. Preston Baker – signed and dated – oil on canvas – 18½ x 10½in.
(Christie's)   **$33,000**   **£17,741**

LOUIS METTLING – Peaches in a basket with a wine glass on a table – signed – oil on canvas – 14 x 17½in.
(Christie's)   **$1,208 £715**

WILLIAM MEYEROWITZ – Village Life, Harbourside – signed – oil on canvas – 27 x 35in.
(Robt. W. Skinner Inc.)   **$4,000 £2,272**

JEAN METZINGER – La Musique – signed – oil on canvas – 26 x 36½in.
(Christie's)   **$70,840 £38,500**

J. C. MICHEL – The Sleigh Ride – indistinctly signed – 31½ x 39in.
(Christie's)   **$2,057 £1,100**

EDWARD MIDDLEDITCH — Trafalgar Square —
signed and inscribed — oil on board — 12 x 26in.
(Christie's)   **$6,371 £3,520**

F. A. KOKO-MICOLETZKY — Alpine view at
Biberkopf-Alberg — signed — 22 x 27½in.
(Christie's)   **$929   £550**

HELMUT MIDDENDORF — Stalker — signed, inscribed and dated — acrylic on canvas — 200 x 250cm.
(Christie's)   **$9,256   £4,950**

WILLIAM HENRY MIDWOOD — On the way home
— signed — 36 x 28in.
(Christie's)   **$12,941**   **£7,150**

HELMUT MIDDENDORF — Nightbirds — signed,
inscribed and dated — acrylic on canvas —
74¾ x 106½in.
(Christie's)   **$18,513 £9,900**

JAN MIEL, Follower of — Townsfolk by ruins at a
quay — 78.5 x 104.5cm.
(Christie's)   **$11,418 £6,600**

MICHAEL MIEREVELDT, Circle of – Portrait of
an elderly man, with high ruff, bust length – oil on
panel – 17.5cm. x 15cm.
(Phillips)   **$962   £550**

PIERRE MIGNARD, After – The Madonna and
Child – 91.2 x 71.8cm.
(Christie's)   **$1,903 £1,100**

WILLEM VAN MIERIS, Follower of – Saint
Sebastian tended by an angel – on copper –
12½ x 9in.
(Christie's)   **$2,093 £1,210**

ROBERT VAN DER MIJN, Attributed to – Still
life of peaches, grapes and cherries on a carpet
draped over a table – indistinctly signed – oil on
canvas – 21½ x 17¾in.
(Phillips)   **$3,401   £1,900**

MILLER

RICHARD EDWARD MILLER — Black Mantilla —
signed — oil on canvas — 91.7 x 87.1cm.
(Christie's) **$28,600** **£15,376**

MAURICE MILLIERE — Motoring — signed and
dated — oil on canvas — 32 x 24½in.
(Robt. W. Skinner Inc.) **$2,500** **£1,479**

GEORGE R. MILNE — Leadbeater's Cockatoo
and frilled lizard (Australia) — signed and dated —
on board — 24 x 29in.
(Christie's) **$2,349** **£1,320**

JEAN FRANÇOIS MILLET — La Baratteuse —
etching on thin Japan paper — 17.8 x 11.7cm.
(Robt. W. Skinner Inc.) **$1,500** **£887**

JOE MILNE — A busy harbour — signed — oil on
canvas — 30 x 40cm.
(Phillips) **$7,273 £4,180**

MACLAUGHLAN MILNE – High Corrie, Arran
– signed – oil on canvas – 50 x 60cm.
(Phillips) **$26,796 £15,400**

JOHN MACLAUGHLAN MILNE – Calva Shore,
Iona – signed – oil on board – 20 x 24in.
(Lawrence Fine Arts) **$18,078** **£10,450**

MACLAUGHLAN MILNE – Figures on a beach,
Western Isles – signed – oil on board – 50 x 60cm.
(Phillips) **$13,398 £7,700**

J. MINARIK – A wooded landscape – signed and
dated – 30 x 40½in.
(Christie's) **$1,028 £550**

JOHN MINTON – Palms and figures – signed and
dated – oil on canvas – 23 x 30cm.
(Phillips) **$9,952 £5,720**

JOAN MIRO – Personnage et Oiseau II – signed
– watercolour, brush and black ink on paper –
17 x 21¾in.
(Christie's) **$92,565 £49,500**

MIRO

JOAN MITCHELL – Untitled – signed – oil on canvas – 28½ x 21¼in.
(Christie's)   **$41,624**   **£24,200**

JOAN MIRO – Personnage et Oiseau II – signed
– watercolour, brush and black ink on paper –
17 x 21¾in.
(Christie's)   **$92,565**   **£49,500**

JOSEPH MISRAKI – Le port du Havre – signed
and dated – oil on canvas – 65 x 81cm.
(Christie's)   **$5,390**   **£3,080**

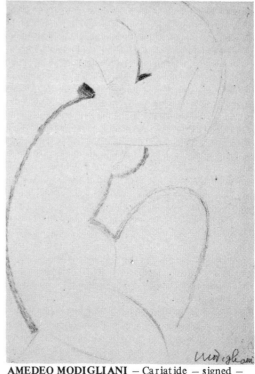

JOSEPH MISRAKI – La Guinguette au Bord de
l'Eau – signed and dated – oil on canvas –
29 x 36½in.
(Christie's)   **$7,315**   **£4,180**

AMEDEO MODIGLIANI – Cariatide – signed –
blue crayon on paper – 13½ x 10½in.
(Christie's)   **$60,544**   **£35,200**

JOHN HENRY MOLE – Gypsy children –
(Morphets) **$2,464 £1,400**

AMEDEO MODIGLIANI – Tete de jeune Homme –
signed – oil on board – 22 x 15½in.
(Christie's) **$253,080 £148,000**

JOHN HENRY MOLE – Patience – angler seated on
a bridge, his mother and sister looking on – signed
and dated – watercolour – 33.5 x 59cm.
(Henry Spencer) **$7,896 £4,200**

LOUIS CHARLES MOELLER – Repairing The Shoe
– signed – oil on canvas – 46.5 x 62cm.
(Christie's) **$16,500 £8,870**

JOHN HENRY MOLE – Collecting shell fish –
signed and dated – 7½ x 12in.
(Anderson & Garland) **$1,512 £840**

ANTONIO MOLINARI, Attributed to – The Sacrifice of Polyxena – oil on canvas – 49½ x 50¾in.
(Phillips) **$6,160 £3,500**

MOLLINGER

ALEXANDER MOLLINGER – Home from the fields – signed and dated – oil on canvas – 70 x 110cm.
(Phillips) **$4,976 £2,860**

FREDERICK WILLIAM MAC MONNIES – Marjorie and Berthe Feed their Pet Rooster, "Coco" – oil on canvas – 21 x 22½in.
(Christie's) **$28,600** **£15,376**

DAVID MONIES – The huntsman – signed – 21 x 19¼in.
(Christie's) **$24,420** **£13,200**

PEDER MONSTED – A wooded river landscape
– signed and dated – 14 x 22½in.
(Christie's)   **$13,090**   **£7,700**

PEDER MONSTED – Algiers – signed and dated
– oil on canvas – 29½ x 47½in.
(Christie's)   **$30,360 £16,500**

PEDER MONSTED – Fra Sicilien – signed and
dated – oil on canvas – 23 x 17½in.
(Christie's)   **$14,572 £7,920**

PEDER MONSTED – Nissastrom, near Halmstad,
Sweden – signed and dated – 71 x 43¼in.
(Christie's)   **$36,630**   **£19,800**

ALFRED MONTAGUE – Market House, Brittany
– signed and dated – on board – 13½ x 9½in.
(Christie's)   **$1,419**   **£825**

MONTASSIER

HENRI MONTASSIER – 'Romance' – signed –
26 x 21½in.
(Christie's) **$1,673 £990**

PIERRE-EUGENE MONTEZIN – Crocq (Creuse)
– signed – watercolour and gouache on paper –
16.3 x 19cm.
(Christie's) **$2,502 £1,430**

PIERRE-EUGENE MONTEZIN – La Rue de la
Fontaine – signed – oil on canvas – 46.6 x 54.3cm.
(Christie's) **$21,175 £12,100**

ADOLPHE MONTICELLI – Fruits sur un Tapis –
signed – oil on panel – 46 x 61cm.
(Christie's) **$37,840 £22,000**

ADOLPH JOSEPH THOMAS MONTICELLI – La
Fete de Flora – signed and dated – oil on canvas
– 21 x 40½in.
(Christie's) **$51,975 £27,500**

LOUIS-MAURICE BOUTET DE MONVEL –
School children – signed – watercolour with pencil
on paper – 9¾ x 6¼in.
(Robt. W. Skinner Inc.) **$2,600 £1,477**

HARRY MOORE – Listening in the moonlight –
signed and dated – oil on canvas – 21 x 16in.
(Christie's)   **$385   £211**

HENRY MOORE – Standing female Nude –
charcoal and grey wash with pen and ink on paper
– 44.1 x 28cm.
(Christie's)   **$7,900   £4,180**

HENRY MOORE – Studies for Sculpture –
signed and dated – on paper – 35 x 25.2cm.
(Christie's)   **$37,840   £22,000**

HENRY MOORE – Dutch Trawlers waiting for the
tide – signed and dated – pencil and watercolour
– 25½ x 39½in.
(Christie's)   **$2,459   £1,430**

H. MOORE – In the park – signed and dated –
20 x 24in.
(Christie's)   **$1,301   £770**

JOHANN MOREELSE, Attributed to – Pan, half
length, wearing a leopard's skin – oil on canvas –
34¼ x 31¾in.
(Phillips)   **$4,654   £2,600**

A. MORALES – Granada – one of a pair –
signed – pencil and watercolour – 26 x 14¾in.
(Christie's)   Two   **$1,236 £715**

R. MORETTI – "Divided opinion" – signed and inscribed – oil on canvas – 22 x 15in.
(Christie's)   **$2,416 £1,430**

BERTHE MORISOT – Fillette jouant avec un Chien – oil on canvas – 10½ x 14in.
(Christie's) **$141,680 £77,000**

GEORGES MORREN – Tete de Femme au Beret blanc – signed and dated – oil on canvas – 45.4 x 50.5 cm.
(Christie's) **$3,118 £1,650**

JOHN FLOYD MORRIS – The Green Mountain – signed and dated – watercolour on paper – 15¼ x 23¼in.
(Christie's) **$1,430 £843**

HARRY MORLEY – The wheelwright's yard – signed and dated – watercolour, pen and black ink – 8¾ x 11¾in.
(Christie's) **$2,937 £1,650**

ERNEST VICTOR PAUL MOROT – A farmyard, St Valary-en-Eahz (?) – signed and dated – oil on canvas – 28 x 36¼in.
(Christie's) **$2,788 £1,650**

JOHN FLOYD MORRIS – – Grotesque Pillar – gouache on paper – 24½ x 18½in.
(Christie's) **$550 £324**

MORTIMER

WILLIAM SIDNEY MOUNT – The Mount Kitchen, Stony Brook – signed – oil on canvas laid down on panel – 18.7 x 35.5cm.
(Christie's) $41,800 £22,473

JOHN HAMILTON MORTIMER – Soldiers resting beneath a tree – pen and black ink – 26 x 20cm.
(Christie's) $2,618 £1,540

P. MOURLOT – An Arab encampment – signed – 32.5 x 55cm.
(Christie's) $2,949 £1,705

GILLIS MOSTAERT, Attributed to – Noah and his sons Shem, Ham and Japheth building the Ark – on panel – 21.3 x 26.8cm.
(Christie's) $4,187 £2,420

RICHARD MULLER – The hummingbird –
oil on panel – 15½ x 20½in.
(Christie's) **$4,048 £2,200**

WILLIAM JAMES MULLER – Lycia – indistinctly
signed – oil on canvas – 31 x 49cm.
(Phillips) **$3,445 £1,980**

AUGUSTUS E. MULREADY – Selling out –
signed, inscribed and dated – on board – 12 x 9in.
(Christie's) **$1,566 £880**

AUGUSTUS E. MULREADY – Visitors to a
London Street – signed and dated – on board –
9 x 7in.
(Christie's) **$1,566 £880**

EDVARD MUNCH – Doppelportrait (Blond und
Schwarz) – oil on canvas – 23¾ x 27¾in.
(Christie's) **$413,820 £242,000**

MICHAEL LIEB MUNKACSY, Follower of – Portrait of a lady standing three-quarter length, at a
window – oil on canvas – 17 x 14in.
(Christie's) **$1,524 £902**

MARTIN MYTENS (The Younger), Follower of
– Portrait of a man, wearing Eastern headdress,
half length – oil on canvas – 29¼ x 23½in.
(Phillips)   **$1,074   £600**

JAN MYTENS THE YOUNGER – Portrait of a
young man, seated half length, wearing a grey coat
and turban – 30 x 23in.
(Christie's)   **$4,948 £2,860**

ANGELO NARDI, Follower of – St Clare praying
before Christ on the cross – oil on panel –
52.5 x 41cm.
(Phillips)   **$792   £450**

EDITH KROGER VAN NAGLER – Hillside with
brush cutter – signed – oil on masonite –
60.7 x 76.2cm.
(Robt. W. Skinner Inc.)   **$1,500   £852**

PAUL NASH – Mixed flowers in a vase, with a
bowl of fruit – signed with monogram –
16 x 13½in.
(Christie's)   **$7,807 £4,620**

ALEXANDER NASMYTH, Follower of – Figures resting in a wooded river landscape, with mountains beyond – 27 x 35 in.
(Christie's) **$1,301** **£770**

ERNST WILHELM NAY – Gelb zu Grau – signed and dated – oil on canvas – 35½ x 49¼ in.
(Christie's) **$90,816** **£52,800**

EDOUARDO NAVONE – La toilette – signed and dated – oil on panel – 14¾ x 17¼ in.
(Christie's) **$12,144** **£6,600**

ERNST WILHELM NAY – Untitled – signed and dated – watercolour on paper – 16 x 23¼ in.
(Christie's) **$25,542** **£14,850**

GEORGE HALL NEALE – Reading on the beach – signed and dated – oil on canvas – 20 x 12¾ in.
(Christie's) **$5,874** **£3,300**

NEAPOLITAN SCHOOL

NEAPOLITAN SCHOOL — Vesuvius erupting by day and by night — gouache — oval.
(Christie's) Two **$1,078 £638**

ALBERT NEUHUYS — The new frock — signed — watercolour — 11¼ x 8¼in.
(Christie's) **$2,974 £1,760**

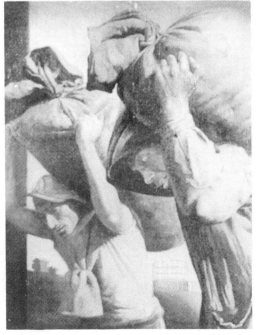

NEAPOLITAN SCHOOL, 19th century — Dancing girls — 21¾ x 17½in.
(Christie's) **$1,234 £660**

ERNST NEUSCHUL — Stone carriers — signed — 39 x 32in.
(Christie's) **$3,346 £1,980**

ALFRED ARTHUR BRUNEL DE NEUVILLE —
Five kittens seated on coloured drapes playing —
signed — 53 x 63cm.
(Henry Spencer)   **$7,400**   **£4,000**

CHRISTOPHER RICHARD WYNNE NEVINSON
— Punts on the Thames at Henley — signed — oil
on canvas — 24 x 30in.
(Christie's)   **$328,515 £181,500**

CHRISTOPHER WYNNE NEVINSON — St Malo
— signed — watercolour and black chalk —
14 x 10in.
(Christie's)   **$5,709**   **£3,300**

JOHN EDWARD NEWTON — The riverside —
signed and dated — 22.6 x 30.9cm.
(Christie's)   **$51,766**   **£28,600**

HART NIBBRIG — Landscape — signed — oil on
canvas — 43 x 81cm.
(Christie's)   **$7,276**   **£3,850**

RICHARD HENRY NIBBS — Entering Port —
signed — 26¼ x 39¾in.
(Anderson & Garland) **$5,760**   **£3,200**

NICHOLLS

SIR WILLIAM NICHOLSON – Glastonbury
Plain – signed with initial – oil on panel –
11 x 15in.
(Christie's) **$18,914 £10,450**

BURR H. NICHOLLS – Glimpse of a Garden:
Venice – signed – oil on artist board –
12 x 8½in.
(Robt. W. Skinner Inc.) **$450** **£266**

WINIFRED NICHOLSON – Vermilion and
Mauve – oil on board – 26 x 21½in.
(Christie's) **$35,205** **£20,350**

BEN NICHOLSON – Ronco 1981 – signed –
on board – 21¼ x 19¼in. overall
(Christie's) **$3,244** **£7,700**

ERSKINE NICOL – Bliss – 'Condition, circum-
stance is no the thing; bliss is the same in subject or
in King' – signed and dated – 26½ x 36in.
(Christie's) **$7,832 £4,400**

VICTOR JEAN NICOLLE – Vue du Pont Au Tuiles, de L'Hotel-Dieux; et des Tours de la Cathedrale de Notre Dame de Paris – signed – pen, brown ink and watercolour – 6 x 9¾in.
(Christie's) **$4,936 £2,640**

BERNARD NINNES – Fishing boats in the harbour St Ives with the slip and town beyond – signed – oil on canvas – 20 x 24in.
(W. H. Lane & Son) **$1,806 £1,050**

EDWARD H. NIEMANN, Circle of – An extensive country landscape – signed – 20 x 30in.
(Christie's) **$1,141 £660**

NIKIFOR – Cityscape Vista – inscribed – crayon with pencil on paper – 5¾ x 8¼in.
(Robt. W. Skinner Inc.) **$475 £281**

POLLOK SINCLAIR NISBET – A Venetian afternoon – signed and dated – 69 x 52.5cm.
(Christie's) **$4,380 £2,420**

VERONICA NISBET – Two costers – signed and
dated – 20½ x 13½in.
(Anderson & Garland)   **$3,740 £2,000**

EMIL NOLDE – Weihnachtskakteen – signed –
watercolour on japan paper – 13¾ x 18½in.
(Christie's)   **$65,824 $35,200**

JOSEPH FRANS NOLLEKENS – The dancing
troupe – oil on canvas – 71.5 x 92cm.
(Phillips)   **$6,688 £3,800**

GIUSEPPE NOGARI, **Attributed to** – Portrait of
a tailor, long bust length – oil on canvas –
55 x 45cm.
(Phillips)   **$2,464 £1,400**

BENGT NORDENBERG – Children playing in an
interior – signed and dated – 25½ x 32in.
(Christie's)   **$28,490   £15,400**

B. L. NORRIS — The new trick — signed —
92 x 72.7cm.
(Christie's) **$4,895 £2,750**

NORTHERN SCHOOL, 19th century — Wooded
landscape with drovers and cattle — signed and dated
— oil on canvas — 18½ x 25½in.
(Robt. W. Skinner Inc.) **$3,500 £1,988**

LEWIS DOYLE NORTON — Along the village path
— signed and inscribed — oil on canvasboard —
24.5 x 30.5cm.
(Robt. W. Skinner Inc.) **$550 £312**

NORTHERN SCHOOL, 18th/19th century — Still
life with flowers — unsigned — oil on canvas —
40¼ x 29¾in.
(Robt. W. Skinner Inc.) **$1,500 £852**

WILLIAM EDWARD NORTON — Cattle grazing
in a wooded landscape — signed — on panel —
29.8 x 40.3cm.
(Christie's) **$1,370 £770**

F. NUNEZ – Kelp gatherers on a coastline – signed
– 21 x 25in.
(Christie's)   **$1,236   £715**

BORGE C. NYROP – Paris in the spring – signed
and dated – 68 x 60.5cm.
(Christie's)   **$22,385   £12,100**

EDGAR H. NYE – Gloucester Schooners – signed
– oil on canvas – 18 x 22in.
(Robt. W. Skinner Inc.)   **$3,600 £2,045**

LUDWIG OBERSTEINER – In the kitchen –
signed and inscribed – 11¾ x 10in.
(Christie's)   **$1,870   £1,100**

JOHN O'CONNOR – Durham Cathedral from the
river – signed with initials – watercolour –
20¾ x 15in.
(Anderson & Garland)   **$2,394 £1,400**

FRANS WILHELM ODELMARK – The snake
charmer – signed and dated – 41 x 28in.
(Christie's) **$20,350** **£11,000**

FRANS OERDER – The bountiful harvest –
signed – on canvas – 31¼ x 23¾in.
(Christie's) **$7,440** **£4,180**

TAKANARI OGUISS – Le Bassin a La Vilette –
signed – oil on canvas – 60 x 80 cm.
(Christie's) **$151,360** **£88,000**

FRANS WILHELM ODELMARK – The Palace
courtyard, Alhambra – signed and dated –
55½ x 37in.
(Christie's) **$22,385** **£12,100**

FREDERICK W. OLIVER – Rockport Harbour
Scene – inscribed – oil on canvas – 41 x 50.5cm.
(Robt. W. Skinner Inc.) **$1,600 £946**

OLIVER

WILLIAM OLIVER – Olivia – signed – 12 x 9in.
(Christie's) **$1,762 £990**

WILLIAM OLIVER, Attributed to – Mont St Michel;
and figures on a track in a wooded river landscape –
17½ x 13¼in.
(Christie's) **$1,892 £1,100**

WILLIAM OLIVER – A fortified hill town with
figures overlooking a valley – 23½ x 35½in.
(Christie's) **$1,324 £770**

WILLIAM OLIVER – Awaiting the fishing fleet
– signed – oil on canvas – 23¼ x 17¼in.
(Anderson & Garland) **$4,959 £2,900**

JULIUS OLSSON – Beach, rowing boats and
lobster pots beneath a cliff – signed – oil on
canvas – 15 x 19in.
(W. H. Lane & Son) **$4,300 £2,500**

G. ONDACHIARI – The Doge's Palace and the entrance to the Grand Canal, Venice – signed – watercolour heightened with white – 12¼ x 25in.
(Christie's) **$822 £440**

JULIAN ONDERDONK – Landscape with dogwoods and house – signed – oil on canvas – 12 x 16in.
(Christie's) **$3,300 £1,813**

UMBERTO ONGANIA – The Grand Canal, Venice – signed – pencil and watercolour – 10¾ x 22¼in.
(Christie's) **$946 £506**

WALTER OPHEY – Eitorf – signed – oil on canvas – 27¾ x 26in.
(Christie's) **$7,700 £4,400**

HENRY NELSON O'NEIL – Portrait of Henry Pelham-Clinton, K.G., 4th Duke of Newcastle, holding a document, in his study – signed and dated – 36½ x 28¼in.
(Christie's) **$4,895 £2,750**

CHARLES OPPENHEIMER – Autumn landscape, Galloway – signed – oil on canvas – 75 x 106cm.
(Phillips) **$9,187 £5,280**

OPPENHEIMER

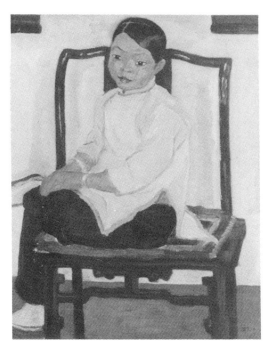

JOSEPH OPPENHEIMER – Piccadilly Circus –
signed and dated indistinctly – oil on canvas –
27 x 22in.
(Christie's) **$45,034** **£25,300**

EMIL ORLIK – Chinesisches Madchen – signed
and dated – oil on canvas – 58 x 49cm.
(Christie's) **$19,228 £10,450**

ALFRED T. ORDWAY – Near Cape Elizabeth –
signed and dated – oil on academy board –
10 x 14in.
(Bruce D. Collins) **$660** **£349**

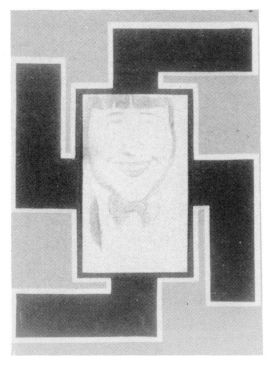

EMIL ORLIK – Pascin zeichnend – signed and inscribed – pen and black ink on paper – 19 x 27cm.
(Christie's) **$2,262 £1,210**

EMIL ORLIK – Kopf – signed – pencil and red
crayon on paper – 7¼ x 4¼in.
(Christie's) **£250** **£143**

J. ORLOFF – Travelling by Troika – signed – oil on panel – 5½ x 11¾in. – and the companion picture. (Two).
(Christie's) **$968 £550**

SIR WILLIAM NEWENHAM MONTAGUE ORPEN – Portrait of Margaret Cruikshank – signed – charcoal – 9 x 7in.
(Christie's) **$1,115 £660**

SIR WILLIAM NEWENHAM MONTAGUE ORPEN – Viewing a masterpiece – signed and dated – pencil, pen and ink on headed writing paper – 10 x 7¾in.
(Christie's) **$650 £385**

FRANCISCO PRADILLA Y ORTIZ – The scholar – signed and inscribed – watercolour – 28 x 20in.
(Christie's) **$36,432 £19,800**

ORZALI

GIUSEPPE ORZALI (after Bartholomeo Manfredi)
– The Fortune Teller – signed, inscribed and
dated – oil on canvas – 98 x 135.5 cm.
(Phillips)   **$2,464   £1,400**

J. OSNAGHI – Still life with cherries and crystal
– signed – oil on canvas – 14 x 24in.
(Du Mouchelles)   **$3,250 £1,719**

A. V. OVERBECK – Goldschneider figure of a
butterfly girl on a draped ledge – signed and dated
– on panel – 13¼ x 11in.
(Christie's)   **$1,301   £770**

AMEDEE OZENFANT – Petite Etude pour 'Vie'
– signed – pen and black ink on thin paper –
5 x 6½in.
(Christie's)   **$374   £198**

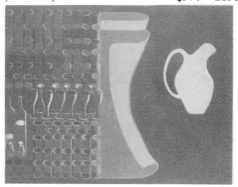

AMEDEE OZENFANT – Nature morte aux
Verres, Bouteilles et Pot blanc – signed –
oil on canvas – 55 x 70¾in.
(Christie's)   **$128,656**   **£74,800**

JOSEPH DE PAES – Saint Emigdio Martyr, in
Glory surrounded with Angels – signed and
inscribed – on copper – 42.9 x 33.7cm.
(Christie's)   **$3,916   £2,200**

ROBERT PAGE — A young poacher avoiding a game keeper — signed and dated — oil on canvas — 29¾ x 24½in.
(Anderson & Garland)   **$4,617 £2,700**

JOHAN DE PALAFOX — Portrait of a Cardinal in an oval frame upon a stone plinth draped with a red curtain — signed — oil on paper — 23 x 17.5cm.
(Phillips)   **$895   £500**

ANTHONIE PALAMEDES (called STEVERS), **Follower of** — The interior of a guardroom — on panel — 30.5 x 38.4cm.
(Christie's)   **$4,567 £2,640**

JEAN DE PALEOLOGU — Pom Pom — signed — pastel — oval — 22 x 17¾in.
(Christie's)   **$761 £440**

FILIPPO PALIZZI — Feeding the goats — signed and dated — oil on canvas — 15 x 20¼in.
(Christie's)   **$133,584 £72,600**

PALIZZI

FILIPPO PALIZZI, Attributed to — Grooming the horses — signed and dated — oil on canvas — 22 x 29in.
(Lawrence Fine Arts) **$5,328** **£3,080**

HARRY SUTTON PALMER — Richmond Bridge — signed — pencil and watercolour — 13½ x 9¼in.
(Christie's) **$1,797** **£1,045**

GIUSEPPE PALIZZI — Peasants herding cattle and goats through a forest — signed — oil on canvas — 55 x 41¼in.
(Christie's) **$36,432 £19,800**

GIUSEPPE PALIZZI — Milking the cow — signed — oil on canvas — 14 x 23½in.
(Christie's) **$24,288 £13,200**

HARRY SUTTON PALMER — "Summer pastures", sheep in the Vale of Conway, Wales — signed — watercolour — 12 x 15in.
(W. H. Lane & Son) **$1,410 £820**

ROBERT PANITZSCH – Garden blooms – signed – 25¾ x 31½in.
(Christie's) **$1,683** **£990**

STUART PARK – A still life of red and white roses – signed – oil on canvas – oval – 49 x 75cm.
(Phillips) **$7,273 £4,180**

EMILIO PANZA – A moment's rest – signed – on panel – 15¾ x 11¾in.
(Christie's) **$1,870** **£1,100**

STUART PARK – A still life of pink, yellow and white roses – signed – oil on canvas – oval – 36 x 61cm.
(Phillips) **$5,359 £3,080**

PARKER

HENRY H. PARKER – Across the stream –
signed – 24 x 36in.
(Christie's) **$13,937** **£7,700**

HENRY H. PARKER – Bredon on the Avon –
signed – 20 x 40in.
(Woolley & Wallis) **$14,878** **£8,600**

HENRY H. PARKER – Pangbourne on Thames
– signed – oil on canvas – 50 x 74cm.
(Phillips) **$11,484 £6,600**

PARKHURST – Portland Head Light – signed –
oil on canvas – 16 x 26in.
(Bruce D. Collins) **$248** **£131**

EVA PARNELL-BAILEY - Plas Mawr – Winter
street scene, a corner shop in the foreground –
signed – oil on canvas – 50 x 59cm.
(Henry Spencer) **$760** **£450**

MAXFIELD FREDERICK PARRISH – The out-
law – initialled – tempera and oil on board –
43.5 x 29.5cm.
(Robt. W. Skinner Inc.) **$75,000 £42,613**

ARTHUR WILDE PARSONS — A barge underway off Gosport — signed and dated — 16 x 24in.
(Christie's)   **$4,307   £2,420**

PHILIP BROWN PARSONS — Bass fishin' — signed — watercolour on paper — 15½ x 21½in.
(Bruce D. Collins)   **$385   £203**

JULES PASCIN — Hermine reposant — signed — oil on board — 61 x 50cm.
(Christie's)   **$61,710   £33,000**

ERNEST PARTON — A mountain river — signed — on canvas — 26 x 17½in.
(Christie's)   **$1,566   £880**

JULES PASCIN — Deux Anglaises — signed — oil on canvas — 55 x 46.5 cm.
(Christie's)   **$128,656   £74,800**

393

PASCIN

JULES PASCIN — Jeunes Filles attablees *(recto)*
— the studio stamp lower right — oil on canvas
— Les Bouquets et les Provisions *(verso)* —
the studio stamp lower right — oil on canvas —
24 x 21¼in.
(Christie's)   **$122,980   £71,500**

JULES PASCIN — Femme se reposant — the studio
stamp — oil on board — 60.5 x 40.5 cm.
(Christie's)   **$32,164   £18,700**

MRS JOHN F. PASMORE — Scenes from rural life; a mother and her family — signed — a pair —
13½ x 11½in.
(Anderson & Garland)   **$5,400 £3,000**

BARON A. DE PASZTHORY — The New Slave
— signed — on board — 11¼ x 13¼in.
(Christie's) **$4,376 £2,530**

JOSEPH PAULMAN — The Gipsy Encampment —
signed and dated — oil on canvas — 16 x 24in.
(W. H. Lane & Son) **$1,738 £950**

CESAR PATTEIN — Children in a meadow —
signed — oil on canvas — 24 x 32in.
(Christie's) **$14,168 £7,700**

P. PAVESI — "The Pool Game" — signed —
watercolour — 20 x 30in.
(Du Mouchelles) **$2,000 £1,058**

GEN PAUL — Les Mesnuls — signed — oil on canvas
— 31 x 25in.
(Prudential) **$5,190 £3,000**

ETHEL PAXSON — Phlox and Butterflies / Kew
Gardens, N.Y. — signed — oil on Masonite —
56.8 x 54cm.
(Robt. W. Skinner Inc.) **$500** **£295**

PAXTON

ELIZABETH V. O. PAXTON – The Silver Coffee
Pot – signed – oil on canvas – 23.8 x 31.2cm.
(Robt. W. Skinner Inc.) **$7,500**   **£4,437**

WILLIAM McGREGOR PAXTON – Portrait of Mrs
Charles Frederic Toppan – signed and dated – oil
on canvas – 44¾ x 36½in.
(Christie's)   **$11,000**   **£5,913**

REMBRANDT PEALE – George Washington –
signed and dated – on paper – 25 x 20.7cm.
(Christie's)   **$24,200**   **£13,010**

REMBRANDT PEALE – Portrait of Olive Foote
Lay – oil on canvas laid down on masonite –
78.4 x 65.8cm.
(Christie's)   **$17,600**   **£9,462**

W. THIRKELL PEARCE – The Smithy – signed and
dated – 21 x 17¼in.
(Christie's)   **$1,702**   **£990**

MARGUERITE S. PEARSON – Fishing vessels,
East Gloucester – signed – oil on board – 8 x 10in.
(Bruce D. Collins) **$660** **£349**

MAX PECHSTEIN – Das rote Beamtenhaus, Nidden
– signed and dated – oil on canvas –
64.5 x 75.5cm.
(Christie's) **$395,010** **£231,000**

MAX PECHSTEIN – Landschaft – signed and
dated – charcoal on paper – 9½ x 13½in.
(Christie's) **$5,405** **£2,860**

MARGUERITE S. PEARSON – Pink roses – signed
– oil on board – 16 x 12in.
(Bruce D. Collins) **$990** **£523**

MARGUERITE S. PEARSON – Pond Lillies –
signed – oil on board – 8 x 10in.
(Bruce D. Collins) **$495** **£261**

MAX PECHSTEIN – Landschaft mit Boote in Rowe
– signed and dated – on card – 19 x 24½in.
(Christie's) **$15,136** **£8,800**

PECRUS

WALDO PEIRCE — After the swim — signed — watercolour on paper — 10 x 13in.
(Bruce D. Collins) **$1,540** **£814**

CAMILLE PECRUS — The Victor — signed — oil on wood panel — 13 x 9in.
(Du Mouchelles) **$850 £449**

THOROLF PEDERSEN — Shipping vessels in Helsingor harbour — signed and dated — 43½ x 54½in.
(Christie's) **$6,545** **£3,850**

J. PEMBERY — A rowing crew at 'The Ship' on the Thames near Mortlake — on board — 41.3 x 36.6cm.
(Christie's) **$489** **£275**

JOSEPH PENNELL — The Putney Bus; Colleoni Statue, Venice: A watercolour and a drawing — both signed — The first watercolour on paper — the second charcoal, pastel and gouache on grey brown paper — 26 x 17.6cm. and 31.7 x 23.6cm.
(Christie's) **$6,050** **£3,252**

J. PEMBERY — A crew rowing past 'The Queen's Head', Mortlake — signed — 41 x 35.6cm.
(Christie's) **$489** **£275**

WILLIAM CHARLES PENN — Playing in the garden — signed and dated — 20 x 23½in.
(Christie's) **$1,859** **£1,100**

SAMUEL JOHN PEPLOE — A still life of apples and pink roses — signed — oil on canvas — 56 x 51cm.
(Phillips) **$220,110** **£126,500**

SAMUEL JOHN PEPLOE – The Harbour, Royan
– signed – oil on board – 27 x 35cm.
(Phillips) **$86,130 £49,500**

JOHN PERCEVAL – Angel in flight – signed –
oil on paper – 69 x 43cm.
(Australian Art Auctions) **$4,472 £2,431**

SIDNEY RICHARD PERCY – Isle of Skye – signed
and dated – 8½ x 14½in.
(Christie's) **$3,027 £1,760**

LILLA CABOT PERRY – Lady in Black – signed
– pastel on paper – 32½ x 26in.
(Christie's) **$9,900 £5,322**

ANTOINE PESNE, Studio of – Portrait of a lady,
half length, wearing a straw hat and carrying a staff
– oil on canvas – 72 x 59cm.
(Phillips) **$2,112 £1,200**

JANE PETERSON — Tomatoes — signed and dated
— oil on board — 45.7 x 45.4cm.
(Robt. W. Skinner Inc.) **$2,400 £1,363**

ANTOINE PESNE, Circle of — Portrait of a gentleman, half length, wearing ceremonial armour and
the badge and sash riband of the House Order of
Fidelity of Baden — oil on canvas — 81 x 68cm.
(Phillips) **$2,200** **£1,250**

EILIF PETERSSEN — 'Pjoka', the artist's house —
signed, inscribed and dated — 24 x 31½in.
(Christie's) **$18,315** **£9,900**

JANE PETERSON — Dogwood Blossoms in a Vase
— signed — oil on canvas — 32 x 32in.
(Christie's) **$14,300** **£7,688**

HIPPOLYTE PETITJEAN — Nu allonge sur l'Herbe
— signed and dated — oil on canvas — 10½ x 18in.
(Christie's) **$41,624** **£24,200**

PFEILLER

M. PFEILLER – Fruits on a draped table with a cockatoo and a young boy holding a salver of fruit – signed – 36½ x 48¾in.
(Christie's)   **$12,342 £6,600**

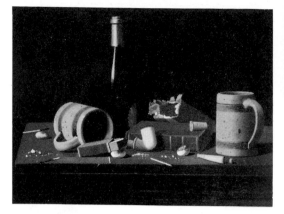

JOHN FREDERICK PETO – Still Life with Mugs, Bottle and Pipe – signed and dated – oil on canvas – 12¼ x 16¼in.
(Christie's)   **$176,000   £94,623**

ADOLPHE PHALIPON – An elegant lady in a blue hat – signed – on panel – 16½ x 10in.
(Christie's)   **$935   £550**

JOHN PHILLIP – The village gossips – on board – 6 x 8in.
(Christie's)   **$939   £528**

SIR JOHN PETTIE – 'Dost know this waterfly?' Hamlet, Prince of Denmark, Act V, Scene II – signed – 40 x 27in.
(Christie's)   **$7,832   £4,400**

SALLY PHILPSEN – Vesterbrogade, Copenhagen – signed – 24¼ x 28¼in.
(Christie's)   **$2,618   £1,540**

GLYN WARREN PHILPOT – Mediterranean coastline – watercolour, pen and ink – 14½ x 11¾in.
(Christie's) **$2,602 £1,540**

GLYN WARREN PHILPOT – Man and the Fates – signed with initials – oil on canvas – 85½ x 71¾in.
(Christie's) **$64,328 £37,400**

GLYN WARREN PHILPOT – Tree in blossom – signed with initials – watercolour – 16½ x 11¾in.
(Christie's) **$2,602 £1,540**

FRANCIS PICABIA – Petit Cabanon a Martiques, Etang de Berre – signed and dated – oil on canvas – 18 x 21¾in.
(Christie's) **$36,432 £19,800**

PABLO PICASSO – Hercule tue le Centaure Nessus, from Les Metamorphoses d'Ovide (G. 160 IIb; Bl. 116; Cf. Cramer 19) – etching – on parchment – from the set of 30 – 12 x 8½in.
(Christie's) **$4,400 £2,596**

PABLO PICASSO – Trois Femmes – signed –
pen and black ink and *sanguine* on paper –
14½ x 10½in.
(Christie's)   **$226,270 £121,000**

PABLO PICASSO – Pomme, Verre et Paquet de
Tabac – signed and dated – oil on canvas –
6¼ x 8½in.
(Christie's)   **$232,760 £126,500**

PABLO PICASSO – Vase de Fleurs – signed –
oil on canvas – 26 x 18¼in.
(Christie's)   **$1,504,800   £880,000**

PABLO PICASSO – Portrait – signed and dated –
coloured ink on paper – 13 x 10in.
(Christie's)   **$4,573   £2,420**

PABLO PICASSO – Deux femmes nues dans un
Arbre (G. 204; Bl. 234) – etching – a proof aside
from the signed edition of 100 – 38.1 x 30cm.
(Christie's)   **$4,950   £2,920**

WALDO PIERCE – Still Life with Wild Flowers –
unsigned – oil on canvas – 24¼ x 18¼in.
(Robt. W. Skinner Inc.)   **$1,300 £738**

ANTONIO PICCINI – Italian beauties – both
signed – on panel – 9¾ x 7¼in.
(Christie's)
Two   **$2,805**   **£1,650**

FREDERICK RICHARD PICKERSGILL – The
four seasons – signed with initials and dated – oil
on canvas – 31 x 36in.
(Christie's)   **$10,120 £5,500**

EVERT PIETERS– Mother's little helper -
signed - 24 x 19½in.
(Christie's)   **$13,090 £7,700**

JOHN PIPER – Le Martyre Finestere – signed and inscribed – gouache, watercolour, wax resist, bodycolour, brush and black ink – 13¾ x 20¼in.
(Christie's) **$3,982 £2,200**

ISIDORE PILS, Attributed to – Civil War soldiers with a new recruit – initialled – pencil, pen and brown ink and grey and red wash – 31.8x22.6cm.
(Christie's) **$799 £462**

CAMILLE PISSARRO – La Charette a Bois – watercolour, pen and brown ink on paper – 4¾ x 8in.
(Christie's) **$12,320 £7,040**

WILMOT PILSBURY – Farmyard scene – signed and dated – watercolour – 24 x 34.2cm.
(Woolley & Wallis) **$2,768** **£1,600**

FERNAND PINAL – Peupliers d'Italie – signed and dated – oil on canvas – 46.1 x 45.7cm.
(Christie's) **$3,534 £1,870**

CAMILLE PISSARRO – La Vache – charcoal and soft pencil on paper – 7¾ x 10½in.
(Christie's) **$4,573 £2,420**

CAMILLE PISSARRO – Paysage avec un Ane, Pontoise (L'Engrais) – oil on canvas – 18 x 21½in. *(Christie's)* **$639,540 £374,000**

LUCIEN PISSARRO – Portrait of Esther, bust length in profile – oil on canvas – 16 x 15in. *(Christie's)* **$87,604 £48,400**

LUDOVICO RODO PISSARRO – Bouquet de Fleurs – signed – oil on canvas – 55 x 46cm. *(Christie's)* **$2,695 £1,540**

PLAS

PIETER PLAS, Attributed to — Goats in a landscape — indistinct signature — oil on panel — 9½ x 8¾in.
(Christie's) **$594 £352**

OGDEN MINTON PLEISSNER — Afternoon in Summer. Chartres — signed — oil on canvas — 24 x 40in.
(Christie's) **$41,800 £22,473**

NICHOLAS POCOCK — Kingweston and the Bristol Channel — watercolour over etched outline — 9¾ x 14¼in.
(Lawrence Fine Arts) **$1,811 £990**

NICHOLAS POCOCK, Attributed to — The loss of the Lady Hobart Packet, Captain Fellowes, on an island of Ice, June 28th 1803 — watercolour — 15¾ x 18½in.
(Lawrence Fine Arts) **$799** **£462**

ARMAND POINT — La Sirene — signed with monogram and dated — oil on canvas — 36¼ x 28¾in.
(Christie's) **$245,960 £143,000**

SERGE POLIAKOFF — Composition Abstraite Rouge et Bleue - signed — on paper — 24.7 x 32.5cm.
(Christie's) **$12,298** **£7,150**

ALFRED POLLENTINE – The Grand Canal,
Venice – signed – 16 x 24¼in.
(Christie's) **$4,307 £2,420**

JACOPO DA PONTE, IL BASSANO, Follower of
– The adoration of the shepherds – on copper –
37.2 x 30.2cm.
(Christie's) **$2,474 £1,430**

ALFRED POLLENTINE – The Palace Pisani,
Venice – signed – 21½ x 30in.
(Christie's) **$3,027 £1,760**

ALFRED POLLENTINE – The Ducal Palace,
Venice – signed – 15¾ x 23¾in.
(Christie's) **$3,216 £1,870**

ARTHUR POND, Attributed to – Portrait of
Alexander Pope, seated three-quarter length –
oil on canvas – 37¾ x 29½in.
(Lawrence Fine Arts) **$4,757 £2,750**

ALEXANDER POPE – "Good dog!" – signed and dated – oil on canvas – 23 x 21in.
(Robt. W. Skinner Inc.) **$900 £511**

ABRAHAM POOLE – Portrait of Carlota Montery (Mrs Eugene O'Neill) – oil on canvas – 186.7 x 114.6cm.
(Christie's) **$4,620 £2,538**

ALEXANDER POPE – "On the Mend/No Hunting!" – signed – oil on canvas – 18 x 24¼in.
(Robt. W. Skinner Inc.) **$10,000 £5,681**

PAUL FALCONER POOLE – A restful moment – on panel – 12 x 10in.
(Christie's) **$979 £550**

LIUBOV POPOVA – Le Village – brush, black ink and grey wash on paper – 5 x 5in.
(Christie's) **$1,871 £990**

ETHEL C. PORTER — Fancy free — 21¼ x 16¼in.
(Christie's) **$7,440 £4,180**

EDWARD HENRY POTTHAST — By the Water —
signed — oil on canvas — 24 x 30in.
(Christie's) **$110,000 £59,139**

JAN FREDERIK PIETER PORTIELJE — The new
bonnet — signed — oil on panel — 9½ x 8in.
(Christie's) **$8,096 £4,400**

GERTRUDE POWYS — Hammersmith Terrace —
overlooking the Thames — signed with monogram —
oil on canvas — 47¼ x 35in.
(Anderson & Garland) **$3,780 £2,100**

SIR EDWARD JOHN POYNTER — Studies for an Israelite Slave in *Israel in Egypt* — on blue paper — 33 x 27 cms.
(Christie's)   **$1,870**   **£1,100**

CLAUDE PRATT — One for the Pot — signed — oil on canvas — 7¾ x 6¾in.
(Anderson & Garland)   **$7,866 £4,600**

SIR EDWARD JOHN POYNTER — Cave of the storm nymphs — signed with monogram and dated — 58¼ x 44¼in.
(Christie's)   **$809,600 £440,000**

CLAUDE PRATT — A boy peeling a turnip in a stable doorway — signed and dated — 18 x 14in.
(Woolley & Wallis)   **$1,245**   **£720**

MAURICE BRAZIL PRENDERGAST – The Balloon – signed – oil on wood panel – 12¼ x 14in.
(Christie's)   **$154,000 £82,795**

LEVI WELLS PRENTICE – Apples in a Hat – signed – oil on canvas – 12 x 18in.
(Christie's)   **$22,000   £11,827**

PREZIOSI

AMADEO, COUNT PREZIOSI — Turks at the
temple of sweet waters, Constantinople — signed
— pencil and watercolour heightened with white
— 144 x 216mm.
(Christie's)   **$5,667 £3,080**

BERNARD PRIESTMAN — River Landscape —
signed and dated — oil on canvas — 9 x 13in.
(Christie's)   **$1,468 £825**

PIERRE PRINS — Nature morte au Pichet et au
Fruits — signed — oil on canvas — 38 x 55cm.
(Christie's)   **$6,160 £3,520**

EDWARD PRITCHARD — Figures in a street by
Roman ruins, Verona — on board — 9¾ x 7¾in.
(Christie's)   **$1,370 £770**

GIULIO CESARE PROCACCINI, Manner of —
The Madonna and child — on panel — 28¾ x 21¾in.
(Christie's)   **$913 £528**

MARGARET FISHER PROUT – Still life with
roses and peaches – signed – oil on canvas –
21½ x 17½in.
(Christie's)   **$7,048   £3,960**

PATRICK PROCKTOR – Twin-portrait of Jane
Kasmin – signed, inscribed and dated – water-
colour – 19¾ x 13¾in.
(Christie's)   **$483   £286**

JOHN SKINNER PROUT – Fort MacQuarie and
Government House from Mrs MacQuarie's Chair
– signed – pencil and watercolour heightened with
white – 6¼ x 10¼in.
(Christie's)   **$5,090 £2,860**

MARGARET FISHER PROUT – A valley in
Sussex – signed – oil on board – 20 x 24in.
(Christie's)   **$14,685   £8,250**

MARGARET FISHER PROUT – An artist at
her easel – signed and dated – oil on board –
23½ x 19½in.
(Christie's)   **$2,545   £1,430**

SAMUEL PROUT — Wells Cathedral — watercolour over pencil — 17 x 20in.
(Phillips) **$1,605** **£950**

HARALD PRYN — A snow-covered road — signed and inscribed — 70.8 x 101cm.
(Christie's) **$2,057** **£1,210**

FERNAND DU PUIGAUDEAU — Le Hezo dans le Golfe de Morbihan — signed — oil on canvas — 20 x 24¼in.
(Christie's) **$32,725 £18,700**

SAMUEL GILLESPIE PROUT — Figures in the interior of the church of the Holy Sepulchre at Eu — signed and inscribed — pencil, pen and brown and grey ink and watercolour heightened with white — 49.5 x 11.1cm.
(Christie's) **$799** **£462**

ALBERT J. PURDY — Toy sail boat — signed and dated — oil on canvas — 42 x 31¾in.
(Christie's) **$6,380 £3,505**

JEAN PUY – Maisons au Toit rouge – signed –
oil on canvas – 19 x 21¾in.
(Christie's) **$11,550 £6,600**

JAMES BAKER PYNE – Shipping on an Italian
mountain lake – signed – oil on metal panel –
(W. H. Lane & Son) **$777 £460**

JEAN PUY – La Plage a Belle Ile – signed –
oil on canvas – 28¾ x 41¾in.
(Christie's) **$34,056** **£19,800**

ALPHONSE QUIZET – Maisons a Rounaville –
signed – oil on canvas – 65.2 x 59.5cm.
(Christie's) **$10,587 £6,050**

ROBIN RAE — Lovers by a moonlit ruin — signed
and dated — 30 x 25in.
(Christie's) $1,487   £880

F. RAINBERGER — Polite conversation — signed
— on panel — 19¼ x 15½in.
(Christie's) $4,114 £2,200

HENRY MACBETH-RAEBURN (After FRANCIS
WHEATLEY) — Portrait of Arthur Phillip,
Commander of the First Fleet and First Governor
of New South Wales — signed and inscribed —
24 x 16¾in.
(Christie's) $548   £308

RAPHAEL, After — The Madonna and child —
on panel — 18½ x 14½in.
(Christie's) $2,093 £1,210

JAN ANTHONISZ VAN RAVESTEYN, Manner of
— Portrait of a lady, bust length, in a gold
embroidered black dress and high ruff collar —
18 x 13¾in.
(Christie's)   **$3,045**   **£1,760**

MAN RAY — La Decoration des Corps Rationnels
— signed and dated — oil on canvas — 15 x 21¾in.
(Christie's)   **$56,672** **£30,800**

RICHARD REDGRAVE, Follower of — An artist at
work in a cornfield — 24 x 35¾in.
(Christie's)   **$1,892**   **£1,100**

ARTHUR WILLIAM REDGATE — The Silver
Birch — signed — oil on canvas — signed —
29½ x 10½in.
(Christie's)   **$1,046**   **£605**

ODILON REDON — Fleurs de Champs dans un
Vase a long Col — signed — oil on canvas —
25½ x 19¾in.
(Christie's)   **$847,305**   **£495,500**

ANNE REDPATH — Storm at Cambrils — signed
— oil on panel — 19½ x 23¾in.
(Christie's)   **$22,896**   **£12,650**

STANLEY REED – Peonies – arranged in an oriental pot – signed – oil on board – 49 x 58 cm.
(Henry Spencer)   **$676**   **£400**

JOHANNES REEKERS Jnr – Grapes, a lemon, a
fig and other fruit on a ledge – signed and dated –
on panel – 15 x 12½ in.
(Christie's)   **$8,415**   **£4,950**

VITTORIO REGGIANINI – The Three Graces –
signed – 39½ x 27 in.
(Christie's)   **$50,000**   **£28,600**

LEA REINHART – Spring blooms – signed – on panel – 15½ x 12¼in.
(Christie's) **$2,044 £1,210**

JOHN ROBERTSON REID – Gathering firewood – signed and dated – oil on canvas – 63 x 50cm.
(Phillips) **$6,699 £3,850**

ROBERT REID – Silvie – signed – oil on board – 30.2 x 40.6cm.
(Christie's) **$15,400 £8,279**

REMBRANDT

GUIDO RENI, Studio of – Suzanna and the Elders – oil on canvas – 116 x 147.5cm.
(Phillips) **$6,160 £3,500**

REMBRANDT, After – An elderly lady with weighing scales – 43 x 37in.
(Christie's) **$913 £528**

GUIDO RENI, Circle of – Charity – oil on canvas laid down on board – 73.5 x 77cm.
(Phillips) **$2,640 £1,500**

GUIDO RENI, Follower of – The Magdalen – oil on copper – 64.5 x 45.5cm.
(Phillips) **$490 £280**

GUIDO RENI, Follower of – Fortuna – oil on canvas – 61¼ x 52½in.
(Phillips) **$3,401 £1,900**

A. RENOIR – Up to mischief – signed – oil on canvas – 22 x 15in.
(Christie's)   **$1,301   £770**

PIERRE-AUGUSTE RENOIR – Le jeune Garcon au Chat – signed – oil on canvas – 48¾ x 26¼in.
(Christie's)   **$2,257,200   £1,320,000**

PIERRE AUGUSTE RENOIR – Marguerites – signed – oil on canvas – 23 x 23cm.
(Christie's)   **$151,800 £82,500**

PIERRE AUGUSTE RENOIR – Promenade sur un Chemin de Campagne – oil on canvas – 27.5 x 40.5cm.
(Christie's)   **$182,160 £99,000**

PIERRE AUGUSTE RENOIR – Portrait de Coco
– signed with monogram – oil on canvas –
3¾ x 3in.
(Christie's) $68,112 £39,600

PIERRE AUGUSTE RENOIR – Tete de Femme
– signed with monogram – oil on canvas –
4½ x 3in.
(Christie's) $132,440 £77,000

PIERRE AUGUSTE RENOIR – Femme en
Blouse de Tulle appuyee sur le Coude gauche
– oil on canvas – 29.5 x 28 cm.
(Christie's) $283,800 £165,000

PIERRE-AUGUSTE RENOIR – Jeunes Arbres
dans la Foret – oil on canvas – 28¾ x 23½in:
(Christie's) $282,150 £165,000

PIERRE-AUGUSTE RENOIR — Peches et Raisins
— oil on canvas — 27 x 46cm.
(Christie's)   **$282,150**   **£165,000**

ERNEST RENOUX — Paris 1912, Porte Maillot —
signed — oil on canvas — 38.1 x 46.1cm.
(Christie's)   **$2,502   £1,430**

ERNEST RENOUX — Paysage dans le Cantal,
Region de St Chamont — signed — oil on panel —
32.7 x 41cm.
(Christie's)   **$1,143 £605**

ERNEST RENOUX — Un Coin de l'Atelier de
l'Artiste — signed — oil on canvas — 28¾ x 21¼in.
(Christie's)   **$3,080   £1,760**

ERNEST RENOUX — Nature morte aux Poissons
— signed — oil on canvas — 27 x 40.6cm.
(Christie's)   **$727   £385**

MARINUS VAN REYMERSWAEL, Manner of —
Saint Jerome — inscribed — on panel — 73.8x105cm.
(Christie's)   **$5,328 £3,080**

425

SEBASTIANO RICCI, Follower of – Cupid –
24½ x 29½in.
(Christie's) **$2,474 £1,430**

PIO RICCI – A helping hand – signed – 19 x 14¼in.
(Christie's) **$4,675** **£2,750**

ANNE ESTELLE RICE – Beach huts, Brittany
– oil on canvas – 46 x 56cm.
(Phillips) **$8,038 £4,620**

SEBASTIANO RICCI – The Assumption of the
Magdalen – oil on canvas – 30¼ x 24¾in.
(Phillips) **$7,920 £4,500**

HENRY WEBSTER RICE – Spring blossoms –
signed – watercolour on paper – 9½ x 13½in.
(Bruce D. Collins) **$55** **£29**

HENRY WEBSTER RICE – Mount Chocorua Peak
– signed – watercolour on paper – 15 x 20½in.
(Bruce D. Collins) **$385** **£203**

GEORGE MATHER RICHARDS – Rocky Shore/
Newport – signed and dated – oil on canvas –
18 x 28in.
(Robt. W. Skinner Inc.) **$500** **£295**

THOMAS MILES RICHARDSON JR – Lake
Maggiori – signed and dated – 11¾ x 19¼in.
(Anderson & Garland) **$4,844 £2,800**

THOMAS MILES RICHARDSON – Borrowdale –
signed and dated – 19 x 26in.
(Anderson & Garland) **$7,020** **£3,900**

CHARLES HENRY RICHERT – Cadillac Mountain,
Mt. Desert Island – signed – watercolour on paper
– 10 x 14in.
(Bruce D. Collins) **$358** **£189**

CHARLES HENRY RICHERT – Mt Desert Island
– signed – watercolour on paper – 14 x 18½in.
(Bruce D. Collins) **$330** **£174**

RICHMOND

LEONARD RICHMOND − West Country harbour with boats upon the hard before a town − signed − oil on board − 19 x 23in.
(W. H. Lane & Son) **$2,287 £1,250**

HERBERT DAVIS RICHTER − Barn interior, Berkshire − signed − oil on canvas − 25 x 30in.
(Christie's) **$2,937 £1,650**

LOUIS RICQUIER − Van Dyck in Frans Hals' Studio − signed − on panel − 21½ x 18¼in.
(Christie's) **$2,468 £1,320**

EDOUARD FREDERIC WILHELM RICHTER − In the conservatory − signed and dated − 32 x 23½in.
(Christie's) **$21,175** **£12,100**

GERHARD RICHTER − Stadtbild − signed, inscribed and dated − oil on canvas − 53 x 43cm.
(Christie's) **$31,790 £17,000**

LEON RIKET − Nature morte aux Fraises − signed − oil on canvas − 28.3 x 39.9cm.
(Christie's) **$2,494 £1,320**

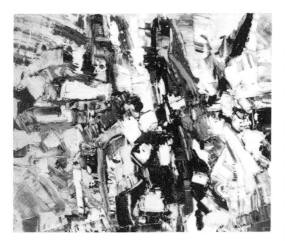

JEAN-PAUL RIOPELLE – Untitled – signed – oil on canvas – 13 x 16¼in.
(Christie's) **$20,812 £12,100**

AIDEN LASSELL RIPLEY – Ducks at Hyde Park – unsigned, stamped on verso – watercolour on paper – 11¼ x 14½in.
(Robt. W. Skinner Inc.) **$550** **£325**

HENRY PARSONS RIVIERE – The Arch of Titus, Rome – signed – pencil and watercolour – 7½ x 5¼in.
(Christie's) **$494** **£286**

JOHN RITCHIE – The old showman – signed – oil on canvas – 24.5 x 18cm.
(Phillips) **$4,976 £2,860**

EDWIN ROBERTS – "Helping mother", interior scene with a young girl peeling apples, a young boy with a mischievous smile – signed – oil on canvas – 24 x 20in.
(Morphets) **$9,774 £5,400**

ROBERTS

EDWIN THOMAS ROBERTS — A good fortune — signed — 35.9 x 30.5cm.
(Christie's) **$2,447 £1,375**

WILLIAM ROBERTS — The see-saw — signed and dated — oil on canvas — 25 x 30in.
(Christie's) **$9,955 £5,500**

WILLIAM ROBERTS — Gateway to the Western Isles — fishermen seated on a quayside — signed — watercolour over ink — 25 x 35.5cm.
(Henry Spencer) **$9,126 £5,400**

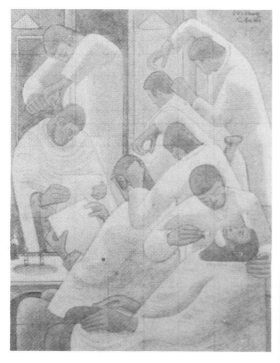

WILLIAM ROBERTS — The barber's shop — signed — watercolour and pencil on squared paper — 15.5 x 12.7cm.
(Christie's) **$5,948 £3,520**

DAVID THOMAS ROBERTSON — The Potato Pickers — signed — oil on canvas — 24¼ x 29in.
(Anderson & Garland) **$2,160 £1,200**

ANDRE FELIX ROBERTY – Le Port de St Tropez – signed – oil on canvas – 66 x 81cm.
(Christie's) **$9,355 £4,950**

MARGARET FORBES ROBINSON – The red shawl – signed with initials – on panel – 12 x 8¾in.
(Christie's) **$1,673 £990**

FLORENCE VINCENT ROBINSON – Wandering Thoughts – signed – watercolour with pencil on paper – 17¾ x 12¾in.
(Robt. W. Skinner Inc.) **$250 £147**

ROBINSON

THEODORE ROBINSON – On the Seine –
signed – pencil and watercolour heightened with
white – 12¾ x 8¼in.
(Christie's)   **$43,076**   **£24,200**

NORMAN ROCKWELL – And Every Lad May
Be Aladdin (Crackers in Bed) – signed – oil on
canvas – 49 x 28in.
(Christie's)   **$242,000**   **£130,107**

VERA ROCKLINE – A Femme decolletee – signed
– oil on canvas – 32 x 25½in.
(Christie's)   **$9,979**   **£5,280**

AUGUSTE RODIN – L'Amour – signed and
inscribed – watercolour and pencil on paper –
45 x 36.5cm.
(Christie's)   **$10,587 £6,050**

FRED ROE — Rue de l'Epicerie, Rouen — signed and inscribed — watercolour heightened with white — 13½ x 9¾in.
(Christie's) **$494** **£286**

AUGUSTE RODIN, Attributed to — Full length portrait of a nude woman, standing — Bears monogram — 18.5 x 10cm.
(Henry Spencer) **$422** **£250**

L. ROELMAN — A Venetian backwater — signed — oil on canvas — 24½ x 35½in.
(Christie's) **$1,673** **£990**

CLARENCE ROE, Attributed to — A mountainous landscape, Westmorland — indistinctly signed — 30 x 50in.
(Christie's) **$1,370 £770**

SEVERIN ROESEN — Flowers and Nest — signed — oil on panel — 27 x 38.1cm.
(Christie's) **$38,500** **£20,698**

CHRISTIAN ROHLFS — Rote Lilien — watercolour on japon nacre paper — 49.9 x 37.8cm.
(Christie's) **$16,456 £8,800**

GEORGE ROMNEY, Follower of — A portrait group of two sisters, one standing full length, the other kneeling, wearing red dresses, one playing a baby viola, the other holding a puppy, in a landscape — 56 x 44in.
(Christie's) **$5,297 £3,080**

SALOMAN ROMBOUTS, Circle of — Peasants resting at the roadside before a barn — oil on panel — 47.5 x 42cm.
(Phillips) **$2,112 £1,200**

PHILIPP PETER ROOS (called ROSA DA TIVOLI), Follower of — A shepherdess in an Italianate landscape — 22¾ x 19½in.
(Christie's) **$1,618 £935**

SALVATOR ROSA, Follower of — A knight directed on his way — 46 x 37.2cm.
(Christie's) **$1,332 £770**

GIULIO ROSATI — The backgammon players — signed — pencil and watercolour — 20¼ x 14in.
(Christie's) **$10,010** **£5,720**

HARRY HERMAN ROSELAND — Budding Scholar — signed — oil on canvas — 18¼ x 26in.
(Christie's) **$35,200** **£18,924**

ROSENSTAND

ALEXANDER M. ROSSI — Beachcombing — signed
— on panel — 19½ x 17¼in.
(Christie's)   **$3,216**   **£1,870**

EMIL ROSENSTAND — The carnival — signed and
dated — watercolour — 21 x 16¼in.
(Christie's)   **$1,347**   **£770**

FREDERICO ROSSANO — A wooded landscape
with drovers and cattle — signed — 50.8 x 30.2cm.
(Christie's)   **$5,610**   **£3,300**

ANTONIO ROTTA — At the cobblers — signed and
dated — 21 x 15¾in.
(Christie's)   **$23,100**   **£13,200**

GEORGES ROUAULT – Danseuse et Pierrot –
signed – gouache on paper – 16 x 11¾in.
(Christie's) **$51,425 £27,500**

GEORGES ROUAULT – Deux Pierrots – signed –
oil on canvas – 47.3 x 28.5cm.
(Christie's) **$601,920 £352,000**

GEORGES ROUAULT – La Sainte Face –
signed – oil on paper laid on canvas – 28¾x21½in.
(Christie's) **$323,840 £176,000**

PHILIPPE ROUSSEAU – The sculptor's studio –
signed – oil on panel – 23½ x 40¾in.
(Christie's) **$1,301 £770**

JOSEPH VICTOR ROUX-CHAMPION – Paysage en Automne avec Personnages pres d'un Ruisseau – signed – oil on canvas – 18 x 21¾in.
(Christie's)   **$37,840**   **£22,000**

PHILIPPE ROUSSEAU, Attributed to – Roman lovers – signed – oil on canvas – 17¼ x 12½in.
(Christie's)   **$483**   **£286**

CHARLES ROWBOTHAM – Lake Lugano and Monte Salvatore – signed and dated – pencil and watercolour heightened with bodycolour – 17 x 27cm.
(Christie's)   **$1,608**   **£935**

CLAUDE H. ROWBOTHAM – Woman and child on a wood path overlooking Falmouth Estuary with a distant view of shipping – signed and dated – watercolour – 12 x 19in.
(W. H. Lane & Son)   **$915 £500**

THEODORE ROUSSEL – The golden scarf – oil on canvas – 24¼ x 18¼in.
(Christie's)   **$5,948 £3,520**

THOMAS LEESON ROWBOTHAM – Mediterranean coastal scene – signed and dated – watercolour – 18.5 x 46.2cm.
(Woolley & Wallis) **$1,176** **£680**

THOMAS ROWLANDSON Monkey Tricks – inscribed — watercolour – 11 x 6½in.
(Phillips) **$2,093** **£1,210**

EDWARD ARTHUR ROWE – An Italian balcony overlooking the sea – signed – 11½ x 9in.
(Michael J. Bowman) **$2,632 £1,400**

THOMAS ROWLANDSON – A Boxing Match – signed – watercolour – 7¼ x 10½in.
(Lawrence Fine Arts) **$4,947** **£2,860**

THOMAS ROWLANDSON – A brace of blackguards, traditionally the artist and George Morland – signed and dated – pencil, pen and brown ink and watercolour on Whatman paper – 10 x 8¾in.
(Christie's) **$15,895 £9,350**

ROYBET

FERDINAND ROYBET, Follower of — The Gay Cavalier — 34½ x 27in.
(Christie's)   **$1,645 £880**

FERDINAND ROYBET, Attributed to — Portrait of a girl with long brown hair, seated on a ledge — indistinctly signed — oil on canvas — 49.5 x 37.5cm.
(Henry Spencer)   **$2,854   £1,650**

HERBERT ROYLE — The Farmyard — oil on canvas — 15¾ x 24in.
(Christie's)   **$2,349   £1,320**

STANLEY ROYLE — Farmyard under the snow — signed — oil on canvas — 20 x 24in.
(Christie's)   **$8,811   £4,950**

SIR PETER PAUL RUBENS, After — Daniel in the Lions' Den — on panel — 19½ x 25¼in.
(Christie's)   **$1,237 £715**

SIR PETER PAUL RUBENS, Manner of — A baby girl handing a boy a laurel crown — 30 x 25½in.
(Christie's) $1,180 £682

SIR PETER PAUL RUBENS, Follower of — The Madonna and child — on copper — 8½ x 6½in.
(Christie's) **$1,294 £748**

ISAAC VAN RUISDAEL — A view of Egmond — signed and dated — 40 x 55in.
(Phillips) **$19,360 £11,000**

SIR PETER PAUL RUBENS, After — Nature adorned by the Three Graces — 33 x 26¾in.
(Christie's) **$1,808 £1,045**

JALMAR RUOKOKSKI — Portrait of Alma Lonnberg — signed and dated — 53 x 38cm.
(Christie's) **$10,175** **£5,500**

RUMMELHOFF

CHR. RUMMELHOFF – A moonlit fjord – signed
– oil on canvas – 9½ x 16½in.
(Christie's)   **$1,078 £638**

SIR HENRY RUSHBURY – Palazzo Barberini,
Rome – signed – watercolour, pen and black ink –
12 x 15in.
(Christie's)   **$1,331   £748**

ROBERT RUSS – The nut harvest at Grenoble
– signed and dated – oil on canvas – 23 x 31in.
(Christie's)   **$26,312 £14,300**

SIR WALTER WESTLEY RUSSELL – Firelight –
indistinctly signed – oil on canvas – 30 x 40in.
(Christie's)   **$11,748   £6,600**

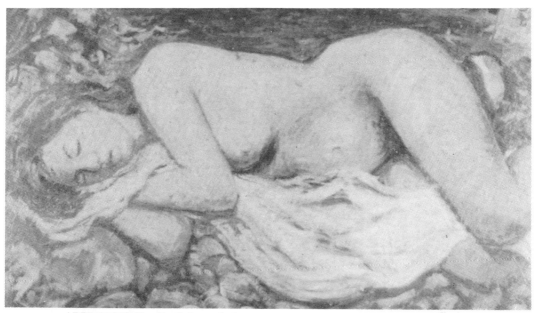

ADRIAN RYAN − Reclining nude female on a beach − oil on canvas − 28 x 36in.
(W. H. Lane & Son)   **$3,870 £2,250**

ZACCHARAI RYBAK −− Sodom and Gomorrah − signed − oil on canvas − 45¾ x 35½in.
(Christie's)   **$36,432 £19,800**

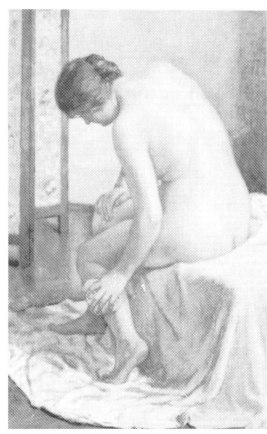

THEO VAN RYSSELBERGHE — Le Champ de Courses a Boulogne-sur-Mer — signed with monogram and dated — oil on canvas — 76 x 88cm.
(Christie's) **$470,250** **£275,000**

THEO VAN RYSSELBERGHE — Baigneuse — oil on canvas — 50 x 37in.
(Christie's) **$37,840** **£22,000**

THEO VAN RYSSELBERGHE — Paysage du Midi — inscribed on reverse — oil on panel — 7½ x 9½in.
(Christie's) **$48,576 £26,400**

CESARE SACCAGGI — Best of friends — signed and dated — 58½ x 38in.
(Christie's) **$6,160** **£3,520**

ROBERT SALMON – Boston Harbor – signed and
dated – oil on panel – 9½ x 13½in.
(Christie's)   **$88,000**   **£47,311**

JOHN FALCONAR SALTER – Poultry in a farmyard – signed – oil on board – 9½ x 13½in.
(Anderson & Garland)   **$1,245 £720**

PAUL SAMPLE – Snow covered village – signed –
oil on canvas – 30 x 36in.
(Christie's)   **$5,280 £2,901**

PAUL SAMPLE – Iceland fisherman – signed –
oil on canvas – 20 x 40in.
(Christie's)   **$2,640 £1,450**

**GIOVANNI BATTISTA SALVI, called IL SASSO-
FERRATO, Studio of** – The Madonna – oil on
canvas – 19¼ x 15¼in.
(Phillips)   **$1,672 £950**

CHRISTOPHER SANDERS – House near
Montilimar – signed – oil on canvas – 20 x 24in.
(Christie's)   **$3,916 £2,200**

SANDYS

ANTHONY FREDERICK AUGUSTUS SANDYS –
Marguerite Ince, aetat 6 – signed with mono-
gram and inscribed – chalks – 13½ x 11¼in.
(Phillips)   **$1,183**   **£700**

RUBENS SANTORO – Canale dei Greci, Venice –
signed – 20 x 14¾in.
(Christie's)   **$32,725**   **£18,700**

MISS EMMA SANDYS – Head and shoulders of a
young lady – signed in monogram – coloured
chalk on tinted paper – 19½ x 15in.
(Fellows & Sons)   **$2,028**   **£1,200**

DIRK SANTVOORT, Circle of – Portrait of a
lady, seated, half length, holding a book – inscribed
and dated – oil on panel – 30 x 24in.
(Phillips)   **$1,232**   **£700**

JOHN SARGEANT — The stolen kiss — signed and
dated — 12 x 13½in.
(Christie's) **$570 £330**

JOHN NOTT SARTORIUS, Circle of — Setting out
for the hunt — oil on canvas — 17¾ x 21in.
(Hy. Duke & Son) **$2,112 £1,200**

GIOVANNI BATISTA SALVI, IL SASSOFERRATO
Manner of — Madonna and child — 29 x 24in.
(Christie's) **$1,713 £990**

GIOVANNI BATTISTA' IL SASSOFERRATO,
After — The Madonna — 16 x 13in.
(Christie's) **$723 £418**

LEONARD SAURFELT — The Porte St Denis,
Paris; and A street scene — both signed — oil on
canvas — 16 x 13in.
(Christie's) **Two** **$1,673 £990**

SCARBOROUGH

FREDERICK WILLIAM SCARBOROUGH –
Sunset – Port of London – signed and inscribed
– 13¼ x 9¼in.
(Anderson & Garland) **$1,496 £800**

ANDREAS SCHELFHOUT, Attributed to – Winter genre scene – signed – oil on cradled panel – 53.3 x 67cm.
(Robt. W. Skinner Inc.) **$4,000 £2,272**

HELENE SCHJERFBECK – Plums in an upturned
pail – signed with initials – watercolour heightened
with white – 10¾ x 14½in.
(Christie's) **$54,760** **£29,600**

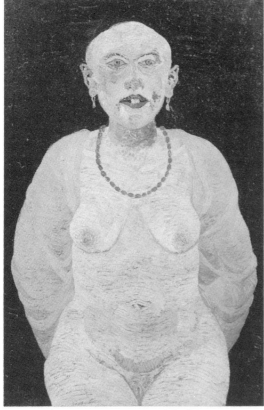

JOSEPH SCHARL – Die Misshandelte Dirne
– signed and dated – oil on canvas – 35¼ x 22½in.
(Christie's) **$16,192 £8,800**

ADRIAAN SCHILL – Reading the Evening Newspaper, a bottle and glass of wine on the table –
signed – oil on panel – 14 x 10½in.
(Geering & Colyer) **$946** **£550**

CARL SCHLEICHTER – The cigar smoker; and The pipe smoker – signed – oil on panel – 4¼ x 3¼in.
(Christie's)   **Two**   **$1,152**   **£682**

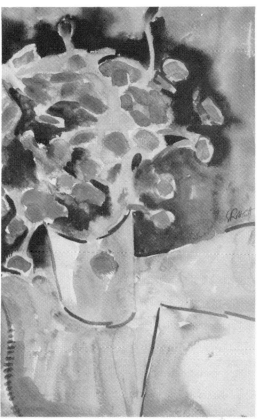

KARL SCHMIDT-ROTTLUFF – Stilleben mit blauen Blumen – signed – watercolour on paper – 26¾ x 19in.
(Christie's)   **$49,368**   **£26,400**

HERBERT GUSTAVE SCHMALZ – A fair beauty – signed and dated – 24 x 20in.
(Christie's)   **$16,055**   **£9,020**

MATHIEU SCHOEVAERTS, Circle of – Figures meeting before a village in a river landscape – oil on panel – 9½ x 14½in.
(Phillips)   **$10,912**   **£6,200**

SCHJERFBECK

HELENE SCHJERFBECK – Self-portrait of the artist – inscribed on the reverse – on paper – 30 x 25 cm.
(Christie's)   **$366,300**   **£198,000**

CLAUDE EMILE SCHUFFENECKER – Saules au Bord d'une Riviere – dedicated, signed and dated – pastel on paper – 17½ x 12¼in.
(Christie's)   **$6,545**   **£3,740**

GUSTAVE SCHRODTER – A reclining nude – signed – oil on canvas – 43¾ x 58¼in.
(Christie's)
$20,240 £11,000

CLAUDE EMILE SCHUFFNECKER – Paris, la Seine, Ile St Louis – signed – oil on canvas – 27.5 x 41cm.
(Christie's)   **$18,287 £10,450**

BERNARD SCHULTZE – Hommage a Ossian – signed and dated – oil on masonite – 46¼ x 40¾in.
(Christie's)   **$47,300 £27,500**

KURT SCHWITTERS – Linea 54 – signed and dated – 13.3 x 10.5cm.
(Christie's)   **$26,488**   **£15,400**

KURT SCHWITTERS – Portrait of Beatrice Bradley – signed and dated – oil on board – 25¾ x 20¾in.
(Christie's)   **$6,160**   **£3,520**

GEORGE SCOTT – George V in Procession – signed and dated – oil on canvas – 34 x 28½in.
(Christie's)   **$6,265**   **£3,520**

SEAGO

EDWARD SEAGO – Piazza Di Duomo, Como –
signed with initials and dated – oil on panel –
8½ x 10½in.
(Christie's) **$8,811 £4,950**

EDWARD SEAGO – Early morning on the Thames
Battersea – signed – oil on canvas – 50 x 75cm.
(Phillips) **$38,280 £22,000**

EDWARD SEAGO – Cloud Shadow, Norfolk –
signed – oil on board – 20 x 30in.
(Christie's) **$29,370 £16,500**

EDWARD SEAGO – Chinese junk in a Hong Kong
Bay – signed – watercolour – 14.2 x 20.2cm.
(Woolley & Wallis) **$1,816** **£1,050**

EDWARD SEAGO – Torremolinos, Spain –
signed – oil on board – 20 x 26in.
(Christie's) **$10,769 £6,050**

RONALD SEARLE – Kiki de Montparnasse –
signed and inscribed – ink on paper – 9 x 10in.
(Robt. W. Skinner Inc.) **$100 £56**

ARTHUR SEGAL – Stilleben mit Blickpunkt
Apfel – signed – oil on board – 60 x 79.5cm.
(Christie's) **$6,160 £3,520**

GERARD SEGHERS, Circle of – The release of
Saint Peter at the hands of the angel – 118.4x95.2cm.
(Christie's) **$2,854 £1,650**

DANIEL SEITER, Follower of – Alexander and
his physician Philip – 36 x 46¼in.
(Christie's) **$2,664 £1,540**

EISMAN SEMENOWSKY – A festival of flowers –
signed – on panel – 17½ x 7in.
(Christie's) **$5,348 £2,860**

SEMENOWSKY

JAMES CLARK SENIOR – A chestnut hunter in a landscape – signed – oil on board – 18¾ x 22¾in. *(Hy. Duke & Son)* **$1,496 £850**

WILLIAM SHAYER SENIOR – Horses and boats on the South Coast – signed – oil on canvas – 17½ x 23½in. *(Anderson & Garland)* **$8,823 £5,100**

EISMAN SEMENOWSKY – The murmur of the sea – signed and dated – on panel – 34 x 11in. *(Christie's)* **$6,660 £3,850**

DOMINIC SERRES – Study of the Inspection of the Fleet at Portsmouth by King George III, June 22, 1773 – one of a set of four – inscribed – pencil, pen and grey ink and watercolour – *(Christie's)* **$5,984 £3,520**

GEORGE SHALDERS – Countryfolk conversing in a farmyard – signed – 12 x 18in.
(Christie's) **$1,762 £990**

GEORGE L. SEYMOUR – Portrait of a young woman – signed – oil on panel – 40.6 x 25.1cm.
(Robt. W. Skinner Inc.) **$2,100 £1,193**

CHARLES HASLEWOOD SHANNON – The Mermaid – oil on canvas – 54 x 60cm.
(Christie's) **$30,272 £17,600**

TOM SEYMOUR – Beneath summer skies – signed and inscribed – oil on canvas – 15½ x 23½in.
(Christie's) **$570 £330**

BEN SHAHN – Silent Music (or Musical Chairs) – signed, numbered and dated – serigraph on paper – 59.1 x 94.2cm.
(Robt. W. Skinner Inc.) **$1,000 £591**

DOROTHEA SHARP – Still Life of Flowers in a Vase – oil on board – 15¾ x 20in.
(Christie's) **$3,720 £2,090**

DOROTHEA SHARP – Gathering Flowers – signed – oil on canvas – 29 x 34¾in.
(Anderson & Garland) **$65,835 £38,500**

DOROTHEA SHARP – On the jetty – signed –
oil on canvas – 63 x 75cm.
(Phillips) **$38,280 £22,000**

DOROTHEA SHARP – The Washing Line –
signed – oil on canvas – 28¼ x 34in.
(Christie's) **$64,614 £36,300**

WILLIAM JOSEPH SHAYER — A farmer with
donkeys and goats in a wooded landscape —
12¼ x 14in.
(Christie's)   **$2,937 £1,650**

DOROTHEA SHARP — Still life of flowers —
oil on canvas.
(Morphets)   **$15,488 £8,800**

CHARLES SHEELER — Birdsnest — signed and
dated — oil on canvas — 24 x 30in.
(Christie's)   **$198,000   £106,451**

HENRY AND CHARLES SHAYER — The
ploughman's rest — 35.8 x 30.8cm.
(Christie's)   **$8,362   £4,620**

CHARLES SHEELER — Grey Barns — signed and
dated — tempera on board — 14 x 20½in.
(Christie's)   **$165,000   £88,709**

SHEERBOOM

DANIEL SHERRIN – A lock with a barge in a landscape – 20 x 30in.
(Christie's)   **$1,174**   **£660**

ANDREW SHEERBOOM – The centre of attention – signed and dated – 17¼ x 21in.
(Christie's)   **$3,524 £1,980**

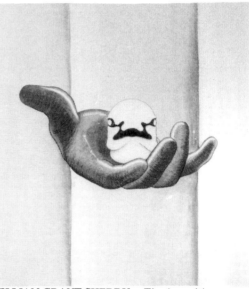

JOSHUA SHELDON – Sunday morning, New England – signed and dated – oil on canvas – 12 x 18in.
(Bruce D. Collins)   **$990**   **£523**

WILLIAM GRANT SHERRY – The Apparition – signed – watercolour on paper – 7½ x 7½in.
(Christie's)   **$330**   **£194**

ALPHONSE J. SHELTON – First snow – signed – oil on board – 12 x 16in.
(Bruce D. Collins)   **$385**   **£203**

KARL SHOU – An interior – signed with initials – 12½ x 15in.
(Christie's)   **$654**   **£385**

WALTER RICHARD SICKERT — The hand cart, or The Basket Shop, Rue St. Jacque, Dieppe — oil on canvas — 24 x 19¾in.
(Christie's) **$99,550 £55,000**

HENRI LE SIDANER — Le Pavillon aux Tournesols — signed — oil on canvas — 26 x 32 in.
(Christie's) **$255,420 £148,500**

HENRI LE SIDANER — Les Toits au Clair-de-Lune, Mouy — oil on canvas — 66.1 x 81.6cm.
(Christie's) **$33,264 £17,600**

PAUL SIGNAC — Barfleur, Voiliers a Quai — signed and dated — on paper — 28 x 44.5cm.
(Christie's) **$25,542 £14,850**

PAUL SIGNAC, Attributed to — Scene de Port, circa 1910 — signed — watercolour with pencil on paper — 9¾ x 13½in.
(Robt. W. Skinner Inc.) **$1000 £568**

HENRI LE SIDANER — Le Buste dans le Jardin au Crepuscule — signed — oil on canvas — 20 x 36½in.
(Christie's) **$131,560 £71,500**

SILVA

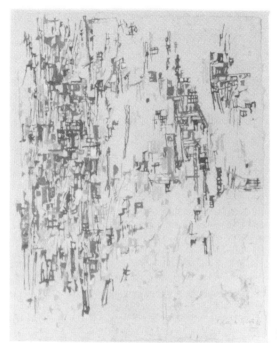

MARIA ELENA VIEIRA DA SILVA – Untitled – signed and dated – watercolour and black ink on paper – 18¼ x 14in.
(Christie's) **$47,300 £27,500**

HUGO SIMBERG – Meditation - signed and dated – pen and black ink and watercolour – 7½ x 6½in.
(Christie's) **$30,525 £16,500**

LUCIEN SIMON – Dans le Parc – signed – oil on board – 10 x 14¾in.
(Christie's) **$7,276 £3,850**

HUGO SIMBERG – Mystery – signed by the artist's wife – canvas laid down on board – 16 x 28¾in.
(Christie's) **$28,490 £15,400**

ATTILIO SIMONETTI – Wine for the weary – signed and dated – 28¼ x 19in.
(Christie's)   **$8,415**   **£4,950**

GUSTAVO SIMONI – A street scene, Biskra – signed – 35 x 23¾in.
(Christie's)   **$10,587**   **£6,050**

NIELS SIMONSEN – Figures fishing from a boat – signed and dated – 13 x 16in.
(Christie's)   **$2,035**   **£1,100**

ATTILIO SIMONETTI – The pet parrot – signed – on panel – 16½ x 12½in.
(Christie's)   **$5,610**   **£3,300**

CHARLES SIMPSON – Rocky Shore – signed – gouache on board – 15 x 21¾in.
(Christie's)   **$1,370**   **£770**

CHARLES WALTER SIMPSON – The Flooded Seine, Paris – signed, inscribed and dated – oil on canvas – 70 x 96in.
(Christie's)   **$9,790**   **£5,500**

CHARLES WALTER SIMPSON – Steer wrestling – signed – gouache – 25 x 37½in.
(W. H. Lane & Son)   **$4,300 £2,500**

CHARLES WALTER SIMPSON – A huntsman at full gallop pursued by others – gouache on board – signed – 25½ x 19½in.
(W. H. Lane & Son)   **$3,268 £1,900**

CHARLES SIMS – The beautiful is fled – signed – oil on panel – 15½ x 20in.
(Christie's)   **$3,916**   **£2,200**

CHARLES SIMS – Girl and a Frog – signed with
initials – watercolour – 16¾ x 11in.
(Christie's) **$5,482** **£3,080**

KNUD SINDING – A dining room – signed
with initials and dated – 17¾ x 22¼in.
(Christie's) **$24,420** **£13,200**

KNUD SINDING – An interior – signed –
17 x 22½in.
(Christie's) **$11,550** **£6,600**

KNUD SINDING – A woman in an interior – signed
and dated – 20½ x 23¾in.
(Christie's) **$2,057** **£1,210**

AXEL SJOBERG – Sommerdag; Sandhamm
(Summer day; Sandhamm) – signed and dated –
pencil and watercolour – 17¼ x 23¾in.
(Christie's) **$4,477** **£2,420**

SKEAPING

JOHN SKEAPING – Cowboys Steering Cattle –
signed and dated – watercolour and bodycolour
– 22¾ x 30¼in.
(Christie's)   **$1,468   £825**

CHRISTIAN SKREDSVIG – Februarabend – signed
and dated – 37 x 47¼in.
(Christie's)   **$16,687   £9,020**

CHARLES HENRY SLATER – Bird's nest and
primroses, and summer roses – signed – watercolour heightened with white – 14½in. x 10in.
(Christie's)   **$3,027   £1,760**

SIGURD SKOU – Gypsies at sea – signed – oil on
panel – 25 x 30in.
(Christie's)   **$3,300 £1,813**

JOHN FALCONAR SLATER – Upland Mist –
signed – oil on canvas – 40 x 50in.
(Anderson & Garland)   **$855 £500**

JOHN FALCONAR SLATER – An extensive view
of North Shields – signed – 21½ x 31¼in.
(Anderson & Garland) **$900** **£500**

JOHN FALCONAR SLATER – A day at the
seaside – signed – oil on board – 10¼ x 12in.
(Anderson & Garland) **$1,368 £800**

JOHN FALCONAR SLATER – A riverside cottage
and church – signed – oil on canvas – 16½ x 20½in.
(Anderson & Garland) **$1,038 £600**

JOHN FALCONAR SLATER – A horseman in the
snow – signed – gouache – 17½ x 23½in.
(Anderson & Garland) **$1,620** **£900**

JOHN FALCONAR SLATER – A garden in summer – signed – oil on board – 18 x 22¾in.
(Anderson & Garland) **$1,440** **£800**

JOHN FALCONAR SLATER – Cockerels and
hens – one of a pair – signed – oil on board –
8½ x 11½in.
(Anderson & Garland) **$2,805 £1,500**

JOHN FALCONAR SLATER – A winter farmyard
– signed – oil on board – 18½ x 14½in.
(Anderson & Garland) **$2,805 £1,500**

MAX SLEVOGT – Angriff der Kavallerie – signed
and dated – pen and brown ink on paper –
8 x 7¼in.
(Christie's) **$1,828 £1,045**

MAX SLEVOGT – Landschaft – signed – oil on
canvas laid down on board – 17¼ x 19¼in.
(Christie's) **$12,512 £7,150**

JOHN FALCONAR SLATER – Jesmond Dene,
Autumn – signed and dated – oil on canvas –
48¼ x 37½in.
(Anderson & Garland) **$2,070** **£1,150**

ERIC SLOANE – West Arlington, Vermont –
signed – oil on Masonite – 20 x 24in.
(Robt. W. Skinner Inc.) **$5,000** **£2,958**

LEON DE SMET − Paysage montagneux − signed − oil on canvas − 23½ x 29in.
(Christie's) **$16,192 £8,800**

GEORGE HENRY SMILLIE − Apple blossoms − signed − oil on canvas − 16 x 24in.
(Christie's) **$3,520 £1,934**

CARLTON ALFRED SMITH − Feeding poultry − signed − 11 x 6½in.
(Anderson & Garland) **$1,346 £720**

ALBERT DELMONT SMITH − Church by the sea (also called Little church on the beach) − signed − oil on canvas − 16 x 20in.
(Robt. W. Skinner Inc.) **$800 £454**

CARLTON ALFRED SMITH − Tending the garden − signed − watercolour − 35.6 x 51.4cm.
(Christie's) **$3,784 £2,200**

CARLTON ALFRED SMITH — The watched pot never boils — pencil and watercolour — 15¾ x 20½in *(Christie's)* $9,081 £5,280

JAMES BURRELL SMITH — A Lakeland view from a terrace — signed and dated — 10¼ x 13¾in. *(Anderson & Garland)* $795 £460

CARLTON ALFRED SMITH — A Girl playing a Mandolin — signed and dated — pencil and watercolour — 38.2 x 26.5cm. *(Christie's)* $11,220 £6,600

JAMES BURRELL SMITH — A View of the Lakes with figures in the foreground — signed and dated — 10¼ x 13¾in. *(Anderson & Garland)* $795 £460

FREDERICK W. SMITH – The Old Corner Bookstore – signed – oil on board – 23.2 x 30.8cm.
(Robt. W. Skinner Inc.) **$1,300** **£769**

SIR MATTHEW SMITH – Reclining girl – signed with initials – oil on canvas – 23¼ x 28¼in.
(Christie's) **$33,847 £18,700**

SIR MATTHEW SMITH – Still life with a statue – signed – watercolour – 19½ x 29in.
(Christie's) **$7,565 £4,180**

CARLTON ALFRED SMITH – Firelight Glow – signed – watercolour – 15½ x 20in.
(Phillips) **$8,112** **£4,800**

JOHN 'WARWICK' SMITH – Monks on a road near a ruined aqueduct in Italy – inscribed – pencil and watercolour – 30 x 36cm.
(Christie's) **$3,179 £1,870**

SPENCE SMITH – Old Mill, East Linton – signed – oil on board – 50 x 60cm.
(Phillips) **$2,296 £1,320**

SMITH

T. NOEL SMITH A Somerset Cottage – Two children and their mother beside garden – signed watercolour 26 x 35 cm.
(Henry Spencer) **$2,422** **£1,400**

THOMAS SMYTHE – The rustic's tryst – one of a pair – signed with initials – circular – 41 cm. diam.
(Christie's) **Two** **$6,853 £3,850**

KNUD CHRISTIAN SOEBORG – A man reading in an interior – signed and dated – 16 x 13in.
(Christie's) **$4,070** **£2,200**

ALICE RUGGLES SOHIER – The Rehearsal – signed and dated – oil on canvas – 63.5 x 76.5cm.
(Robt. W. Skinner Inc.) **$9,000** **£5,325**

FRANS SNYDERS, Studio of – A concert of birds – oil on canvas – 31¾ x 45½in.
(Phillips) **$11,635 £6,500**

WILL SOHL – Vase of flowers in a window overlooking a square of houses – signed and dated – oil on canvas – 39 x 31in.
(W. H. Lane & Son) **$2,535 £1,500**

HARALD SOHLBERG — Viksfjord (The boat)
— signed and dated — 17¾ x 22½in.
(Christie's) **$101,750** **£55,000**

HARALD SOHLBERG — Summer night on the Oslo
fjord — signed and dated — 34¾ x 44½in.
(Christie's) **$244,200** **£132,000**

ANDREA SOLDI — Justice and Peace — signed
and dated — oil on canvas — 36¼ x 29in.
(Phillips) **$2,685** **£1,500**

G. SOLLI – The harpsicord lesson – signed and
inscribed – pencil and watercolour – 7 x 9⅜in.
(Christie's) **$575 £308**

SIMEON SOLOMON – Head of a woman in
profile, as Sappho – signed and dated – on board
– 17¾ x 15in.
(Christie's) **$783 £440**

HENRI SOLLIER – Bretonnes apres la Messe –
signed – oil on canvas – 65 x 81cm.
(Christie's) **$3,465 £1,980**

ABRAHAM SOLOMON – The artist abroad –
signed and dated – 29½ x 24¾in.
(Christie's) **$11,352 £6,600**

SIMEON SOLOMON – Judith and her attendant
– signed with monogram and dated – 32¼ x 22¼in.
(Christie's) **$3,916 £2,200**

WILLIAM LOUIS SONNTAG – Scene Near Grafton,
West Virginia – signed and dated – oil on canvas –
30¼ x 50in.
(Christie's)   **$27,500**   **£14,784**

THOMAS JACQUES SOMERSCALES – The
Battle of Punta Gruesa, the 'Independencia'
abandoning ship with the 'Covadonga' beyond –
signed and dated – on canvas – 9¾ x 14½in.
(Christie's)   **$8,811 £4,950**

WILLIAM LOUIS SONNTAG – Finery In Peril –
signed – watercolour on paper laid down on board
– 35.5 x 53.1cm.
(Christie's)   **$13,200**   **£7,096**

K. R. H. SONDERBORG – 8.V.59, 17.39.–18.12h
– signed and dated – egg tempera on heavy paper
– 42½ x 27¾in.
(Christie's)   **$41,624 £24,200**

HENDRIK MARTIN SORGH, Attributed to – Two
peasants near a table in an interior – oil on panel –
21.5 x 17cm.
(Phillips)   **$262 £150**

JOSEPH EDWARD SOUTHALL − Ariadne in
Naxos − signed with monogram and dated − oil
on canvas − 15 x 20½in.
(Christie's) **$58,740 £33,000**

JOSEPH EDWARD SOUTHALL − Italian
lakeside village − signed with monogram and
dated − watercolour − 8 x 9½in.
(Christie's) **$7,048 £3,960**

JOSEPH EDWARD SOUTHALL − The Mystic
Burial − signed with monogram and dated −
watercolour and bodycolour − 10 x 7½in.
(Christie's) **$5,874 £3,300**

JOSEPH EDWARD SOUTHALL − Clee Hills,
Shropshire − signed with monogram and dated
− watercolour − 5¾ x 9¼in.
(Christie's) **$3,916 £2,200**

FRANCIS N. SOUZA – City with Red Sun –
signed and dated – oil on canvas –
35½ x 35¾in.
(Anderson & Garland) **$342** **£190**

GERARD VAN SPAENDONCK, Follower of –
A still life of flowers in a glass vase, a snail and a
butterfly on a ledge nearby – oil on canvas.
(Phillips) **$2,362 £1,350**

RAPHAEL SOYER – Street Scene with Moses
Soyer – signed – oil on canvas – 30 x 22in.
(Christie's) **$35,200** **£18,924**

SPANISH SCHOOL – A flower filled terrace beside
a villa – indistinctly signed and dated – pencil
and watercolour – 23¾ x 14¾in.
(Christie's) **$371 £220**

SPANISH SCHOOL

SPANISH SCHOOL – On the Seine; and Notre
Dame – both indistinctly signed – oil on board –
6 x 9in.
(Christie's)   Two   **$1,394 £825**

RUSKIN SPEAR – Portrait of Violet Stanley,
the Artist's Niece – signed – oil on panel –
15¾ x 20in.
(Christie's)   **$3,132   £1,760**

GABRIEL SPAT – The ballet rehearsal – signed
– oil on canvas board – 9¾ x 15½in.
(Christie's)   **$1,980 £1,087**

RUSKIN SPEAR – The Girl and a Plant – signed
– oil on canvas – 19¾ x 23¾in.
(Christie's)   **$9,790   £5,500**

CHARLES SPENCELAYH – A Tasty Morsel –
signed – oil on canvas – 23¼ x 17¼in.
(Anderson & Garland) **$30,600** **£17,000**

SIR STANLEY SPENCER – Amaryllis,
Chauntrey Court – oil on canvas – 30 x 20in.
(Christie's) **$83,622 £46,200**

JOHN C. SPENCER – Playful kittens – signed and
dated – oil on canvas – 14 x 22in.
(Robt. W. Skinner Inc.) **$1,900 £1,079**

R. B. SPENCER – Men-o-war in a heavy gale off a
coastline – signed and dated – 24 x 36in.
(Christie's) **$1,332 £770**

IGNACE SPIRIDON – The visitors – signed – on
panel – 16 x 12½in.
(Christie's) **$16,830** **£9,900**

SPIRO

EUGEN SPIRO – Portrait of the artist's sister –
signed and dated – 62 x 47½in.
(Christie's) **$17,204** **£10,120**

CARL SPITZWEG – Der Sonntagsjager – signed –
16 x 9in.
(Christie's) **$154,000** **£88,000**

L. S. SPITRIM – A portrait of the snow-rigged brig 'Thankful' of Blyth – signed and dated –
watercolour – 17½ x 24¼in.
(Anderson & Garland) **$936 £520**

FRIEDRICH STAHL – Adam and Eve – signed and inscribed – oil on canvas – 27¾ x 27¾in.
(Christie's) **$17,028 £9,900**

JACOB VAN SPREEUWEN, Circle of – A Philosopher sitting at a desk in an interior – oil on panel – 51 x 45cm.
(Phillips) **$880** **£500**

ELOISE HARRIET STANNARD – A vase of roses – signed – 15 x 12in.
(Christie's) **$7,832 £4,400**

FRIEDRICH STAHL – The Judgement of Paris – signed and dated – oil on canvas – 42 x 58in.
(Christie's) **$66,220 £38,500**

ELOISE HARRIET STANNARD – A melon, pineapple, grapes, plums, peaches and other fruit, with a silver cup on a marble ledge – signed and dated – canvas laid down on board – 25in.
(Christie's) **$23,496 £13,200**

STANNARD

HENRY SYLVESTER STANNARD – Home from school – signed – 10¼ x 14in.
(Anderson & Garland) **$8,131 £4,700**

HENRY STANNARD – Thatched cottage with garden in full bloom, and chickens in the lane – signed – watercolour – 9½ x 13in.
(W. H. Lane & Son) **$2,580 £1,500**

SYLVESTER STANNARD – Study of a country cottage – signed – watercolour – 26 x 35.5cm.
(Henry Spencer) **$6,600 £3,600**

HENRY STANNARD – The Water Mill – signed – watercolour – 32.6 x 47cm.
(Christie's) **$681** **£396**

HENRY JOHN SYLVESTER STANNARD – Little gleaners, Bedfordshire – signed – 14 x 20¼in.
(Anderson & Garland) **$10,285 £5,500**

CLARK STANTON – In the Artist's Studio – signed – watercolour and bodycolour – 24½ x 15¾in.
(Phillips) **$1,352** **£800**

GEORGE CLARK STANTON – Making Bouquets
– signed – oil on canvas – 28 x 36in.
(Lawrence Fine Arts) **$7,231** **£4,180**

WILLIAM STEELINK – Shepherdess with her
flock – signed – 31 x 28in.
(W. H. Lane & Son) **$4,225 £2,500**

LILIAN STANNARD – A Summer Border –
signed – watercolour – 14 x 10in.
(Phillips) **$2,957** **£1,750**

ARTHUR JAMES STARK – A King Charles
spaniel, lying on a red-covered bed – signed –
35.8 x 45.6cm.
(Christie's) **$4,307 £2,420**

EDWIN STEELE – Still life of mixed spring flowers
in a green vase, on a ledge – signed and dated –
24 x 20in.
(Christie's) **$1,208** **£715**

PHILIP WILSON STEER – The Teme at Ludlow – signed and dated – pen, black ink and grey wash – 9½ x 14in.
(Christie's)   **$2,153**   **£1,210**

EDWIN STEELE – Roses on a mossy bank – signed and dated – 19½ x 15¼in.
(Christie's)   **$1,141 £660**

PHILIP WILSON STEER – Harwich Harbour from Landguard Point, Felixstowe – signed and dated – watercolour – 7½ x 10¾in.
(Christie's)   **$2,153**   **£1,210**

PHILIP WILSON STEER – In the Conservatory – signed – oil on canvas – 30 x 25in.
(Lawrence Fine Arts)   **$232,166**   **£134,200**

PHILIP WILSON STEER – The River at Dusk – signed – oil on panel – 11½ x 18½in.
(Christie's)   **$3,328**   **£1,870**

POUL STEFFENSEN – On the beach – signed
– 16 x 20¾in.
(Christie's)   **$6,512**   **£3,520**

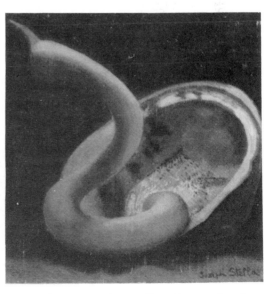

THEOPHILE ALEXANDRE STEINLEN – Femme
nue assise – signed – charcoal on paper –
46.1 x 39.4cm.
(Christie's)   **$5,405 £2,860**

JOSEPH STELLA – Abstract Green Form – signed
– oil on canvas – 33.2 x 33.4cm.
(Christie's)   **$9,350**   **£5,026**

STELLA

JOSEPH STELLA – Pink Rose – pencil and coloured pencil on paper – 47.8 x 30.7cm.
(Christie's) **$6,600** **£3,548**

WILLIAM LESTER STEVENS – Old Mill – signed – oil on canvas – 107 x 121.9cm.
(Christie's) **$5,500 £3,021**

WILLIAM LESTER STEVENS – Autumn Hills – signed – oil on Masonite – 24 x 30in.
(Robt. W. Skinner Inc.) **$750** **£443**

AGAPIT STEVENS – Indecision – signed and dated – 30¼ x 22¼in.
(Christie's) **$13,464** **£7,920**

WILLIAM LESTER STEVENS – The red silo – signed – oil on canvas – 30 x 36in.
(Robt. W. Skinner Inc.) **$2,500 £1,420**

J. E. STEWART — Bamburgh Castle — signed and dated — 14 x 21in.
(Christie's)   **$1,174   £660**

FRANK ALGERNON STEWART — The Vine Hunt — watercolour and bodycolour — 12½ x 10in.
(Christie's)   **$3,916   £2,200**

HARRY JAMES STICKS — A lakeland river lined by trees — signed — oil on canvas — 15½ x 25½in.
(Anderson & Garland)   **$1,453 £840**

MORITZ STIFTER — Views through keyholes: the Bath; and Love — both signed — on panel — 18½ x 12¼in.
(Christie's)   Two   **$7,854 £4,620**

ST LAURENT

EDWARD ST. LAURENT – White House, Green
Trim – signed and dated – oil on board – 12 x 16in.
(Bruce D. Collins)   **$303**   **£160**

EDWARD ST. LAURENT – Boatyard – signed and
dated – oil on board – 12 x 16in.
(Bruce D. Collins)   **$385**   **£203**

JOSEPH STOITZNER – Kahlenbergerdorf –
signed -- oil on canvas – 27 x 21¾in.
(Christie's)   **$4,427   £2,530**

ARTHUR STOCKS – A Flower for Grand-daddy
– signed and dated – watercolour – 22¾ x 17¾in.
(Christie's)   **$1,776**   **£1,045**

JAMES STOKELD – 'Must be in love, they jest at
scars that never felt a wound' – signed and dated
– 24 x 19in.
(Christie's)   **$2,937 £1,650**

WILLIAM STONE — An old house on crossroad near Bromsgrove — signed — 16¼ x 24¼in.
(Christie's) **$1,958 £1,100**

ABRAHAM STORCK — Figures feasting and bathing on a shore overlooking Amsterdam — oil on canvas — 24 x 30in.
(Phillips) **$93,080 £52,000**

MARCUS STONE — Courtship — signed with monogram and dated — 29.9 x 24.5cm.
(Christie's) **$1,958 £1,100**

EVA STORT — View of Stockholm — signed and dated — oil on canvas — 27¼ x 35in.
(Christie's) **$3,326 £1,760**

HERBERT MORTON STOOPS — The Posse — oil on canvas — 26 x 36in.
(Christie's) **$880 £483**

ARTHUR CLAUDE STRACHAN – "By the cottage door" and "My favourite cat" – both signed – watercolours – 10 x 7in.
(Prudential)   **Two $9,515   £5,500**

JAMES PHILIP S. STREATFIELD – Bathers on the rocks – signed and dated – 39 x 60in.
(Christie's)   **$2,788   £1,650**

JURIAN VAN STREECK, Manner of — Flowers
and fruit on a draped ledge — 31½ x 26in.
(Christie's) **$4,758 £2,750**

JOHANN ANTHONIE BALTHASAR STROBEL
— In the game larder — signed — on panel —
9½ x 8in.
(Christie's) **$1,589** **£935**

DANIELE DE STROBEL — San Giorgio — signed — pastel on canvas — oval — 27½ x 37¾in.
(Christie's) **$10,406 £6,050**

STRUDWICK

CHARLES STUART – Deer by a loch in a Sutherlandshire glen – signed – oil on canvas – 29¼ x 49in.
(Anderson & Garland)   **$1,384 £800**

FRANZ VON STUCK – Sommer – signed – oil on canvas – 30¼ x 26¾in.
(Christie's)   **$10,120 £5,500**

JOHN MELHUISH STRUDWICK – Falling leaves – signed with initials and dated – oil on canvas – 34¼ x 21¼in.
(Christie's)   **$242,880 £132,000**

JOHN MELHUISH STRUDWICK – Love and Time – signed – oil on canvas – 15 x 38in.
(Christie's)   **$80,960 £44,000**

ARTHUR STUDD – Portrait of a Lady standing
– oil on board – 21½ x 15½in.
(Christie's)   **$761**   **£440**

FRANZ VON STUCK – Die Tanzerin – inscribed
– watercolour on paper – 36¼ x 13¼in.
(Christie's)   **$4,812**   **£2,750**

JINDRICH STYRSKI – 'One's good fortune, the
other's misfortune' – signed, dated and inscribed –
collage – 16¾ x 13in.
(Christie's)   **$1,975**   **£1,045**

LEOPOLD SURVAGE — Le Soleil — signed — pen, brush and indian ink and pencil on paper — 27.6 x 21.9cm.
(Christie's) **$956 £506**

HAROLD SWANWICK — The plough team returning home — signed and dated — 7¼ x 10¼in.
(Christie's) **$3,973 £2,310**

SWEDISH SCHOOL, 19th century — Stockholm — 24½ x 34¾in.
(Christie's) **$6,993 £3,740**

LEGHE SUTHERS — "The broken pitcher", a young girl in tears before the village well, consoled by a man and woman — signed — oil on canvas — 40 x 32in.
(W. H. Lane & Son) **$14,640 £8,000**

PER ADOLF (PELLE) SWEDLUND — Jakobs kyrka, Stockholm — signed with monogram — 42½ x 34½in.
(Christie's) **$13,838 £7,480**

PER ADOLF (PELLE) SWEDLUND — Gathorn i
Fiskabackskil (Streetcorner in Fiskabackskil) —
signed with initials — 32½ x 38in.
(Christie's) **$6,105** **£3,300**

WALTER H. SWEET — The Warren, St Ives,
fishwives before sail lofts with a view of the
harbour at St Ives — signed — watercolour —
10 x 14in.
(W. H. Lane & Son) **$1,354 £740**

MICHAEL SWEERTS, Circle of — A boy blowing
a horn — oil on canvas — 23½ x 19in.
(Phillips) **$14,080 £8,000**

SYMONS

GEORGE GARDINER SYMONS — Summer landscape with pond — signed — oil on board — 16.2 x 21.9cm.
(Robt. W. Skinner Inc.)   **$650   £369**

GEORGE GARDINER SYMONS — European village and aquaduct — signed and initialled — oil on panel — 16.5 x 21.9cm.
(Robt. W. Skinner Inc.)   **$600   £340**

ARNALDO TAMBURINI — An Arab guard — signed — 14 x 11¾in.
(Christie's)   **$9,873 £5,280**

ROBERT S. TAIT — A Mother and child — 50 x 40in.
(Christie's)   **$5,874 £3,300**

DOROTHEA TANNING — The Truth about Comets and Little Girls — signed and dated — oil on canvas — 24 x 24in.
(Christie's)   **$33,000   £19,473**

ANTONI TAPIES — Untitled: Grey and Black — signed and dated — oil, ink, chalk and sand on paper laid down on masonite — 43½ x 30½in.
(Christie's)   **$94,622 £50,600**

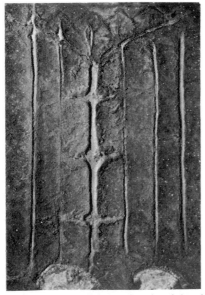

ANTONI TAPIES — Untitled — signed and dated —
oil and sand on canvas — 28¾ x 19¾in.
(Christie's) **$85,140 £49,500**

JAMES C. TARR — Making Camp Beds — oil on
canvas — 25 x 30in.
(Christie's) **$1,617** **£935**

JAMES C. TARR — Chiltern Landscape — signed
and dated — oil on panel — 15 x 20in.
(Christie's) **$2,093** **£1,210**

GEORG TAPPERT — Zwei Akte im Wald — oil
on canvas — 189.5 x 118.2cm.
(Christie's) **$14,168 £7,700**

WILLIAM TAVERNER — A horseman crossing
a bridge in an Italianate landscape — pencil,
watercolour and bodycolour, on grey green paper
— 22 x 35cm.
(Christie's) **$935** **£550**

ALBERT CHEVALLIER TAYLER — The garden party — signed — on panel — 9¼ x 13¼in.
(Christie's) **$22,308 £13,200**

CHARLES TAYLOR — A breeze off the south foreland — signed in monogram — 16 x 31½in.
(Fellows & Sons) **$2,704** **£1,600**

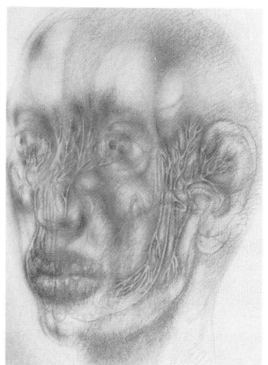

PAVEL TCHELITCHEW — Head: Interior Landscape — signed and dated — coloured chalks on paper — 13¾ x 9¾in.
(Christie's) **$4,620** **£2,726**

LEONARD CAMPBELL TAYLOR — Reminiscences — signed — oil on panel — 12½ x 9in.
(Christie's) **$5,482 £3,080**

PAVEL TCHELITCHEW — Still Life with Apples — signed — oil on canvas — 25¾ x 21¼in.
(Christie's) **$4,950** **£2,920**

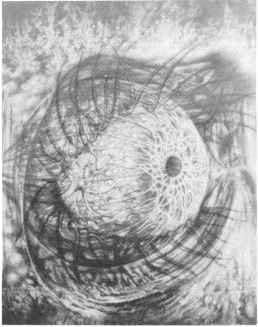

PAVEL TCHELITCHEW – The Flower of Sight –
signed   gouache on three pieces of paper, joined –
17 x 13in.
(Christie's)   **$4,950**   **£2,920**

PAVEL TCHELITCHEW – The Shepherd – signed
and dated – oil on canvas – 100 x 73cm.
(Christie's)   **$17,600**   **£10,385**

PAVEL TCHELITCHEW – Three Sitting Together
– signed and dated – oil on board – 29¼ x 41¼in.
(Christie's)   **$14,300**   **£8,138**

TCHELITCHEW

PAVEL TCHELITCHEW – Figures in Geometric Landscape – signed and dated – gouache, pen and black ink on paper – 9¼ x 13½in.
(Christie's)   **$4,950**   **£2,920**

DOUGLAS ARTHUR TEED – Interior of a mosque – signed – oil on canvas laid down on board – 42 x 33in.
(Du Mouchelles)   **$1,500 £793**

TELBISZ – A Vanitas: Books, a Crucifix and a Skull on a ledge in a niche – signed – oil on panel – 16 x 15cm.
(Phillips)   **$880**   **£500**

HANS TEMPLE – The love token – signed – on panel – 13 x 18in.
(Christie's)   **$3,740**   **£2,200**

HERMAN FREDERIK CAREL TENKATE – A 17th century interior scene – signed – 6¾ x 9¾in.
(Anderson & Garland)   **$1,193 £690**

JAN MARIE TEN KATE – Far away thoughts – signed – 27 x 30½in.
(Christie's)   **$4,114 £2,200**

DAVID TENIERS II, Follower of – An old woman spinning – 13½ x 9¾in.
(Christie's)   **$1,903 £1,100**

MARIE TEN KATE – The dead fawn – signed – oil on panel – 32 x 42cm.
(Christie's)   **$3,908 £2,090**

DAVID TENIERS II, Follower of – An old woman sleeping in a kitchen – on panel – 41.6 x 62.2cm.
(Christie's)   **$2,474 £1,430**

TENIERS

DAVID TENIERS, The Younger, Circle of — Interior of a pig-sty, with figures standing nearby — oil on canvas — 40 x 58cm.
(Phillips)   **$3,500 £2,000**

HENRY TENRE — Morning tea — signed — oil on panel — 8½ x 13¼in.
(Christie's)   **$1,394 £825**

DAVID TENIERS, the Younger and BONAVENTURA PEETERS — Sailing vessels off a rocky coast — signed — oil on panel — 50.5 x 60.5cm.
(Phillips)   **$51,240 £28,000**

WILLEM DE FAMARS TESTAS — Vue a Senouris (province du Fayoum, Egypte) — signed — 20¾ x 31¾in.
(Christie's)   **$4,114 £2,200**

JOHN F. TENNANT — From Haddon Hall — signed — on panel — 8¾ x 5¾in.
(Christie's)   **$2,153 £1,210**

FRITS THAULOW — A wooded landscape — signed and dated — oil on panel — 37 x 46cm.
(Christie's)   **$17,028 £9,900**

FRITS THAULOW – A town on a river – signed
and dated – oil on canvas – 100 x 65cm.
(Christie's)   **$48,576 £26,400**

T. THEURICH – Country folk by an alpine
farmhouse – both signed and dated – 21 x 26½in.
(Christie's)   **$3,085 £1,650**

ABBOT HANDERSON THAYER – A woman
reading – oil on canvas – 14 x 10in.
(Christie's)   **$1,540   £846**

ANTHONY THIEME – Rockport motif – signed
– oil on canvas – 25 x 30in.
(Bruce D. Collins)   **$7,150   £3,783**

ANTHONY THIEME – Gloucester Harbour – signed – oil on canvas – 26 x 31in.
(Christie's) **$3,740 £2,054**

ANTHONY THIEME – Rockport afternoon –
signed – oil on canvas – 63.2 x 76.8cm.
(Robt. W. Skinner Inc.) **$3,900 £2,215**

ANTHONY THIEME – Blue water – signed – oil
on canvas – 30 x 36in.
(Christie's) **$7,700 £4,230**

JAMES CRAWFORD THOM – The Shopping
List – signed – on canvas – 20 x 30in.
(Christie's) **$2,153 £1,210**

PAULINE THOMSEN – Summer day, Shordager,
Aarhus – signed with initials and dated –
36½ x 50½in.
(Christie's) **$5,298 £3,080**

ARCHIBALD THORBURN, Attributed to – Study
of a kingfisher perched on a branch – signed and
dated – watercolour on brown paper – 30 x 24cm.
(Henry Spencer) **$657 £380**

ARCHIBALD THORBURN – A Turnstone, a Grey
Plover and a Golden Plover – signed and dated –
pencil and watercolour – 8½ x 12in.
(Christie's) **$9,350 £5,500**

ARCHIBALD THORBURN – A Stoat in Winter –
signed – pencil, watercolour and bodycolour on
grey paper – 9¾ x 12in.
(Christie's) **$12,155 £7.150**

ARCHIBALD THORBURN – Eagle owl on
a rock – signed and dated – watercolour –
14 x 10in.
(W. H. Lane & Son) **$912 £540**

SIR JAMES THORNHILL – Neptune and Amph-
ritrite – 47¾ x 30in.
(Christie's) **$5,297 £3.080**

ARCHIBALD THORBURN – A peregrine falcon –
signed and dated – watercolour and bodycolour –
9½ x 13in.
(Christie's) **$13,500 £7,500**

ARCHIBALD THORBURN – A Pointer and
Setters – pencil and watercolour heightened with
white on buff paper – 18.1 x 24.1cm.
(Christie's) **2 in 1 frame** **$6,844 £3,740**

CHARLES THORNLEY – Northfleet – signed
and inscribed – 10½ x 8½in.
(Christie's) **$1,958 £1,100**

WENZEL THORNOE – The bead makers –
signed – oil on canvas – 31¼ x 40in.
(Christie's) **$16,192 £8,800**

ADOLPH TIDEMAND – The orphan (In a Swedish
farmer's cottage) – signed and dated – 24 x 21in.
(Christie's) **$97,680 £52,800**

SHEILA TIFFIN – Children on the sands – signed
– oil on canvas – 11 x 14in.
(W. H. Lane & Son) **$677 £370**

TILBORCH

GILLIS VAN TILBORCH — A village kermesse — signed — 45 x 48in.
(Christie's) $30,448 £17,600

JOE TILSON — Thesmophoria Version I (Project) 1987 — signed — oil on burlap mounted on wood panel — 48 x 35cm.
(Christie's) $3,520 £2,000

CHRISTIAN TILEMANN-PETERSEN — An interior, Ledreborg — signed and dated — 24 x 22in.
(Christie's) $2,442 £1,320

CHRISTIAN TILEMANN-PETERSEN — An interior with an empire bed — signed and dated — 16 x 14in.
(Christie's) $1,131 £605

JAMES JACQUES JOSEPH TISSOT — A portrait of Mr Edward Fox-White — signed — oil on canvas — 29 x 21¼in.
(Christie's) $101,200 £55,000

TITIAN, Manner of – Hagar and Ishmael –
21¼ x 25½in.
(Christie's) **$913 £528**

LODEWYK TOEPUT (called POZZOSERRATO),
Follower of – The Forge of Vulcan – 68 x 49¾in.
(Christie's) **$28,545 £16,500**

THEO TOBIASSE – Deborah la Prophetesse –
signed, inscribed and dated – oil on canvas –
33.4 x 24.5cm.
(Christie's) **$6,545 £3,740**

LODEWYK TOEPUT (called POZZOSERRATO),
Follower of – The formal gardens of a country
mansion, by a river, with an imperial lily, tulips
and other figures in pots in the foreground
– 68 x 49¾in.
(Christie's) **$108,471 £62,700**

HENRY TONKS — An Autumn morning — signed
with monogram — 30 x 50in.
(Christie's) **$1,566 £880**

JACOB TOORENVLIET — A school room — signed
— oil on panel — 19½ x 16in.
(Phillips) **$4,475 £2,500**

GIOVANNI BATTISTA TORRIGLIA — The
farmer's family — signed — oil on canvas —
29 x 43½in.
(Christie's) **$91,080 £49,500**

HENRI DE TOULOUSE LAUTREC — Au Lit —
huile a l'essence — on board — 14 x 10½in.
(Christie's) **$141,900 £82,500**

PAUL TREBILCOCK — Seated nude — signed —
oil on aluminium — 26 x 20in.
(Christie's) **$1,045 £574**

ADOLPH TREIDLER — Venice — signed — water-colour on paper — 10 x 14in.
(Bruce D. Collins) **$110** £58

FRANCESCO TREVISANI, Circle of — St Joseph and the Christ Child — oil on canvas — 40 x 31cm.
(Phillips) **$792** £450

FRANCESCO CAVALIERE TREVISANI, Manner of — Saint Joseph and the infant Christ — 53 x 39in.
(Christie's) **$856 £495**

TRIER

HANN TRIER – Zeit totschlagen – signed with initials and dated – egg tempera on canvas – 76¾ x 45 in.
(Christie's)   **$34,056 £19,800**

JEAN FRANCOIS DE TROY – Ceres – oil on canvas – 73 x 90.5 cm.
(Phillips)   **$12,810 £7,000**

PRINCE PAUL TROUBETSKOY, Follower of – A carriage at full speed – indistinctly inscribed – on canvas laid down on board – 12½ x 7½ in.
(Christie's)   **$1,851 £990**

JEAN FRANCOIS DE TROY, Follower of – Ladies playing backgammon in an elegant interior – 60.8 x 50.4 cm.
(Christie's)   **$3,045 £1,760**

JEAN FRANCOIS DE TROY – The massacre of the Jews by King Antiochus – oil on canvas – 81.5 x 113.5 cm.
(Phillips)   **$21,960 £12,000**

JOSIAH T. TUBBY – Oak, Crotched Mountain – signed – watercolour on paper – 10½ x 14 in.
(Bruce D. Collins)   **$55**   **£29**

ADA ELIZABETH TUCKER – What can it be? –
signed – 13½ x 22¾in.
(Christie's)   **$3,720 £2,090**

HENRY SCOTT TUKE – Man in a rowing boat
– signed and dated – oil on panel – 8¼ x 11½in.
(Christie's)   **$5,874   £3,300**

HENRY SCOTT TUKE – Three-Masters, Falmouth
– signed and dated – watercolour – 6¾ x 10in.
(Christie's)   **$2,937   £1,650**

HENRY SCOTT TUKE – A two masted sailing
vessel with sails partly furled in Falmouth
Harbour – signed and dated – watercolour –
17½ x 11½in.
(W. H. Lane & Son)   **$5,070 £3,000**

511

TURNER

GEORGE TURNER — A Sunny Day on the Hillside — landscape with a cottage and sheep — signed and dated — 20 x 30in.
(Woolley & Wallis)   **$5,190**   **£3,000**

JAMES GALE TYLER — On a Reach — signed — oil on canvas — 12 x 18in.
(Robt. W. Skinner Inc.) **$1,300**   **£769**

GEORGE TURNER — The way to the village — signed — 20 x 30in.
(Christie's)   **$9,081**   **£5,280**

EDGARD TYTGAT — Sheherazade — signed and dated — 78 x 66in.
(Christie's)   **$28,875**   **£16,500**

LAURITS TUXEN — A girl paddling in the sea *(recto)*; and Venus *(verso)* — signed with initials and dated — on panel — 26.5 x 35cm.
(Christie's)   **$2,849**   **£1,540**

KARL KRISTIAN UCHERMANN — The uninvited guest — signed — 46.5 x 55.5cm.
(Christie's)   **$14,190 £8,250**

LEON UNDERWOOD — The Trawl Hand — signed and dated — pencil — 22.5 x 17.5cm.
(Phillips) **$1,352 £800**

S. JEROME UHL — "The Midget"/Seated girl with bouquet — signed, inscribed and dated — oil on canvas — 12 x 10in.
(Robt. W. Skinner Inc.) **$325 £186**

LEON UNDERWOOD — Men and birds — signed and dated — oil on board — 17¾ x 21¾in.
(Christie's) **$3,574 £2,090**

B. C. ULNITZ — Wild roses in a vase on a ledge — signed and dated — 12½ x 9¾in.
(Christie's) **$3,406 £1,980**

FRANZ RICHARD UNTERBERGER — Anacapri — signed — 35¾ x 53½in.
(Christie's) **$28,380 £16,500**

UNTERBERGER

FRANZ RICHARD UNTERBERGER — A terrace, Posilipo — signed — on panel — 15½ x 23¾in.
(Christie's) **$23,375** **£13,750**

FRANZ RICHARD UNTERBERGER — Fisherfolk in a rocky coastal landscape — signed — 10½ x 16¾in.
(Christie's) **$3,927 £2,310**

FRANZ RICHARD UNTERBERGER — The Lagoon, Venice — signed — oil on panel — 10½ x 10¾in.
(Christie's) **$12,727 £7,150**

JOHN WILLIAM UPHAM — Carisbrooke Castle, Isle of Wight — inscribed — pencil, pen and grey ink and watercolour — 29.2 x 45cm.
(Christie's) **$1,861 £990**

LESSER URY — Haus Vaterland, Berlin — signed — oil on canvas — 13 x 9½in.
(Christie's) **$52,976** **£30,800**

LESSER URY — Das Brandenburger Tor, Berlin — signed — oil on canvas — 14¼ x 20½in.
(Christie's) **$101,200 £55,000**

LESSER URY — Der Uferdamm, London — signed, dated and inscribed — oil on canvas — 19¾ x 27¾in.
(Christie's) **$60,720 £33,000**

LESSER URY – Brandenburger Tor, Berlin –
signed – 49 x 34cm.
(Christie's)   **$87,032**   **£50,600**

STEFANO USSI – The Angel – oil on panel –
11¾ x 7¼in.
(Christie's)   **$3,784**   **£2,200**

LESSER URY – Strassenszene bei Regen –
signed – drypoint on wove paper – 118 x 84mm.
(Christie's)   **$1,028 £605**

ADRIAEN VAN UTRECHT, Attributed to – A
young woman beside a fishstall – oil on canvas –
127 x 159.5cm.
(Phillips)   **$29,600 £16,000**

UTRILLO

MAURICE UTRILLO – La Maison de Mimi Pinson a Montmartre – signed and dated – oil on canvas
– 50 x 65cm.
(Christie's) **$225,720 £132,000**

MAURICE UTRILLO – Rue de Paris a Asnieres – signed – oil on board – 20¼ x 29in.
(Christie's) **$245,960 £143,000**

MAURICE UTRILLO – Vase de Fleurs sur une Table – signed and dated – oil on board laid down on canvas – 18 x 15in.
(Christie's) **$111,320 £60,500**

MAURICE UTRILLO – Eglise de Saint Michel, Andorra – signed and dated – gouache on paper – 17½ x 12in.
(Christie's) **$60,544 £35,200**

MAURICE UTRILLO – Le Lapin Agile – signed – oil on board – 39 x 26cm.
(Christie's) **$90,816 £52,800**

MAURICE UTRILLO – Montmartre – signed – oil on canvas – 41 x 33cm.
(Christie's) **$157,872 £85,800**

UTRILLO

MAURICE UTRILLO – Montmartre, Moulin de la Galette – signed – oil on paper laid down on canvas – 11 x 14¾in.
(Christie's) **$125,488 £68,200**

MAURICE UTRILLO – Scene de Rue – signed and dated – coloured crayons and charcoal on paper – 9¼ x 12¼in.
(Christie's) **$36,432 £19,800**

MAURICE UTRILLO – Bourg-la-Reine – signed – oil on canvas – 46 x 54 cm.
(Christies) **$245,960 £143,000**

MAURICE UTRILLO — La Moulin de la Galette
— signed — oil on canvas — 13¾ x 16½in.
(Christie's)   **$132,440 £77,000**

THOMAS UWINS, Follower of — Portrait of a
gentleman, three-quarter length, wearing a tail
coat and carrying a top hat and cane — pencil
and watercolour — 11¼ x 8¾in.
(Christie's)   **$321**   **£187**

ANDREA VACCARO, Studio of — St Lucy — oil
on canvas — 47¼ x 37¾in.
(Phillips)   **$3,872 £2,200**

THEODORE V. C. VALENKAMPH – Marine Scene – signed – oil on canvas – 28 x 36in. *(Robt. W. Skinner Inc.)* **$850**   **£502**

PERINO DEL VAGA, Follower of – The Holy Family – oil on panel – 55 x 40cm. *(Phillips)*   **$2,275 £1,300**

THEODORE V. C. VALENKAMPH – Off a rocky coast – signed and dated – oil on canvas – 18x24in. *(Robt. W. Skinner Inc.)*   **$1,200   £681**

JOHN VALENTINE – Mare with her foal at Guyzance Hall, Northumberland – signed, inscribed and dated – oil on canvas – 19½ x 29½in. *(Anderson & Garland)*   **$864 £480**

THEODORE VALERIO – An Arab warrior and his horse – signed – pencil and watercolour – 265 x 195mm.
(Christie's) **$2,695** **£1,540**

FELIX VALLOTTON – Bouquet de Fleurs et Citron – signed and dated – gouache on board – 12½ x 9½in.
(Christie's) **$52,624 £28,600**

LORENZO VALLES – Coming from church, Rome – signed – oil on canvas – 27¾ x 19¼in.
(Christie's) **$16,192 £8,800**

LOUIS VALTAT – Oeuillets au Vase jaune – the studio stamp lower left *L.V.* – oil on canvas – 51 x 33.3 cm.
(Christie's) **$24,596** **£14,300**

VALTAT

LOUIS VALTAT – Le Saut d'Obstacle – signed
– oil on canvas – 24 x 29cm.
(Christie's) **$6,930 £3,960**

LOUIS VALTAT – La Roseraie, Bagatelle –
signed – oil on canvas – 15 x 22in.
(Du Mouchelles) **$25,000 £14,790**

LOUIS VALTAT – Madame Valtat au Jardin –
signed with initials and dated – oil on canvas –
61 x 81cm.
(Christie's) **$141,680 £77,000**

EUGENIE VALTER – Society Pets – three
kittens at play – signed – watercolour – 11½ x 9¼in.
– one of a set of two.
(Hy. Duke & Son) **(Two)** **$2,464 £1,400**

CORNELIUS VARLEY – Tegwin Ferry, North
Wales – signed, inscribed and dated – pencil and
watercolour – 13¼ x 20½in.
(Christie's) **$4,488 £2,640**

GEZA VASTAGH – A pride of lions – signed and
dated – oil on canvas – 80 x 135cm.
(Christie's) **$14,572 £7,920**

KEITH VAUGHAN – The lake with bathers –
signed – oil on canvas – 28 x 42in.
(Christie s) **$17,919 £9,900**

KEITH VAUGHAN – Two nudes – oil on board
– 22¼ x 16¼in.
(Christie's) **$3,583 £1,980**

ELIHU VEDDER – Etruscan Girl – signed with
initial and dated – oil on paper laid down on
canvas – 9 x 7½in.
(Christie's) **$9,900** **£5,322**

VEDDER

ELIHU VEDDER — The Tinker — oil on panel —
31.4 x 40.6cm.
(Christie's)   **$18,700**   **£10,053**

MARTEN-JACOBSZ VAN VEEN (called
HEEMSKERK), Manner of — Portrait of a lady,
small bust length, in a dark coat — dated — on
panel — 24.7 x 19.4cm.
(Christie's)   **$2,284 £1,320**

CORNELIS VAN DER VELDE, Circle of — A flag-
ship and other shipping sailing under strong winds
— oil on canvas — 25 x 32½in.
(Phillips)   **$5,280 £3,000**

HENRI VAN DE VELDE — Soleil d'Hiver — signed
and dated — oil on canvas — 17¼ x 23¾in.
(Christie's)   **$132,440**   **£77,000**

PETER OLSEN VENTEGODT – A temple of
Heracles at Agrigento – signed and dated –
25¾ x 38¼in.
(Christie's) **$4,812** **£2,750**

EUGENE VERBOECKHOVEN – A cairn terrier on
a rug in a landscape – signed and dated – oil on
board – 9 x 12in.
(Christie's) **$3,532** **£2,090**

VENETIAN SCHOOL, 19th century – A wine
seller – oil on panel – 13 x 9in.
(Anderson & Garland) **$1,620** **£900**

EUGENE JOSEPH VERBOECKHOVEN – Skaters
on a frozen river in a winter landscape – signed and
dated – on panel – 10 x 8in.
(Christie's) **$13,464** **£7,920**

P. VERBERGHEN – Landscape scene, horse
drawn firewood cart and man loading firewood –
signed – oil on canvas – 20 x 28in.
(Du Mouchelles) **$600 £317**

LOUIS VERBOECKHOVEN, Attributed to – A
shady spot – signed – oil on canvas – 17 x 26in.
(Christie's) **$1,766 £1,045**

VERBOECKHOVEN

LOUIS VERBOECKHOVEN — Sailing vessels off a jetty in a choppy sea — signed — oil on panel — 20½ x 27½in.
(Christie's) $17,811 £9,680

JAN PEETER VERDUSSEN — Elegant figures picnicking near a waterfall in the Italian campagna — oil on canvas — 21 x 25¼in.
(Phillips) $4,752 £2,700

JAN HENDRIK VERHEYEN — A courtyard in Utrecht — signed and dated — oil on panel — 19 x 14in.
(Christie's) $18,216 £9,900

H. DUNCHENE DE VERE — A tambourine girl — one of a pair — signed and dated — 24 x 18in.
(Christie's) $2,468 £1,320

CHARLES MICHEL MARIA VERLAT — Deshabillee — signed, inscribed and dated — on panel — 28½ x 23¼in.
(Christie s) $4,675 £2,750

JOSEPH CLAUDE VERNET, Follower of —
Peasants watching a ship depart at sunset — oil on
canvas — 46 x 74cm.
(Phillips) **$2,362 £1,350**

BONIFAZIO VERONESE, Circle of — The Holy
Family with the infant Saint John offering fruit —
100.8 x 117.7cm.
(Christie's) **$7,231 £4,180**

**LOUIS PIERRE VERWEE and EUGENE JOSEPH
VERBOECKHOVEN** — Skaters on a frozen river
— signed by both artists and dated — oil on canvas
— 26¼ x 36¾in.
(Christie's) **$32,384 £17,600**

ANTONIO VERRIO — A modello for the decoration of the ceiling of the king's staircase at Hamp-
ton Court — 32½ x 40½in.
(Christie's) **$6,432 £3,740**

SALOMON LEONARDUS VERVEER — A coastal
village — signed and dated — 15½ x 24in.
(Christie's) **$18,700 £11,000**

BORIS THEO VESELY — The tomb of Sultana
Seliman II, Constantinople — signed, inscribed
and dated — oil on canvas — 29½ x 19½in.
(Christie's) **$6,072 £3,300**

VICKERS

ALFRED H. VICKERS — A riverside village — signed and dated — 18 x 32in.
(Christie's)   **$3,185**   **£1,760**

LATE VICTORIAN SCHOOL — Life size study of a black retriever — oil painting — 93 x 71cm.
(Henry Spencer)   **$709**   **£420**

VIENNA SECESSION SCHOOL — Maidens with offerings in a casket — oil on panel inlaid with coloured glass — 22¼ x 13½in.
(Christie's)   **Two**   **$856**   **£495**

VICTORIAN SCHOOL — The Letter, full length portrait of a young peasant girl reading a letter — monogrammed — oil on canvas — 60 x 49.5cm.
(Henry Spencer)   **$5,365 £2,900**

HARRY AIKEN VINCENT — The rocky inlet/ Gloucester — signed — oil on board — 10½ x 13¾in.
(Robt. W. Skinner Inc.)   **$1,300**   **£738**

HARRY AIKEN VINCENT – Gloucester Harbour scene – signed – oil on canvasboard – 11 x 14in.
(Robt. W. Skinner Inc.) **$1,800 £1,022**

ANTONIO VISENTINI, Circle of – A Venetian lady at her toilet, and a woman and child with a dog – oil on paper, laid down on board – 10¼ x 15½in.
(Phillips) **$3,168 £1,800**

LEONARDO DA VINCI, Manner of – La Belle Ferronniere – 24 x 19¾in.
(Christie's) **$1,618 £935**

MAURICE DE VLAMINCK – Vase de Fleurs – signed – oil on canvas – 21¾ x 18¼in.
(Christie's) **$94,600** **£55,000**

DAVID VINCKBOONS – A stag hunt near a river in dense woodland – oil on panel – 8½ x 13in.
(Phillips) **$5,632 £3,200**

MAURICE DE VLAMINCK – Paysage aux Arbres – signed – oil on canvas – 71 x 90cm.
(Christie's) **$172,040 £93,500**

MAURICE DE VLAMINCK – Les Ramasseurs de Pommes de Terre – signed – oil on canvas – 18¼ x 21¾in.
(Christie's)   **$1,034   £605,000**

MAURICE DE VLAMINCK – Le Pont du Canal
– signed – gouache, watercolour pen and ink on
paper – 45 x 53cm.
(Christie's)   **$36,575 £20,900**

MAURICE DE VLAMINCK – Rue a Heronville
– signed – oil on canvas – 54 x 65.1cm.
(Christie's)   **$98,175 £56,100**

MAURICE DE VLAMINCK – Vase de Fleurs –
signed – oil on canvas – 79 x 64.2 cm.
(Christie's)   **$179,740   £104,500**

MAURICE DE VLAMINCK – Vase de Fleurs sur
une Table – signed – oil on canvas – 25½ x 19¾in.
(Christie's)   **$137,632 £74,800**

MAURICE DE VLAMINCK – Le Tracteur rouge
– signed – oil on canvas – 34 x 41.9cm.
(Christie's)   **$47,817 £25,300**

ANTOINE VOLLON — A fan, oranges and a basket of flowers on a table — signed — on panel — 24 x 19¼in.
(Christie's)   **$10,285   £6,050**

VINCENT DE VOS — Circus friends — signed — on panel — 8¾ x 6¾in.
(Christie's)   **$905   £484**

ALEXIS VOLLON — Pecheur sur les Quais de la Seine — signed, dated and inscribed — 33 x 41cm.
(Christie's)   **$5,775   £3,300**

SEBASTIEN VRANCX, Circle of — The Vendage — 31¼ x 46in.
(Christie's)   **$15,224 £8,800**

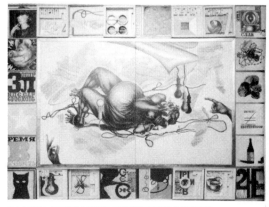

SERGEI ALEXANDROVICH VOLOCHOV — Russland — signed and dated — oil, tempera and mixed media on canvas and wood — 192 x 260cm.
(Hauswedell & Nolte)   **$25,982   £15,106**

ALFRED WAHLBERG — The village church — signed — oil on panel — 11½ x 15½in.
(Christie's)   **$4,461   £2,640**

BERNARD FLEETWOOD WALKER – By the
Wayside – signed and dated – oil on canvas laid
down on panel – 13½ x 13½in.
(Christie's)   **$1,958 £1,100**

WILLIAM AIKEN WALKER – Boy with Torn
Jacket – signed and dated – oil on canvas –
20.3 x 18.1cm.
(Christie's)   **$5,500**   **£2,956**

DAME ETHEL WALKER – Portrait of a lady –
26 x 21in.
(Christie's)   **$1,580 £935**

WILLIAM AIKEN WALKER – Cuban man – oil
on canvas – 25.1 x 20.3cm.
(Christie's)   **$3,520 £1,934**

ABRAHAM WALKOWITZ — The fishermen —
signed — watercolour and pencil on paper —
22¼ x 30¾in.
(Christie's) $2,420 £1,329

JOHN WALLACE — A bather in a woodland lake —
signed and dated — oil on canvas — 23¼ x 17¼in.
(Anderson & Garland) $1,260 £700

HENRY WALL — An eastern fabric bazaar — signed
— watercolour — 12 x 13in.
(Woolley & Wallis) $622 £360

WALT DISNEY STUDIOS — Goofy as a Knight on
Horseback — unsigned — chalks on tan paper —
6 x 8¼in.
(Robt. W. Skinner Inc.) $225 £133

WILLIAM GUY WALL — West Point on the Hudson
— signed — oil on panel — 20.3 x 25cm.
(Christie's) $8,800 £4,731

EMMA WALTER — Flowers; and Christmas roses
and fruit — signed — pencil and watercolour —
10 x 14¾in.
(Christie's) $3,594 £2,090

HENRIETTA WARD – An interior at Knole House, Seven Oaks – signed and dated – 12 x 14in.
(Christie's) **$1,530 £860**

WILLIAM H. WARD – The hurdy gurdy player – signed and dated – 10 x 8in.
(Christie's) **$1,723 £968**

VERNON WARD – Canadian geese in flight over a winter mainland landscape – signed – oil on canvas – 11 x 21in.
(W. H. Lane & Son) **$1,634 £950**

ARTHUR WARDLE – "Melgrange Marquis", a bull dog – signed and dated – on card – 10¼ x 14¼in.
(Christie's) **$1,324 £770**

WARDLE

SOPHY S. WARREN — Crossing the River —
signed with monogram — watercolour over pencil —
6 x 10in. — and companion
(Phillips)   Two   **$1,352**   £800

HOWARD WARSHAW — Sacks — signed and dated
— oil on canvas — 5 x 8in.
(Christie's)   **$1,430**   £843

FRANK WASLEY — Venice, Festival of St Marks
— signed — watercolour — 14½ x 21in.
(Prudential)   **$4,675**   £2,500

ARTHUR WARDLE — Terriers on a staircase —
signed — 22 x 15in.
(Christie's)   **$14,685 £8,250**

FRANKLIN C. WATKINS — Reclining nude — initialled — oil on canvas — 14 x 24in.
(Du Mouchelles)   **$1,100   £582**

HARRY WILLSON WATROUS – Lake scene –
signed – oil on canvas – 63.5 x 76.5cm.
(Christie's) **$1,100** **£604**

FRANKLIN C. WATKINS – Portrait of Mrs
Steinman – initialled – oil on canvas – 40 x 36in.
(Du Mouchelles) **$1,300** **£687**

JOHN DAWSON WATSON – The Turnip Field –
signed with initials and dated – 12 x 16½in.
(Anderson & Garland) **$1,656** **£920**

FRANKLIN C. WATKINS – Still life with flowers
– signed – oil on canvas – 30 x 25in.
(Du Mouchelles) **$2,000 £1,058**

GEORGE FIDDES WATT – The young goatherd
– signed and dated – oil on canvas – 60 x 45cm.
(Phillips) **$10,527 £6,050**

GEORGE FREDERICK WATTS – Portrait of
Kharilaos Trikoupis – signed and dated –
24 x 19in.
(Christie's) **$4,235** **£2,420**

WILLIAM HARRIS WEATHERHEAD – A fisher-
girl mending a net at a window – signed – 28 x 16in.
(Anderson & Garland) **$2,162 £1,250**

WILLIAM EDWARD WEBB – Douglas Harbour,
Isle of Man – signed, inscribed and dated –
20 x 30in.
(Chrystals) **$10,846** **£5,800**

WILLIAM EDWARD WEBB – In Poole Harbour
– signed and dated – 14 x 10in.
(Christie's) **$1,370 £770**

WILLIAM EDWARD WEBB – Whitby from the
bridge – signed – 15 x 18in.
(Chrystals) **$4,862** **£2,600**

WESLEY WEBER – Sailboats by moonlight – signed – oil on canvas – 20 x 16in.
(Du Mouchelles) **$1,000 £529**

HERBERT WILLIAM WEEKS – The ambush – signed – 11¼ x 8in.
(Christie's) **$5,482 £3,080**

EINAR WEGENER – Versailles – signed and dated – on panel – 37.5 x 46cm.
(Christie's) **$2,645 £1,430**

BERTHA WEGMANN – Wildflowers in a vase on a table – signed and dated – 62 x 55cm.
(Christie's) **$13,227 £7,150**

BERTHA WEGMANN – Resting – signed – canvas laid down on board - 12¼ x 15¼in.
(Christie's) **$16,362 £9,350**

CAREL WEIGHT – The village road – 15¾x17¾in.
(Christie's) **$5,577 £3,300**

JOHN REINHARD WEGUELIN – Herodias and her daughter – signed and dated – oil on canvas – 48¾ x 34in.
(Christie's) **$24,288 £13,200**

CAREL WEIGHT – Windermere – oil on board – 8 x 14¼in.
(Christie's) **$7,440 £4,180**

CAREL WEIGHT – Old woman in a garden – signed – oil on canvas – 36 x 48in.
(Christie's) **$23,496 £13,200**

LUCY KEMP WELCH – Cart Horses – signed and
dated – 11½ x 14¼in.
(Christie's)   **$1,419   £825**

RUDOLF WEISS – The new acquisition – signed
and dated – on panel – 61 x 49.3cm.
(Christie's)   **$15,400   £8,800**

LUCY KEMP-WELCH – The Lumber Team –
signed and dated – oil on canvas – 37½ x 55½in.
(Hy. Duke & Son)   **$132,000 £75,000**

LUCY ELIZABETH KEMP-WELCH – A Guernsey
cow – dated and inscribed – oil on canvas-board –
5¼ x 8in.
(Christie's)   **$1,370   £770**

J. V. WELLER – The Oxford-Cambridge Boat Race, 1909 – signed and dated – 21½ x 33½in.
(Christie's) **$929 £550**

HUBERT LINDSAY WELLINGTON – Country cottage – signed – 18 x 24in.
(Christie's) **$1,635 £968**

DENYS GEORGE WELLS – An interesting story – signed and dated – oil on canvas – 28 x 23½in.
(Christie's) **$7,832 £4,400**

DENYS GEORGE WELLS – Woman Seated at a Table – signed – oil on panel – 17¾ x 14¼in.
(Christie's) **$1,566 £880**

WILLIAM WELLS – Gathering mussels – signed – oil on board – 20 x 30cm.
(Phillips) **$3,636 £2,090**

STOW WENGENROTH – Season's End (Edition 40) and Sunlight, Wicasset (Edition 75) – signed and numbered – lithographs – 23.5 x 39cm.
(Robt. W. Skinner Inc.)
Two **$1,600 £946**

STOW WENGENROTH – River Light – signed – lithograph on wove paper – 26.9 x 40.4cm. *(Robt. W. Skinner Inc.)* **$700**   **£414**

STOW WENGENROTH – Serenity – signed – lithograph on wove paper – 28.6 x 45.4cm. *(Robt. W. Skinner Inc.)* **$1,100**   **£650**

CARL FRIEDRICH HEINRICH WERNER – The Doge's Palace with Porta della Carta and the Marcus Basilica – signed and dated – oil on canvas – 16½ x 14in. *(Christie's)*   **$13,156 £7,150**

EMIL AUGUST THEODOR WENNERWALD – A lake at sunset – signed – 30½ x 40in. *(Christie's)*   **$935**   **£550**

REINHOLD WERNER – A farm near Rome and The road to market – the first signed and inscribed – watercolour – 9¾ x 17in. *(Christie's)*   **$1,028 £550**

ALFRED WENT – Portrait of a Terrier – signed – 9½ x 13in. *(Prudential)*   **$3,272**   **£1,750**

RAPHAEL LAMAR WEST — The fall of the Rebel Angels — pen and brown ink, brown wash — 24½ x 18¼in.
(Christie's) **$2,805 £1,650**

GEOFFREY S. WESTLAKE — Archie Shepp with his saxophone and John Coltrane — signed — on board — 38 x 28in.
(Christie's) **$1,394 £825**

CONSTANT WESTCHILOFF — Harbour Scene — signed — oil on cardboard — 21.7 x 26.5cm.
(Robt. W. Skinner Inc.) **$300 £177**

FRITZ WESTENDORF — Blick auf Notre Dame, Paris — signed and dated — oil on canvas — 17¼ x 22in.
(Christie's) **$12,512 £7,150**

ROGIER VAN DER WEYDEN, Follower of — The Madonna and Child — oil on panel — 29.5 x 21.5cm.
(Phillips) **$8,800 £5,000**

JOHN ALFRED WHEELER – Flying Fox with
a jockey – signed and inscribed – 20 x 24in.
(Christie's)   **$10,769 £6,050**

ALFRED WHEELER, Jnr – A head study of a bull
terrier – signed – oil on board – circular – 12in.diam.
(Christie's)   **$951   £550**

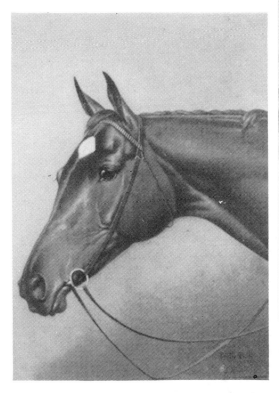

JOHN ALFRED WHEELER – Pretty Polly – one
of a pair – signed, inscribed and one dated – on
board – 21 x 18¼in.
(Christie's)   **Two $4,307 £2,420**

JAMES ABBOTT McNEIL WHISTLER – St James
Street – signed – etching and drypoint on Japan
wove paper – 28.3 x 15.7cm.
(Robt. W. Skinner Inc.) **$1,700   £1,005**

ETHELBERT WHITE – Tractor in a field – on panel – 9½ x 13½in.
(Christie's) $1,078 £638

ETHELBERT WHITE – The Church, Great Coates – signed – watercolour – 15 x 22in.
(Christie's) $1,076 £605

ETHELBERT WHITE – In a Paris Market – signed – watercolour, pen and black ink – 11¾ x 14½in.
(Christie's) $1,860 £1,045

MILDRED WHITE – A portrait of a pair of horses, Amazon and Bradley, on the practice polo ground at Ranelagh – signed with initials and dated – 20 x 30in.
(Woolley & Wallis) $657 £380

ETHELBERT WHITE – Cows Grazing in an Upland Landscape – signed – oil on canvas – 31 x 39in.
(Christie's) $3,524 £1,980

FREDERICK WHITEHEAD – Cattle watering at a stream – signed – oil on canvas – 14 x 21in.
(Christie's) $1,664 £935

SARAH E. WHITEHOUSE – Young girls picking flowers in a walled garden at springtime – signed – oil on canvas – 16 x 22in.
(W. H. Lane & Son) **$1,183 £700**

ROBERT DODD WIDDAS, Attributed to – Fallen at the fence: and The runaway horse – the latter with signature and date – oil on canvas – 11½ x 15¾in.
(Christie's) **Two** **$1,807 £1,045**

FREDERIC WHITING – Huntsman and Hounds – signed – watercolour – 18½ x 22in.
(Christie's) **$1,370 £770**

BERNHARDT WIEGANDT – Watercarriers at Para De Belem – signed and inscribed – pencil and watercolour heightened with white – 12¾ x 20in.
(Christie's) **$2,153 £1,210**

JOHN WHORF – A scene in Provincetown – signed – watercolour on paper – 15½ x 22in.
(Robt. W. Skinner Inc.) **$2,200 £1,250**

GUY CARLETON WIGGINS – Landscape with Cows – signed – oil on Academy board – 30.2 x 40.5cm.
(Robt. W. Skinner Inc.) **$550** **£325**

GUY CARLETON WIGGINS — Lower Broadway in Winter — signed and dated — oil on canvas — 20 x 24in.
(Christie's) **$19,800** **£10,645**

GERARD WIGMANA, Circle of — A Philosopher reading at a table — oil on panel — 28 x 21.5cm.
(Phillips) **$739** **£420**

JOHANNES MARTIN FASTINGS WILHJELM — On the beach — signed and dated — 26 x 32½in.
(Christie's) **$4,114 £2,420**

ARTHUR STANLEY WILKINSON – A woman feeding birds and a woman gathering flowers – signed – a pair – 15 x 10½in.
(Anderson & Garland) $2,772   £1,540

ARTHUR WILLAERT – Voiliers au Couchee du Soleil – signed – oil on canvas – 33½ x 45¾in.
(Christie's) $2,310   £1,320

TERRICK JOHN WILLIAMS – Sardine boats, Concarneau, Brittany – signed and dated – oil on canvas – 18 x 24in.
(Christie's) $10,769   £6,050

MAURICE WILKS – Collecting Peat, West of Ireland – signed – oil on canvas – 20 x 24in.
(Christie's) $3,132   £1,760

TERRICK JOHN WILLIAMS – After Vespers, Brittany – signed – oil on canvas – 32½ x 41in.
(Christie's) $17,622   £9,900

HENRY BRITTAN WILLIS – On the Stour –
signed and indistinctly dated – oil on canvas –
11½ x 15½in.
(Anderson & Garland) **$11,700**   **£6,500**

HENRY BRITTAN WILLIS – Cattle in water-
meadow – signed and indistinctly dated –
9 x 18in.
(Anderson & Garland)   **$1,989 £1,150**

CHARLES EDWARD WILSON – An Interruption
– signed – pencil and watercolour – 10 x 7in.
(Christie's)   **$8,976**   **£5,280**

CHARLES EDWARD WILSON – Primrose Gatherers – signed – 13½ x 20¾in.
(Anderson & Garland)
$27,000 £15,000

CHARLES EDWARD WILSON – Study of an old fish wife, wearing a mauve poke bonnet, blue checked shawl, black dress and white apron – signed – 35.5 x 25.5cm.
(Henry Spencer) **$10,285 £5,500**

CHARLES EDWARD WILSON – Teasing the kitten – signed and dated – watercolour – 15¼ x 10½in.
(Phillips) **$14,365 £8,500**

CHARLES EDWARD WILSON – A mute Appeal – signed – pencil and watercolour – 25.5 x 17.2cm.
(Christie's) **$14,025 £8,250**

CHARLES EDWARD WILSON – Off to the Hay Fields – A young woman carrying a wooden hay rake, walking along a country track – signed and dated – watercolour – 38.5 x 26cm.
(Henry Spencer) **$21,625 £12,500**

JOHN WILSON – Shipping off a rocky coastline
– signed and dated – oil on canvas – 12 x 20in.
(Christie's) **$1,332 £770**

EDMUND MORISON WIMPERIS – Wood-
gatherers at a forest edge – signed with initials
and dated – 23 x 34½in.
(Anderson & Garland) **$1,215 £650**

JOHN JAMES WILSON – A summer stroll – figures
on a path in a river meadow at harvest time –
initialled and dated – watercolour – 9½ x 13in.
(W. H. Lane & Son) **$420 £230**

FRITZ WINTER – Kommendes (B.3) – signed
and dated – tempera on paper – 19¾ x 27½in.
(Christie's) **$10,406 £6,050**

ROBERT WINTER – Farmhouse across the meadow
– signed – watercolour – 11½ x 18½in.
(Prudential) **$1,122 £600**

OSCAR WILSON – A Venetian Cafe – signed and
dated – oil on canvas – 19 x 12½in.
(Christie's) **$6,470 £3,740**

WITKOWSKI – Boys fishing on dock – signed
– oil on canvas – 24 x 30in.
(Christie's) **$1,650 £906**

ERICH WOLFSFELD – Study for Two Arabs –
oil on canvas – 18½ x 22in.
(Christie's)   **$608**   **£352**

FRANZ XAVIER WOLF – The last throw – signed
– on panel – 19¾ x 23½in.
(Christie's)   **$4,114**   **£2,420**

WILLIAM BARNES WOLLEN – The Ambush –
signed and dated – oil on canvas – 20 x 28in.
(Lawrence Fine Arts)   **$10,466**   **£6,050**

EDWARD WOLFE – Girl with pearls – signed –
pastel – 20 x 14in.
(Christie's)   **$2,190** **£1,210**

ALFRED WOLMARK – Hampstead Village –
signed – oil on canvas – 19 x 23in.
(Christie's)   **$6,265**   **£3,520**

ALFRED WOLMARK – Self Portrait – signed and dated – oil on canvas – 13 x 10in.
(Christie's)   **$2,153**   **£1,210**

ALFRED WOLMARK – Distraught Figures – signed – charcoal and pencil on board – 12¼ x 6¾in.
(Christie's)   **$2,093**   **£1,210**

ALFRED WOLMARK – Breton Girl – oil on canvas-board – 17¾ x 14¾in.
(Christie's)   **$3,524**   **£1,980**

ALFRED WOLMARK – Sarah and Gitel – signed with initials – 36 x 28in.
(Christie's)   **$12,727**   **£7,150**

ALFRED AARON WOLMARK — Girl in a turquoise dress — 16 x 12in.
(Christie's) **$1,022 £605**

ALFRED AARON WOLMARK — Two boxers *(recto)*, Wolmarks pots *(verso)* — signed — on board — 24½ x 35½in.
(Christie's) **$2,974 £1,760**

THOMAS WATERMAN WOOD — Arguing the Question — signed and dated — gouache, watercolour and pencil on paper laid down on canvas — 51.5 x 72.1cm.
(Christie's) **$93,500 £50,268**

WOODVILLE

WILLIAM P. CATON WOODVILLE − Study of a reclining nude woman − signed and dated − oil on canvas − 15½ x 24½in.
(W. H. Lane & Son)
$608 £360   556

ROBERT STRONG WOODWARD − The Hale House, Buckland, Massachusetts − signed − oil on canvas − 25 x 30in.
(Robt. W. Skinner Inc.) **$600**   £355

ALFRED JOSEPH WOOLMER − The birth of Venus − 40 x 50in.
(Christie's)
$4,307 £2,420

ALFRED JOSEPH WOOLMER – "There is a rapture on a lonely shore" – Byron – signed and inscribed – 12 x 18in.
(Christie's) **$780** **£462**

ABRAHAM BRUININGH VAN WORRELL – Milkmaids and their herds in a riverside pasture – signed – oil on canvas – 25¼ x 30¼in.
(Phillips) **$4,576** **£2,600**

CHARLES NATHAN WOOLNOTH – Angling in Scotland – signed – 17¾ x 24¾in.
(Anderson & Garland) **$761** **£440**

HAROLD WORKMAN – Figures crossing a bridge, city sky-line in the distance – Oil on board – 23.5 x 30.5cm.
(Henry Spencer) **$642** **£380**

JULIA WORSWICK – Tete en Profile – signed – oil on canvas – 13¾ x 10½in.
(Christie's) **$913** **£528**

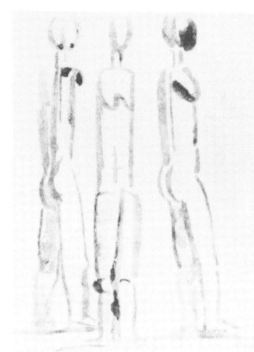

GEORGE WRIGHT — Before the hunt — signed —
10 x 16in.
(Christie's) $10,950   £6,050

FRITZ WOTRUBA — Untitled — signed —
airbrush on paper — 19 x 19in.
(Robt. W. Skinner Inc.) **$650**   **£384**

GEORGE WRIGHT — Belvoir Hunt — oil on
canvas.
(Morphets)   **$51,040 £29,000**

GEORGE WRIGHT — A hunter and a hound in a
loose-box — signed and indistinctly dated —
40.7 x 50.5cm.
(Christie's)   **$2,545 £1,430**

JAMES WRIGHT – The candy man, children buying sweets and balloons from a donkey cart in Dunfermline – signed – watercolour – 12 x 14in.
(W. H. Lane & Son) $2,745 £1,500

ROBERT W. WRIGHT – The little warbler; and Interesting pictures – both signed and dated – on panel – 8¼ x 6in.
(Christies) Two $6,853 £3,850

GEORGE WRIGHT – A jig on a country road – signed – oil on canvas – 6½ x 8½in.
(Christie's) **$1,338 £748**

FERDINAND VON WRIGHT – Redstarts – signed and dated – 16 x 13in.
(Christie's) **$32,164 £18,700**

GILBERT SCOTT WRIGHT – Outside the Crown Inn – signed – 24 x 36in.
(Christie's) **$14,520 £8,250**

ROBERT W. WRIGHT – Cottage interior, an old man seated playing a fiddle, a young girl by his side – signed and dated – oil on panel – 39 x 28.5cm.
(Henry Spencer) **$6,574** **£3,800**

MANUEL WSSEL – The musician – signed and dated – on panel – 21¾ x 15¾in.
(Christie's) **$2,992** **£1,760**

CARL WUERMER – The wintry river – signed
– oil on canvas – 25 x 30in.
(Christie's) **$7,700 £4,207**

CARL WUERMER – Old Lyme, Conn. – signed
– watercolour and gouache on paper – 20½ x 27½in.
(Christie's) **$1,650 £906**

FRANZ WULFHAGEN, Attributed to – Christ healing the paralysed – oil on panel – 50.5 x 66.5cm.
(Phillips) **$4,862 £2,600**

WUNDERLICH

JAN WYCK, Follower of – An ambush in a gorge
– oil on canvas – 69.5 x 82cm.
(Phillips)   **$1,458**   **£780**

PAUL WUNDERLICH – Die Fusse – signed and
dated – oil on canvas – 161.6 x 130.2cm.
(Christie's)   **$10,230 £5,500**

WILHELM WUNDERWALD – Preparing to bathe
– signed and inscribed – pastel – 680 x 1070mm.
(Christie's)   **$11,132 £6,050**

JAN WYCK, Follower of – A stag hunt –
83 x 133.4cm.
(Christie's)   **$8,639 £4,620**

THOMAS WYCK – Coastal scene with merchants before a sailing vessel – oil on canvas – 26.5 x 32.2cm.
(Phillips)   **$6,954 £3,800**

NEWELL CONVERS WYETH – The moose call – signed – oil on canvas – 36 x 40in.
(Christie's)   **$66,000 £36,065**

ANDREW WYETH – The Blackberry Picker – signed – tempera on panel – 28¾ x 48¼in.
(Christie's)   **$385,000**   **£206,989**

ANDREW NEWELL WYETH – British General at Brandywine – signed – watercolour on paper laid down on board – 17¾ x 25¾in.
(Christie's)   **$13,200 £7,213**

NEWELL CONVERS WYETH – Supply Waggons – signed and dated – oil on canvas – 38 x 25¾in.
(Christie's)   **$37,400**   **£20,107**

WYETH

WILLIAM WYLD — Prague — signed — water-colour heightened with white — 16 x 23.1cm.
(Christie's) **$5,997 £3,190**

NEWELL CONVERS WYETH — The bucking bronco — signed — oil on canvas — 34 x 25in.
(Christie's) **$66,000 £36,065**

HENRI VAN WYK — Arab horsemen in a landscape — signed — 35 x 65cm.
(Christie's) **$2,244 £1,320**

WILLIAM WYLD — Genoa — signed and inscribed — pencil and watercolour heightened with white — 13 x 21¾in.
(Christie's) **$1,452 £825**

CHARLES WILLIAM WYLLIE – 'Rainham Quay'
– signed – oil on canvas – 10 x 18in.
(Bonhams) **$3,872 £2,200**

WILLIAM LIONEL WYLLIE – Sailing barges in
a French port – signed and dated – oil on canvas
– 10 x 7in.
(Christie's) **$2,937 £1,650**

WILLIAM LIONEL WYLLIE – The 'Teutonic'
leaving Liverpool – signed – oil on canvas –
22 x 12in.
(Phillips) **$26,100 £15,000**

WILLIAM LIONEL WYLLIE – H.M.S. Resolution
guarding the high sea fleet – signed and inscribed
– pencil and watercolour – 10¼ x 16½in.
(Christie's) **$2,710 £1,540**

WILLIAM LIONEL WYLLIE – The Channel fleet
off Scarborough – signed and dated – oil on
canvas – 16 x 24¼in.
(Bonhams)   **$10,560 £6,000**

WILLIAM LIONEL WYLLIE – 'Greenwich
Hospital' – signed and dated – oil on canvas –
18 x 32in.
(Bonhams)   **$19,360 £11,000**

WILLIAM LIONEL WYLLIE – 'A tide-race' –
signed and inscribed – watercolour – 10½ x 17in.
(Phillips)   **$2,576 £1,400**

WILLIAM LIONEL WYLLIE –'A Whole Gale of
Wind'– signed and dated – oil on canvas –
48 x 84in.
(Bonhams)   **$9,504 £5,400**

JAN WYNANTS – Landscape with drover and cattle on a sandy path – signed – oil on canvas – 52 x 73.5cm.
(Phillips) **$12,810 £7,000**

JAN WYNANTS – Hunters before a stream in a wood – signed – oil on canvas – 83 x 66cm.
(Phillips) **$25,620 £14,000**

BRYAN WYNTER – Sandspoor XIII – signed – oil on canvas – 56 x 44in.
(Christie's) **$7,147 £4,180**

BRYAN WYNTER – Towards evening No. 20 – oil on board – 31¾ x 23¾in.
(Christie's) **$4,138 £2,420**

FRED YATES – The ladies of Lake Wobegon – oil on board – 38 x 33in.
(David Lay) **$840 £480**

JOSEPH YARNOLD – A river landscape with a bridge – one of a pair – signed – 36 x 28in.
(Christie's) **$4,963 £2,640**

FRED YATES – Street corner, Cornwall – signed – on board – 13¾ x 13¼in.
(Christie's) **$146 £82**

FRED YATES – '4 o'clock St Just Primary' – signed – oil on board – 19 x 26½in.
(Bonhams) **$498 £280**

FRED YATES – 'End of Term' – signed – oil on board – 35 x 41in.
(Bonhams) **$925 £520**

YATES

FRED YATES – God's Garden – oil on board –
44 x 45in.
(W. H. Lane & Son) **$851 £460**

WILLIAM FREDERICK YEAMES – The morning
rehearsal – signed – oil on board – 20¼ x 14in.
(Christie's) **$2,481 £1,320**

W. YATES – One of a pair – Near Reigate,
Surrey; and Farnborough, Kent – signed –
14 x 12in.
(Christie's) **Two** **$2,153 £1,210**

JACK BUTLER YEATS – Sleep beside falling
water – signed – oil on canvas – 18 x 24in.
(Christie's) **$66,188 £37,606**

JACK BUTLER YEATS – The Fair at Tubber – pen and black ink – 5¾ x 8¾in.
(Christie's)   **$6,949 £3,948**

JACK BUTLER YEATS – Where fresh water and
salt water meet – signed – oil on canvas –
16 x 20in.
(Christie's)   **$94,050 £55,000**

JACK BUTLER YEATS – Summer storm – signed
– oil on canvas – 17¾ x 24in.
(Christie's)   **$56,259 £31,965**

JACK BUTLER YEATS – The basin in which
Pilate washed his hands – oil on canvas –
40 x 60in.
(Christie's)   **$263,340 £154,000**

JACK BUTLER YEATS – The Bailiff – signed
– watercolour, pen and black ink – 11½ x 9in.
(Christie's)   **$20,691 £12,100**

JACK BUTLER YEATS – The Falls of Sheen –
signed – oil on panel – 9½ x 14in.
(Christie's)   **$15,801 £9,350**

JACK BUTLER YEATS – The Barrel Man – signed – watercolour and bodycolour – 10 x 14in.
(Christie's)   **$13,942 £8,250**

JACK BUTLER YEATS – Gaff in the East End
– signed – pen and black ink – 13½ x 20½in.
(Christie's) **$4,647 £2,750**

JACK BUTLER YEATS – The Music – signed –
watercolour, pen, brush and black ink – 8 x 5½in.
(Christie's) **$12,226 £7,150**

JACK BUTLER YEATS – The Ringmaster –
signed – pen and black ink – 10 x 7½in.
(Christie's) **$15,988 £9,350**

JACK BUTLER YEATS – The Pookah – signed – pen, brush and black ink – 7½ x 10in.
(Christie's)   **$7,900 £4,620**

JACK BUTLER YEATS – Tumblers at the circus – signed and inscribed – pen, brush, black ink and brown wash – 9½ x 6½in.
(Christie's)   **$16,929   £9,900**

JACK BUTLER YEATS – The Circus poster – signed – watercolour, pen, brush and black ink – 8 x 5½in.
(Christie's)   **$22,572 £13,200**

JACK BUTLER YEATS -- The bold Belfast shoemaker – signed with monogram – pen and black ink – 11.8 x 13.3cm.
(Christie's)   **$1,489 £846**

LAETITIA YHAP – A Man with a large Cod at Night – signed, inscribed and dated – oil on canvas – 20 x 24in.
(Christie's)   **$1,294**   **£748**

JACK BUTLER YEATS – The Fair – signed – pen, brush and black ink – 8 x 5¾in.
(Christie's)   **$9,405 £5,500**

MODESTO URGELL Y INGLADA – Low tide – signed – 11¼ x 22in.
(Christie's)   **$9,790 £5,500**

HENRY JOHN YEEND KING – A view of Worcester Cathedral – indistinctly signed – watercolour – 10¼ x 14¼in.
(Bonhams)   **$626 £360**

FRANS YKENS – A still life with a plate of oysters before a basket of grapes – oil on canvas – 78.5 x 114cm.
(Phillips)   **$21,000 £12,000**

MARCELINO UNCETA Y LOPEZ – Spanish horsemen – oil on panel – 5¼ x 2¾in.
(Christie's)   **$3,133 £1,760**

EDMOND CHARLES JOSEPH YON – A house on the edge of a river – signed and dated – 9½ x 13¼in.
(Christie's) **$1,762 £990**

EDUARDO ZAMACOIS Y ZABALA – Bufones – signed and dated – 19¾ x 24in.
(Christie's) **$27,412 £15,400**

WILLIAM S. YOUNG – Hudson River Scene – signed and dated – oil on canvas – 24½ x 41¼in.
(Christie's) **$6,204 £3,300**

CHRISTIAN ZACHO – Cattle grazing by a pond in a wooded landscape – signed – oil on panel – 10½ x 13¾in.
(Christie's) **$1,566 £880**

JAN THOMAS VAN YPEREN, Circle of – The rest on the flight into Egypt – 38 x 44½in.
(Christie's) **$4,567 £2,640**

CHRISTIAN ZACHO – A wooded landscape – signed with initials – 14½ x 21in.
(Christie's) **$1,157 £650**

CHRISTIAN ZACHO — Monte Carlo — signed and dated — 23 x 32in.
(Christie's) **$10,120 £5,500**

OSSIP ZADKINE — Figures — signed and dated — pen and black ink and ink wash on paper — 28 x 21in.
(Christie's) **$16,192 £8,800**

JOSE LUIS DE ZAMORA — A fashion design — pencil and watercolour heightened with silver — 32.5 x 25cm.
(Christie's) **$979 £550**

JOSE LUIS DE ZAMORA − A fashion design −
signed, inscribed and dated − pencil and watercolour, heightened with silver − 31.5 x 22cm.
(Christie's) **$979 £550**

JOSE LUIS DE ZAMORA − Danseuses au
Camboose − signed and inscribed − pencil and
watercolour and bodycolour heightened with silver
− 12½ x 9½in.
(Christie's) **$1,416 £770**

JOSE LUIS DE ZAMORA − A fashion design −
pencil and watercolour heightened with gold on
Bristol paper − 31.5 x 24cm.
(Christies) **$979 £550**

EUGENIO ZAMPHIGI − Music hath charms −
signed − 24 x 18in.
(Christie's) **$9,790 £5,500**

EUGENIO ZAMPIGHI – "A work of art", interior scene, lady and gentleman playing cards with lady standing holding jug of wine – signed – oil on canvas – 14 x 20in.
(Du Mouchelles) $4,000 £2,366

EUGENIO ZAMPIGHI – "An important decision", interior scene, gentleman standing with two ladies seated at table – signed – oil on canvas – 14 x 20in.
(Du Mouchelles) $3,750 £2,218

E. ZANINI — Children fishing in a mountain
stream — signed and dated — 18 x 14in.
(Christie's) **$2,442 £1,320**

JAKOB JOSEPH ZELGER — The Matterhorn
— signed — oil on canvas — 60 x 47cm.
(Christie's) **$9,715 £5,280**

HANS ZATZKA — A heavenly trio — signed —
oil on canvas — 19 x 37¼in.
(Christie's) **$8,500 £4,620**

CATHRINE HELENE ZERNICHOW — Holly-
hocks in a jug — signed with initials —
25¼ x 23¾in.
(Christie's) **$935** **£550**

NELLIE EVELYN ZIEGLER – Coastal Scene/
California – signed – oil on canvas – 20 x 24in.
(Robt. W. Skinner Inc.) **$1,400** **£828**

MARTIN ZEROLO – The Dove – signed and dated
– acrylic on canvas – 51 x 38in.
(Christie's) **$1,936 £1,100**

**FELIX FRANCOIS GEORGES PHILIBERT
ZIEM** – Sur la cote du Maroc – signed –
55.5 x 85cm.
(Christie's) **$5,984 £3,520**

JOHAN JACOB ZIEGLER – Portrait of a man,
half length, in ceremonial military costume – oil
on canvas – 15 x 12¼in.
(Phillips) **$844 £480**

EDOUARD ZIER – Portrait of a young lady in
ball gown – signed and dated – oil on canvas –
17 x 14in.
(Du Mouchelles) **$2,750 £1,455**

VITTORE ZANETTI ZILLA – A Venetian backwater – signed and inscribed – pencil and watercolour – 15¼ x 22¾in.
(Christie's) **$1,229 £715**

THEODORE ZIMMERMAN – In the cornfield – signed – pastel – 24.5 x 33.6cm.
(Christie's) **$1,017 £550**

THEODORE ZIMMERMAN – Hyde Park – signed and inscribed – coloured chalks – 5½ x 6½in.
(Christie's) **$610 £330**

DORIS ZINKEISEN – "Troublesome", a lady
riding sidesaddle on a rearing horse – signed –
oil on canvas – 20 x 23½in.
(W. H. Lane & Son)   **$1,462 £850**

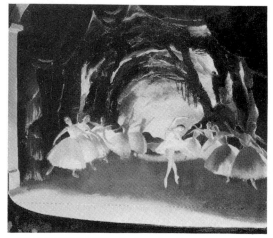

DORIS ZINKEISEN – Le Lac des Cygnes –
signed – oil on canvas – 25 x 30½in.
(Christie's)   **$3,425   £1,980**

DORIS ZINKEISEN – The soloist – signed – oil
on canvas – 20 x 16in.
(Phillips)   **$1,318 £780**

DORIS ZINKEISEN — La Chanteuse — signed —
oil on canvas — 24 x 20in.
(Christie's) $4,919 £2,860

DORIS ZINKEISEN — Costume design for Miss
Alexandre from Cocl... Rean — signed — water-
colour and pencil — 21½ x 14in.
(Christie's) $380   £220

DORIS ZINKEISEN — Picking flowers — signed
— oil on canvas — 24 x 20in.
(Phillips) $6,422 £3,800

DORIS ZINKEISEN — Jack O'Lantern: Costume
Design — signed — watercolour — 14½ x 10½in.
(Christie's) $761   £440

ZINKEISEN

DORIS ZINKEISEN – The Laundry Maid –
signed – oil on canvas   19 x 15in.
(Christie's)   **$5,482   £3,080**

DORIS ZINKEISEN – Welsh Cob, Scole Cam –
signed – oil on canvas – 20 x 24in.
(Christie's)   **$2,545   £1,430**

DORIS ZINKEISEN – Pavilion Dauphine,
Champs Elysees – signed – oil on canvas –
64.5 x 76cm.
(Phillips)   **$8,788 £5,200**

DORIS ZINKEISEN – The Great Horse Fair –
signed – oil on canvas – 19 x 29¼in.
(Christie's)   **$4,540 £2,640**

DORIS ZINKEISEN – Prima ballerina – signed –
oil on canvas – 20 x 16in.
(Phillips)   **$1,318 £780**

DORIS ZINKEISEN – Blackheath – signed –
oil on canvas – 51 x 76cm.
(Phillips)   **$6,516   £3,600**

DORIS ZINKEISEN – The Bandstand – signed
– oil on canvas – 25 x 30in.
(Christie's)   **$6,853   £3,850**

DORIS ZINKEISEN – Little girl in a field of
buttercups – signed – 16 x 12in.
(Christie's)   **$780   £462**

EMIL ZOIR – The fishermen's return – signed and dated – 116 x 140cm.
(Christie's) **$4,730 £2,750**

ANDERS ZORN – Galli I – signed – drypoint on wove paper – 5 x 3½in.
(Robt. W. Skinner Inc.) **$325** **£192**

VENANZIO ZOLLA – A quiet moment – signed – oncard – 7 x 6½in.
(Christie's) **$905 £484**

FAUSTO ZONARO – The musical party – signed – 23 x 31½in.
(Christie's) **$15,785** **£9,020**

ANDERS LEONARD ZORN – Naket (Nudes) – signed and dated – canvas laid down on board – 20½ x 12¾in.
(Christie's) **$359,480 £209,000**

ANDERS LEONARD ZORN – The Swan –
signed – etching on laid paper –
(Christie's) **$1,309 £770**

ANDERS LEONARD ZORN – Portrait of Jeanna
Heijkenskjold – signed and dated – watercolour
and bodycolour – 16¾ x 13in.
(Christie's) **$132,440 £77,000**

ANDERS LEONARD ZORN – Kuvadorren (The
chamber door) – signed and dated – canvas laid
down on board – 21 x 13¼in.
(Christie's) **$510,840 £297,000**

ANDERS LEONARD ZORN – Ida – signed and
dated – 67 x 43.2cm.
(Christie's) **$473,000 £275,000**

ANDERS LEONARD ZORN – Pa sangkanten (On the bed) – signed and dated – 91 x 61.3cm. *(Christie's)* **$407,000** **£220,000**

ANDERS LEONARD ZORN and BRUNO LILJEFORS – Natteffekt 11, a study by Anders Zorn (recto), and another – signed and dated on panel – 9¼ x 13in. *(Christie's)* **$227,040 £132,000**

RAMON DE ZUBIAURRE – The carpenter – signed and dated – canvas laid down on board – 18 x 23in.
(Christie's) **$12,139 £6,820**

VALENTIN DE ZUBIAURRE – Self-portrait of
the artist, head and shoulders – signed and dated –
61 x 46cm.
(Christie's)   **$18,920 £11,000**

TADDEO ZUCCARO, Circle of – Study of three
heads – pen and ink – 98 x 80mm.
(Phillips)   **$347 £190**

TADDEO ZUCCARO, Circle of – The Miracle of
the Vernicle – oil on copper – 25.5 x 20cm.
(Phillips)   **$2,464**   **£1,400**

ANTONIO ZUCCHI, Manner of – An extensive
landscape with the murder of Jehovah (?) –
73 x 91.7cm.
(Christie's)   **$2,854   £1,650**

HEINRICH VON ZUGEL – A shepherdess and
sheep in a wooded lane – signed – 27½in. x 22in.
(Christie's)   **$36,575**   **£20,900**

ARTS REVIEW

ZUCCHI

ANTONIO ZUCCHI – A Capriccio; peasants
gathered on a riverbank before a bridge – signed
– pen and ink with grey washes heightened with
white – 515 x 650mm.
(Phillips)   **$915 £500**

SOTOMAYOR Y ZUNIGA – The black mantilla –
signed – 24 x 22¾in.
(Christie's)   **$6,993 £3,740**

FRANCESCO ZUGNO – The Vision of St Teresa
of Avila – oil on canvas – 25¾ x 13¼in.
(Phillips)   **$2,464 £1,400**

ANTON ZWENGAUER – The angler's return –
signed and dated – 33½ x 27¾in.
(Christie's)   **$2,992**   **£1,760**

Do you have a £2,400 biscuit tin? What about a bird-cage for £16,500, or a pair of high heeled shoes worth £8,000?

This book is certain to intrigue and fascinate, with over 3,000 illustrations and prices of just the sort of collectable which is possibly pushed out of sight and forgotten until now!

448 pages 245 x 170mm. paperback
SBN 0-86248-053-1   **£7.95**

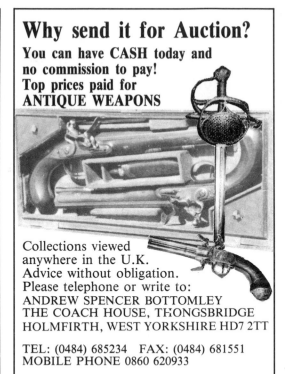

BRITISH ANTIQUE EXPORTERS LTD

WHOLESALERS, EXPORTERS PACKERS SHIPPERS
HEAD OFFICE: QUEEN ELIZABETH AVENUE, BURGESS HILL, WEST SUSSEX, RH15 9RX ENGLAND
TELEPHONE BURGESS HILL (04 44) 245577   FAX (04 44) 232014

To: Auctioneers, Wholesalers and Retailers of antique
    furniture, porcelain and decorative items.

Dear Sirs

We offer the most comprehensive service available in the UK.

As wholesalers we sell 20 ft and 40 ft container loads of antique
furniture, porcelain and decorative items of the Georgian, Victorian,
Edwardian and 1930's periods. Our buyers are strategically placed
throughout the UK in order to take full advantage of regional pricing.

You can purchase a container from us for as little as £7500. This
would be filled with mostly 1880's to 1930's furniture. You could
expect to pay approximately £10,000 to £15,000 for a shipment of
Victorian and Edwardian furniture and porcelain. £15,000 to £35,000
would buy a Georgian, Queen Anne and Chippendale style container.

Containers can be tailored to your exact requirements - for example,
you may deal only in office furniture and therefore only buy desks,
file cabinets and related office items.

Our terms are £1,500 deposit, the balance at time of arrival of the
container. If the merchandise should not be to your liking for any
reason whatsoever, we offer you your money back in full, less one-way
freight.

We also have a large showroom where you can purchase individual items.

If you wish to visit the UK yourself and purchase individually from
your own sources, we will collect, pack and ship your merchandise with
speed and efficiency. Our rates are competitive and our packing is
the finest available anywhere in the UK. Our courier-finder service
is second to none and we have experienced couriers who are equipped
with a car and the knowledge of where to find the best buys.

If your business is buying English Antiques, we are your contact.
We assure you of our best attention at all times.

Yours faithfully
BRITISH ANTIQUE EXPORTERS LTD

Norman Lefton
Chairman & Managing Director

DIRECTORS: N. LEFTON (Chairman & Managing),   P. V. LEFTON,   THE RT. HON. THE VISCOUNT EXMOUTH   A. FIELD, MSC FBOA DCLP FSMC FAAO.
REGISTERED No. 893406 ENGLAND
BANKERS: NATIONAL WESTMINSTER BANK LTD. 155 NORTH STREET, BRIGHTON, SUSSEX   THE CHASE MANHATTAN BANK, N.A., 410 PARK AVENUE, NEW YORK

THERE ARE MANY ANTIQUE

… few, if any, who are as quality conscious as Norman Lefton, Chairman and Managing Director of British Antique Exporters Ltd. of Burgess Hill, Nr. Brighton, Sussex.

Nearly thirty years' experience of shipping goods to all parts of the globe have confirmed his original belief that the way to build clients' confidence in his services is to supply them only with goods which are in first class saleable condition. To this end, he employs a cottage industry staff of over 50, from highly skilled antique restorers, polishers and packers to representative buyers and executives.

Through their knowledgeable hands passes each piece of furniture before it leaves the B.A.E. warehouses, ensuring that the overseas buyer will only receive the best and most saleable merchandise for their particular market. This attention to detail is obvious on a visit to the Burgess Hill showrooms where potential customers can view what must be the most varied assortment of Georgian, Victorian, Edwardian and 1930s furniture in the UK. One cannot fail to be impressed by, not only the varied range of merchandise, but also the fact that each piece is in showroom condition awaiting shipment.

As one would expect, packing is considered somewhat of an art at

B.A.E. and the manager in charge of the works ensures that each piece will reach its final destination in the condition a customer would wish. B.A.E. set a very high standard and, as a further means of improving each container load, their customer/container liaison dept, invites each customer to return detailed information on the

BRITISH ANTIQUE EXPORTERS LTD,
SCHOOL CLOSE, QUEEN ELIZABETH AVENUE, BURGESS HILL, WEST SUSSEX RH15 9RX, ENGLAND.
Telephone BURGESS HILL (04 44) 245577.
Fax (04 44) 232014.
Members of L.A.P.A.D.A. and Guild of Master Craftsmen

SHIPPERS IN BRITAIN BUT...

£10,000 container will immediately it is unpacked at its final destination realise in the region of £15,000 to £20,000 for our clients selling the goods on a quick wholesale turnover basis."

When visiting the warehouses various container loads can be seen in the course of completion. The intending buyer can then judge for himself which type of container load would be best suited to his market. In an average 20-foot container B.A.E. put approximately 75 to 100 pieces carefully selected to suit the particular destination. There are always at least 10 outstanding or unusual items in each shipment, but every piece included looks as though it has something special about it.

B.A.E. have opened several new showrooms based at its 15,000 square feet headquarters in Burgess Hill which is 15 minutes away from Gatwick Airport, 7 miles from Brighton and 39 miles from London on a direct rail link, (only 40 minutes journey), the Company is ideally situated to ship containers to all parts of the world. The showrooms, restoration and packing departments are open to overseas buyers and no visit to purchase antiques for re-sale in other countries is complete without a visit to their Burgess Hill premises where a welcome is always found.

saleability of each piece in the container, thereby ensuring successful future shipments.

This feedback of information is the all important factor which guarantees the profitability of future containers. "By this method" Mr. Lefton explains, "we have established that an average

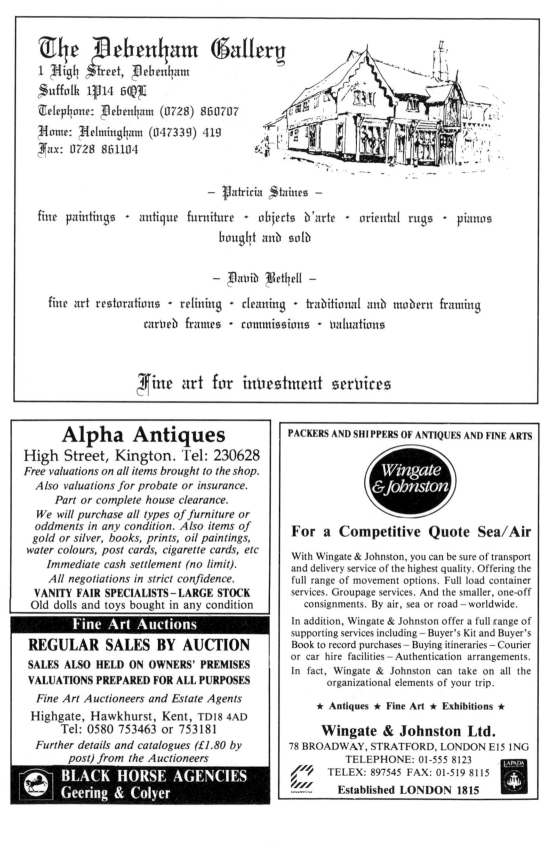

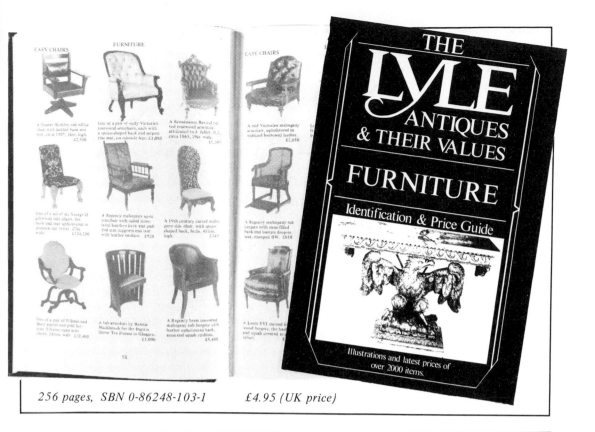

603

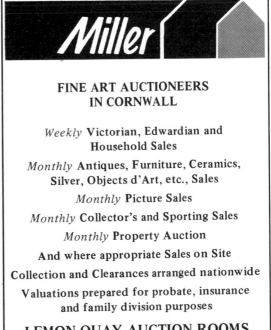

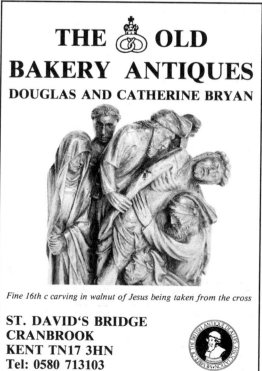